the good
website
guide
2001

SIMON EDWARDS

Revised and updated by David Williams

the good website guide

2001

MITCHELL BEAZLEY

The Good Website Guide 2001
by Simon Edwards
Revised and updated by David Williams

Published in Great Britain in 2001 by Mitchell Beazley,
an imprint of Octopus Publishing Group Ltd,
2–4 Heron Quays, Docklands, London, E14 4JP

ISBN 1 84000 418 5

A CIP catalogue record for this book is available from
the British Library

The author and publishers would be grateful for any
information that will assist them in keeping future editions
up-to-date. Although all reasonable care has been taken in
the preparation of this book, neither the publishers nor the
author can accept liability for any consequences arising from
the use thereof, or from the information contained therein.

Commissioning Editor	Vivien Antwi
Project Editor	Chloë Garrow
Editor	Claire Musters
Design	Kenny Grant
Production	Nancy Roberts
Checkers	David Folkman, Lydia Garrow, Maxine McCaghy

Typeset in Clearface Gothic, Franklin Gothic,
and Helvetica Neue

Printed and bound by Bath Press, Bath

CONTENTS

INTRODUCTION

This handbook will help to guide you through your explorations of the exciting world wide web. Many people have already discovered the huge amounts of useful services, shops, and information that are available. Don't worry if you are not one of these people. If you have a computer, an Internet connection, and this book then you will soon be zooming around the web, visiting the places you need, and learning how to avoid the ones that you don't.

— Getting connected —

Essential terms

There are a few technical terms that you will need to know. Don't worry, though. You don't have to understand how the Internet works to use it, but knowing a few buzzwords will help make your journey much easier. The Internet can be divided into different areas. The bit people are talking about, where you "surf" for information, look at lush pictures, and generally "get connected", is called the web. Other places include Newsgroups, Chat, and FTP sites. We will concentrate on the web here as it will be the most useful for you.

Sites and addresses

The web itself is made up of many different areas, called sites. Each one has a unique name, or address. Web addresses frequently appear in advertisements or at the end of television programmes. The proper name for a web address is an URL (often pronounced "earl"), which means Uniform Resource Locator. Most of the time you won't need to know this, but the writers of some websites assume their readers have lots of technical knowledge, and will refer to URLs. If you are having trouble with the concept of the web, imagine that it is similar to the teletext service available with most televisions. But instead of typing in a three figure number to find the news headlines, television programme showing times, or sports results, you enter words. And you'll find that the web can be much more powerful, too, with photographic-quality pictures and interesting articles.

Browsers and plugins

To access a website your computer needs to be connected to the Internet and be able to run a program called a web browser – the two most commonly used are Microsoft Internet Explorer and Netscape Navigator. It is almost certain that Internet Explorer will already be installed on your PC. The browser acts as your window on to the web. It will show you pictures, text, and will sometimes play sounds. Modern browsers also support moving video images and other technologies that provide animations and interactive buttons. Sometimes a website might expect your browser to be equipped with a piece of software to display multimedia – Flash is the most common – but don't worry if you don't have it as most of the time you'll be offered the opportunity to download the appropriate program. This program is called a plugin.

An example site

Here's an example of a website. *The Times* newspaper has a website that contains much of the same information that you would find in the physical paper version. Its address is **www.the-times.co.uk**. You would visit this site by connecting to the Internet, loading your web browser program, and typing the web address (URL) into the address box, or bar.

Once you have connected you will be given the option to look at the various areas covered by the site, such as world news, sport, or business. The site is updated daily, so you can refer to it in much the same way as you would a newspaper. The added benefit, however, is that new stories can be included as soon as they happen, so readers – like you – don't have to wait until the next day for articles to be published.

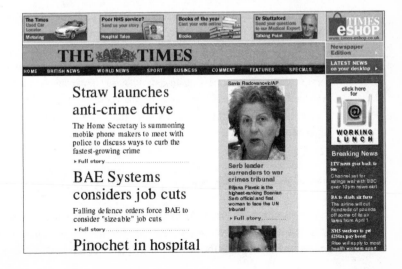

SPORT
Foo(ba)ll
shee(te)st

When you position your cursor over words providing links to other websites your cursor will change from an arrow shape to a pointing hand.

Navigating sites using links

Once you have found an interesting website (this book contains the addresses to over 1500 of these), you'll obviously want to read its contents. The beauty of the web is that you can choose which bits to look at without having to plough through the whole thing. Websites are not like books, which you should read from beginning to end. Web pages allow you to link a word or phrase to another page so that when you click on it with your mouse, your browser goes straight to another article without you having to type in a further address. By clicking on the link you will be sent immediately to the related site that usually offers further information. The linked text is usually written in a different colour and is often underlined, although different sites have different styles. Some links merely change colour when your mouse moves over them – the cursor also changes to a hand when you hover over a link. Most websites have simple menus that make browsing easier. It's usually obvious.

For example, if this book was a website, you might expect to click on the underlined text to find out what the term "website" actually means. These links are called hyperlinks, and are not just restricted to the text. Pictures are also used as hyperlinks. Alternatively, when visiting an art gallery's site you can expect to click on any of their small pictures, called thumbnails, to view a larger version.

Making a list

Armed with this knowledge you are ready to take your first tentative steps on to the web. Once you've found a site you like, it is often a good idea to make a note of its address so that you can return to it easily. Your web browser program will be able to do this for you, by using its Bookmark (Netscape Navigator) or Favourites (Internet Explorer) list.

Once you have found a set of sites you really like, you'll probably want to keep returning to them, particularly those that provide regular news stories. It's worth spending a bit of time really whittling down the numbers. If you try to visit too many, you'll end up not bothering at all in the long run, which would be a shame because the Internet is more up-to-date than any newspaper or magazine can ever be. Create a short list and get into the habit of checking the sites on it regularly. Alternatively, many sites now have newsletters that they send to you by email on a daily basis.

— A brief history of the web —

The Internet has been around for ages, although the web has only really caught on in the last six or seven years. Until 1991, the web was dominated by the experts that developed it. The first proper web browser, which could show pictures and run on the common PC, was introduced in 1993. It was called Mosaic and was the forerunner to modern browsers like Internet Explorer and Navigator. It was so easy to use that the use of the web grew by 341,634 per cent within the browser's first year. Since then, web browsers have had more features added to them, including the ability to make secure financial transactions.

The most important thing to happen to increase the web's popularity has been the introduction of free access. Generally, those in the US have to pay subscription fees to Internet Service Providers (ISPs) but don't pay for the phone calls used to establish connections. In the UK, Internet users pay for phone calls but are signing up in droves for free subscriptions to ISPs. So far there have been a few attempts to introduce completely free access, with no subscription fees or call charges. Most, though, have been unsuccessful or over-subscribed so far.

The chances are that you will be accessing the web by computer, either at home or at work. It may be a Mac, but is more likely to be a PC. However, a new generation of machines has meant an end to sitting in front of a monitor at a desk. They will be easier to use than normal computers, and won't crash as often. Technicians have developed boxes that plug into your TV to pipe web pages straight into your living room. WAP (Wireless Application Protocol) phones give a limited kind of access to the web through specially designed pages, and more powerful, portable devices will be with us any time now.

How to use this book

This Guide brings you over 1500 of the best websites available on the Internet. Whether you are a keen traveller, a bookworm, or a sports fanatic you will find something here for you. If you can't find what you are looking for in the main area then look to the "see also" section at the back of each chapter, where a number of other sites are concisely described. They may well take you to the ideal site.

Each entry is given in alphabetical order, either according to its official company name or a brief summary of the site's contents. The website address, or URL, is then given. While all addresses have "http://" in front of them, it is not necessary to type this into the address bar as your computer should do this automatically. Please note, however, that not all websites begin "www" and in this book this prefix has only been given when it is actually part of the address.

Unfortunately the nature of the Internet and e-commerce means that websites are prone to change, both in design and location. Although we can warrant that the sites included in this book were correct at the time of going to press we, the author and the publishers, do not accept responsibility for any errors that may occur as a result of these changes, but apologize for any inconvenience this may cause you.

SURFING THE NET

The Internet is packed with information about absolutely everything. Most of it is free, much of it is accurate, but actually finding the bits you need is not always as straightforward as you might hope. Don't panic, though. Once you've read this crash course in Internet navigation, the tangled mess that is the web will be under your control. You'll learn about web directories, search engines, and even how to guess a site's address, sometimes with astonishing accuracy. Remember, too, that many sites provide links to other, similar pages. A directory or search engine might not give you exactly the information you want, but the pages they do yield can take you closer to your ultimate goal.

Web directories

There is more than one way to find useful information on the web. The simplest method is to use a website directory. This is a site that stores lists and lists of Internet sites, a bit like the "A–Z guide" in this book. The best web directories have clearly defined categories that will make it easy for you to find your particular area of interest. If you want to find out about health-related issues, perhaps to learn more about asthma, then browse through the available categories until you find one called "Health". This would contain sub-categories for you to burrow down into – and eventually you should find a shortlist of websites referring to asthma. Some website directories have an often quite basic search feature, which you can use to help you find the best categories to attack.

Searching with a web directory

Yahoo! (**www.yahoo.com** or **uk.yahoo.com**) is the world's most popular web directory and we are using it here to show you what a search is actually like. In this instance we are searching for information on the hit film *The Matrix*. Initially you might enter something like "the matrix" into the search box and then press the Search button to start things moving (see step 1, opposite). The

Add some key words and press Search

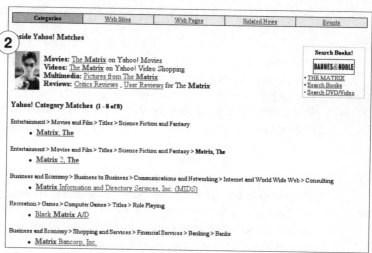

This is just a small number of the sites Yahoo! has listed

"Entertainment > Movies and Film" section looks like a safe bet, so click on it to see a list of sites, and other sub-categories (see step 2, above). A website's title and address can often give you a clue as to how useful it's going to be. It is worth remembering that the official websites are not necessarily the best. Once you get a feel for a directory, you'll be able to head straight for the right categories. For example, it makes sense to start at "Recreation and Sport" when searching for your favourite soccer team's home page.

Local information

If you are looking for information on local businesses then the easiest method is to use the electronic equivalent of the local telephone directory. Many will go further than just providing telephone numbers and addresses. Some, like Scoot (**www.scoot.co.uk**), will give you information about what films your local cinema is showing. It will also provide access to a full timetable, as well as giving you the option to book tickets online. Links to the companies' websites, if they exist, are also available.

Guestimate

If you know the company's name then there is a very simple and very fast way to find its website – guess! Imagine that there is a hardware store that sells nails, screws, and other bits and pieces. It's called "Mr Grommet". There is a fair chance that if the company has a website, its address would be **www.mrgrommet.com**. You can type the address right into your web browser and see what comes up. The worst thing that can happen is an error message saying that the page doesn't exist. If so, try **www.mrgrommet.co.uk**, **www.mrgrommet.uk.com**, and possibly **www.mrgrommet.net**. What about **www.mr-grommet.com**? Try generic names when starting out with such searches. Do you want to know about hamsters? Then try **www.hamsters.com**.

How web addresses work

Most website addresses are in three parts – beginning with www, which stands for world wide web. The words that follow can be almost anything, but usually make up the name of the company in question. The last bit, the ".com", ".co.uk", or ".net" indicates where or what the site is. You can deduce the basic nature of a site from its address. See the list opposite for descriptions of common endings.

Check a website's ending to see if it belongs to a government department, an educational facility, or if it is located on the other side of the world. The latter sites can often load much more slowly than sites that are closer to home. This is because it takes time for digital information to flow through the many computers that make up the Internet – and the further away a site is, the more computers will become involved. Some of these computers may well be too busy to help straight away.

Some popular sites exist in more than one place. For example, the main Microsoft website is in America, but there are copies of it hosted all over the world. Americans will find that the **www.microsoft.com** address will work just fine for them. However, British users would be much better off going to **www.microsoft.co.uk**, or **www.microsoft.com/uk**. If you are given a choice, it is always best to choose a site that is either in or near your own country. Links to international "mirror" sites are almost always provided on the main site's first page so they are easy to find.

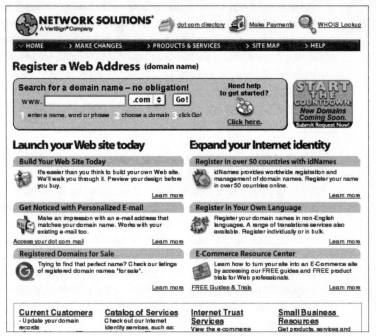

Register your domain name with a domain name registration service like networksolutions.com

Common web address suffixes

Here are some common web address suffixes, called Top Level Domains (TLDs):

.com	A company, often based in the United States – but not always.
.org	A non-commercial organization, sometimes charitable.
.net	Usually reserved for networks, like your Internet Service Provider.
.co.uk	A British company.
.org.uk	A British organization.
.gov	These sites are run by US governmental departments.
.gov.uk	Add a country's suffix for other nations' governments.
.mil	The military
.ac.uk	British academic sites, run by universities and colleges.
.edu	US educational facilities.
.au	Australian site
.fr	French site
.de	German site
.it	Italian site
.jp	Japanese site
.ru	Russian site

Judge a site by its cover. A site address such as **www.nhsdirect.nhs.uk** (NHS Direct) or **www.fda.gov** (Food and Drug Administration) is much more likely to contain trustworthy information than an amateur one. And remember that there is no guarantee that a site has been designed for English readers. If the address ends with a Japanese or German code, you're likely to need a phrase book. You can find more information on TLDs at the NetNames domain register (**www.netnames.co.uk**).

Search engines

A search engine is a website that has access to an incredibly large index of websites right across the network. You tell it what you want to find by using key words and phrases and it consults the index, throwing up links to possibly useful sites. Because there is no single official index that these sites can use, search engines have to create their own. Some share, but the main ones use different technologies to gather and sort information. The result is that not all search engines are of equal quality. But even the best search engines cannot search the whole internet thoroughly. One of the best, general search engines is AltaVista (**www.altavista.com** or **uk.altavista.com**). It provides a basic directory of the web for beginners to browse through, while also offering you various different levels of searching. It also allows you to search the web solely for images, videos, or music.

Search engines are not very discriminating, and won't be able to second-guess your intentions. Search for "star wars", and you'll find millions of pages about the science fiction film, as well as related games and books. You'll also find documents about the Reagan administration's defence policies mixed in. But by using the special techniques detailed over the page, you'll be able to sift out the bits you don't want.

It is a sad fact that even the most innocent of keywords can bring up links to a variety of potentially offensive websites, even when used with the best intentions. One way to deal with rude sites is to ignore them. Another is to use a security system (**www.netnanny.com** and **www.cyberpatrol.com** are just two examples) that will block out offensive sites. They are always obvious from the description and address shown by the search engine. Unfortunately, the site descriptions are usually exceedingly graphic so parental guidance when using the Internet is definitely advised. The advantage of web directories is that they keep adult material in the adult material categories. Regular Internet search engines are not so discriminating. It's not their fault – the automatic indexing systems are easy to trick. See "Security on the Internet" on pages 304-306 for more details on avoiding the less tasteful parts of the Internet.

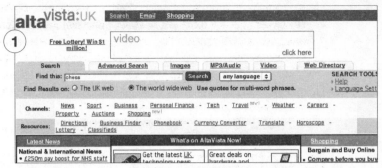

Start off with a general word or phrase before narrowing down your search

Nearly a million results, most of which are of no use

Searching with a search engine

We have chosen **uk.altavista.com** as our search engine. If you want to search, for example, for coverage of the chess game between Garry Kasparov and the computer Deep Blue, type "chess" into the search box and press the Search button (see step 1, above). An intimidating number of pages will appear, most of which will mean nothing to you (see step 2, above). Now try this: type "+chess +kasparov" and press Search. The plus signs mean that the search engine will only look for webpages that contain both of these words. You can see that the number of sites has decreased dramatically and the chance of picking up relevant pages is looking more likely. But there are still thousands of pages listed. Now try "+chess +kasparov + "deep blue"" (see step 3, next page). The inverted commas are needed when using a phrase containing more than one word, such as "deep blue". The more words you add, the more specific your search is likely to be, but be warned – do not use too many words or your search is likely to come up with

At last. Still more than 5000 web pages listed, but the first few options should do fine

no results at all. You can continue to use this technique to pare down the results until your list is of a manageable size, which you can then read through.

Advanced searching

You can really narrow down your searches using a standard set of commands known as Boolean operators. The most common are AND, OR, and AND NOT. A search for "cocktail AND recipe AND NOT whisky" using capitals will save you a lot of time that you would otherwise waste trawling through useless pages. Some search engines support extra features like NEAR, which will find key words that appear within a certain number of words from each other.

You can also try searching for exact phrases. If you are looking for a transcription of a speech, and you know a small quote, enclose it in inverted commas and give it a try. Search for ""i have a dream" AND "martin luther king" AND speech AND mp3", and the list you get is going to be very specific – probably including links to actual recordings of the event that you can listen to over the Internet.

Some search engines let you narrow down the search to images, videos, or sounds. If you want to search several search engines at once, you can use a metasearch engine, such as **www.dogpile.com**. This will increase your chances of finding some hard-to-find information – remember that not all the search engines look at the same pages, and so the more search engines you use the better. However, this can be time consuming if you are conducting a more general search and, in these cases, one may suffice.

Many modern web browsers have a self-contained search facility, but these are limited in their scope, and it is therefore best to stick with using the professional search engines that are very easy to use.

— Usenet

One of the most active parts of the Internet is called Usenet, which contains Newsgroups. These are like electronic bulletin boards that people use to ask questions and post their opinions. There are certain rules within newsgroups – you would do well to have a look at the "Netiquette section" at the back of the book. You may not have the time to spend hours reading all the articles in a Newsgroup, but you can still take advantage of other people's knowledge by using a web-based search site called **Deja.com**. It stores online discussions, known as threads, and provides a power search function.

Searching Usenet with Deja.com

Enter your keywords. We'll use tree and fungus in this example (see below). This will bring up a list of discussions, rather than websites. You may well find people asking the same questions that you have, but with luck there will also be replies from other, well-informed individuals. Click through a few to see if they are on the right track. Your keywords will be highlighted where they appear in each message. If you need to narrow the search, there is an easy-to-use Power Search option. Once you've found your answer you can be on your way, but some people will want to ask more questions, or even add their opinions to a discussion. This is also possible, using the Reply feature attached to each message.

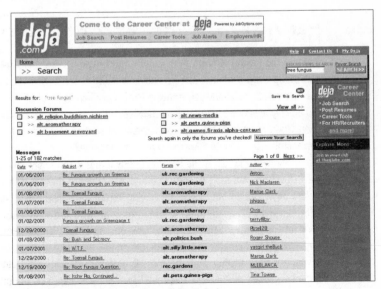

Visit deja.com to join newsgroups on your favourite topics

SHOPPING ON THE INTERNET

Using the Internet to buy goods and services has become very popular. Over the last two or three years the number of online shops has exploded, and no matter what you want to buy, it is very likely that there will be a website willing to sell it to you. Every high street and retail store that is worth their salt has its own website for you to buy from, almost certainly at discounted prices. You can buy prescription drugs, specialist food you would not find in your local supermarket, and rare records and CDs. By the beginning of 2000, it was estimated that 10 per cent of people in the UK alone had bought something over the Internet. More than 55 per cent of Americans have shopped online.

— The online high street

You may be feeling left out. Perhaps you can't imagine why you'd want to buy something via a computer screen. And how do you even begin? You can't touch the merchandise and any descriptive pictures are likely to be small and lacking in detail. Maybe you are worried about how you're going to pay for things. After all, surely there is an invisible army of hackers just waiting to pounce on your credit card number the minute you send it over the Internet?

The reality is that using the Internet to buy things is incredibly convenient and safe. Obviously, you can't squeeze fruit and vegetables to check that they are fresh before buying them but, if you are buying commodities like books, videos, and CDs then you will already know what to expect anyway. And some music sites will even let you preview album tracks before you buy. In fact, if you have a mind to buy a particular item, the Internet provides an excellent way to shop around while saving on shoe leather and patience. It also means that you can avoid the Saturday crowds and browse through shops online in a fraction of the time that you could in the high street.

Buying from a website is like buying from a catalogue. If you're happy to spend based on a stamp-sized picture in a magazine, why not when it's on a monitor? The fact that the Internet is always up-to-the-minute and up-to-date also means that prices can change every day. And competition between companies and the lack of overhead costs means the prices usually come down. From a business point of view, running a shop on the Internet costs a lot less than renting, lighting, and heating a property in a city centre and some of the savings are passed on to the customer.

Internet shopping

How do you dip your toe into the Internet shopping centre? Your best option is to start off small. Buy something that will fit through your letterbox, like a book or CD. That way you won't be worried about sending money off into the ether, and you won't have to wait in to receive a large package. There are plenty of online shops that will sell you a single novel or album. You don't have to buy in bulk.

Shopping walkthrough

In this virtual shopping trip I will be looking for a cookery book. Because I spend far too much time using the Internet, the meals must be quick and easy – I don't want to waste any valuable time that I could use to be online!

I've chosen to shop at **Amazon.co.uk**. As I don't know the title of the book I'm after, I'll browse the book section, rather than search for a particular title. Click on the "Books" tab to get the next screen (see step 1, above).

After negotiating a few sub-categories, we come to the "Food & Drink" menu (see step 2, next page). The "Quick & Easy" section looks suitable so let's have a look at it.

This one fits the budget, and other customers have rated it well. Press the Add to Shopping Basket button to select this title (see step 3, next page). If I find

another book that I decide I prefer, I can easily remove this book from my Shopping Basket. We could continue shopping for other books at this point or go straight to the online checkout to pay.

The next step would be to create an account with the online shop, as this makes it possible to track the order later on. It's only necessary to give them my address and credit card details once though as the shop will remember my details, reducing the tiresome job of typing it in each time I shop. It will also remember the items that you have shopped for, and make recommendations based on the books or CDs that you buy from Amazon. You can also keep a wishlist of items if you do want to buy an item on that particular e-shopping expedition. I can also ask for books to arrive at addresses other than mine, which is useful when sending last minute birthday presents to friends and relatives. Some sites will even giftwrap an item for you!

A padlock on the bottom left of your window means that your details are encoded before they are sent.

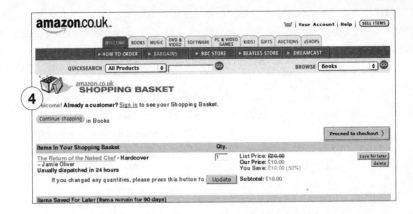

When you submit your details you will notice a yellow padlock at the bottom of the screen. This means that the website is "secure" and that until the transaction has been completed all the information added to the forms will be sent in secret code to the shop.

When we are setting up the account, we will be asked to choose a password. This will have to be entered each time the account is used and so, in order to do this, we are asked to sign in (see step 4, above). It is important to remember whatever password you choose or you won't be able to track your order.

The system will give us a final chance to check that all the details – address, list of purchases, etc – are correct before we decide to go through with the order. Postage and packaging, if not free, should be displayed at this point. When you are sure everything is correct, you can then press the Place Your Order button (see step 5, below).

When a parcel arrives, two or three days later, I guarantee you will be sold on the idea of using the Internet to shop. And I bet that the CD/DVD/bestseller you found was available at a discounted rate.

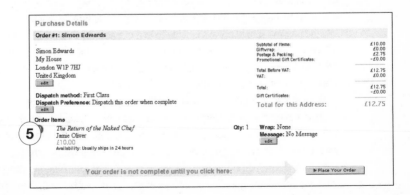

Order tracking is an interesting and useful feature you'll find on all the best websites. You identify yourself to the site using a unique user name and password, and the screen will tell you if your item has been placed into stock yet, whether or not it's actually been shipped out to you, and will possibly also give an estimated delivery date. Sometimes, when you order more than one thing, one item will be in stock while another needs to be ordered from the supplier. Companies like **Amazon.co.uk** will sometimes send the first item and forward the other ones as soon as they become available. You shouldn't be expected to pay extra postage charges for this service. If you use the order tracking facility, you will be able to see exactly what's going on without having to sit in a phone queue to speak to customer services.

What happens if the goods are faulty when they arrive? Or perhaps you don't like the colour of the shirt that looked so appealing on the web page. Maybe you've been sent a completely different item from the one you ordered! As with any business, an Internet shop will have a returns policy that will deal with any such problems.

Buying tips

Use a price comparison site, such as **www.shopsmart.com** or **www.kelkoo.com**, to get the best price on a product. These sites allow you to search for the best price on an item by searching a list of retail sites and giving you the biggest discount, including postage costs and often telling you how long it will take to be delivered.

Given the choice, always use a credit card rather than a debit card. The former protects you when goods are faulty, or don't turn up, and the seller refuses to co-operate. You get your money back, and the credit card company chases the lost money itself. A debit card just provides a way to pay money from your bank account, and can be useful for small purchases, but you don't get any protection from fraudsters.

A good online shop will clearly publish its prices and include any tax you might have to pay. You should always be able to find out how much postage and packing will cost. Some Internet shops provide free delivery, but not all. Reading the small print can be painful – there's usually loads of it – but it is essential that you know what you're letting yourself in for.

Many stores will remember your details, so you won't have to type in your address and card number every time you buy something. "Cookies" are often stored on your computer by the store, so that each time you log into the site, it recognizes your details. If an online shop gives you a user name and password, make sure you keep it in a safe place. You won't want to lose it, and you certainly don't want someone else to find it and go on a spree at your expense. That said, the worst that can happen is that you'll receive a massive package one day. Any customer services department worth its salt will be happy to sort the mess out. It's no different from someone finding your catalogue card and ordering goods with it.

A well-run business in the high street will have a nice, big shop with excellent displays and polite staff. An Internet site can be made to look equally fantastic by anyone with a computer, some cheap software, and a half-decent eye for design. So how can you tell if an e-shop is all it appears? Many major retailers recognize that Internet customer service needs to be of a consistently high quality, but this is no guarantee. Some sites join schemes where they agree to follow a certain code of conduct and, in return, are permitted to display a logo that certifies them as good traders. This is intended to instil confidence in consumers. Don't be taken in by any old certificate, though, as they can be falsely copied or created out of thin air. If in doubt, check the organization's website and see if the shop is listed. The Consumers' Association run a scheme called "Which? Web Trader", with details at **www.which.net/webtrader**.

Buying from foreign websites

You can buy things from websites in other countries very easily. There are bargains to be had, and exclusive luxuries on offer. An increasing number of places will ship goods to anywhere on the planet, and at reasonable rates. But please remember that you will probably have to pay duty and tax. Depending on what you have bought, you may be expected to pay VAT and some other local duty. The Post Office might also make a charge. Always expect to receive a bill from Customs when buying "bargains". That cheap CD could turn out to be more expensive than you think. UK shoppers should visit HM Customs and Excise (**www.hmce.gov.uk**) to get the latest details on import duties, while US customers will find US Customs (**www.customs.ustreas.gov**) useful.

Delivery

As with any mail order transaction, the hardest part of Internet shopping is receiving the goods. Small items that come through the mail will pose little or no problem, but order a computer, freezer, or TV then you'd better make sure you're at home when the courier comes knocking. This is no different from waiting for a delivery from a high-street electrical shop though, and the prices on the Internet are almost certainly cheaper.

The problem of delivery is a bugbear to supermarkets, which desperately want to get on with the serious business of creating massive online stores. Unfortunately, having large, refrigerated delivery lorries hammering through urban areas every five minutes is neither practical nor desirable. As demand rises, we might see vans or even pizza delivery-style motor bikes fulfilling orders. Not yet, though.

Internet auctions

Online auctions can be a fun way to spend or make money via the Internet. Here's how they work. An online auction acts a bit like a classified advertisement page in a local paper. The seller puts up a price that he or she believes is reasonable for their item. If you want an item, click on it and offer an amount, which will be sent to the auction and published on the page – remember that you will have to be a registered user to do this. Other people will do the same, and the price will rise, as with a conventional auction. Online auctions run for a set period of time, possibly one day, but frequently a week or more, and the person who bids the highest at the end gets to buy. Sometimes there is a catch, though. Even if the offer price seems low, that probably means that a reserve price has been placed, so although you may be the highest bidder on an item, if that bid does not reach the reserve price, you can't buy it.

There are a few things to think about when taking part in one of these auctions. First of all, know who you're buying from. If it isn't the auction house itself, or a well known, affiliated company, treat the deal as if it were a classified advert. Don't just send money off to a stranger, because should things go wrong and you end up without your vacuum cleaner/guitar/vase, the auctioneers won't help. Auction sites run self-policing communities, where naughty people are given black marks against their names, but this will be of no comfort to you if your cheque is cashed. Therefore, always check a user rating – if they have a number of dissatisfied customers, then refrain from buying from them. Continual offenders are suspended from trading, though there is no method to stop these people from rejoining under a different user name. Some auction sites are developing schemes where you send the money to them and they release it to the seller once they know that you've actually got the goods. There are also payment schemes using credit cards. Companies such as **www.paypal.com** allow sellers to send the money to the seller electronically. This cuts out the need to send money through the post.

Also bear in mind how you will receive the things you've bought. Will the seller deliver, or will you have to pick them up yourself? Is this feasible if you live in different areas, or even different countries? What about warranties? Don't be blinded by the high-tech fun you're having on the websites. Anyone, including you, can sell through online auctions. And anyone can try to rip you off. Generally, though, honesty prevails, and auctions provide a great hunting ground – just be careful.

How to buy safely

Although your computer isn't being constantly monitored by electronic criminals, all good Internet shops still take serious security measures to make absolutely sure that your credit or debit card numbers remain safe. They do this by creating a special connection between your PC and their site, which encodes the information exchanged between the two. So when you send your name, address, and bank details, they are wrapped up in a secret code and sent to the shop, which can decrypt your details. You may see the abbreviation SSL (Secure Sockets Layer) being mentioned. This is the technical name for a secure connection.

There is a simple way to detect a secure connection. Look at the bottom part of your web browser program. If you can see a small padlock then it is safe to send your details. The website address will also begin https:// rather than the normal http:// – the extra "s" stands for "secure". Sites also provide information about how they will stop people stealing customers' details. If you're still not convinced, did you realize that it is much easier for waiters, shop assistants, and even refuse collectors to find and use your card number than it is for an unauthorized individual on the Internet?

Even though hackers may be a negligible threat, what about the companies themselves? This is where common sense comes in. We are yet to see a viable electronic equivalent to cash, so Internet purchases have to be made using a card of some sort. When you go shopping in town you wouldn't (or at least shouldn't) give your details to every here-today-gone-tomorrow business. Sensible Internet shoppers only use online shops backed up by well known businesses, or at least ones with a genuine postal address and phone number. In the event that something goes wrong, it's easier to chase a company that exists in the physical world than one whose details only consist of a website and email address. Be sensible and I guarantee that you will enjoy the Internet shopping experience!

You can make or spend money at auction sites such as www.ebay.co.uk

(a) # ART, DESIGN, AND ARCHITECTURE

Whether you want to research a 16th-century printmaker or find out about the latest imaging technologies, these sites can help you locate and expand your visual interest. There is an extensive range of museum-based sites and a host of art galleries to sample from around the world. Alternatively, owners of crumbling old historic houses can also find help on the Internet, where the art of masonry restoration is documented, while potential visitors can locate said properties and arrange a viewing. Clothes fashions are equally well catered for and you can click online to find out which pair of trainers is in fashion this week...

— Architecture

Architecture magazine online
www.architecturemag.com
An industry journal and art publication, this bright website gives you all that you might want to know about the world of architecture. Check out previous issues of the magazine, search through the evergrowing database of architecture firms, and also consult the (very much US-based) events calendar. Like some modern architecture, this site is clean to look at, and I assure you, it will definitely grow on you.

Castles on the Web
www.castlesontheweb.com
This site pays homage to hundreds of medieval castles throughout the world. You can take virtual tours of castles or take part in the castle question and answer area. The site is updated regularly, and has a featured castle every day of the year. Marvellous.

The professional architect's online magazine at www.architecturemag.com is a bright affair

Conservation of historic buildings
www.buildingconservation.com

If you own an old building in need of repair and want to either hire a professional to help or go on a course to learn about masonry or stone conservation, then the Building Conservation site is the place to try first. A good selection of online articles by leading authorities covers such areas as repairing reinforced concrete, and fire protection in historic buildings.

Database of buildings and architects
www.greatbuildings.com

Experience the world's best architectural feats with Great Buildings Online, which features a database that can be browsed by place, building, and architect. This handy resource includes a brief history of the constructions and the constructors, bibliographical sources, close-up photographs of buildings from different angles, and in some cases with 3D models. All this will certainly help to answer those awkward architectural arguments and aid with school projects.

The National Trust
www.nationaltrust.org.uk

The National Trust has a great website full of information about places of historic interest or natural beauty in the UK. Find one of their sites through their searchable database by name or by area. A large educational site is also available, with a small photo gallery. Older students may find the Sites of Scientific Interest particularly enjoyable.

Art and artists

Art, artists, galleries, and exhibitions
www.artincontext.com

The stylish, minimalist appearance of Art In Context hides a complex work of reference, containing details of art galleries and dealers, exhibitions, and artists the world over (albeit with a large bias to the United States). You can search for art by genre — every discernable style is listed here — and there is also an image database.

Art database and news
www.artcult.com

An up-to-date news service and a database of 30,000 paintings, complete with average auction prices, makes Artcult a compelling site for all art investors. The site also includes detailed advice for collectors on how to avoid fake goods, and

The world's most famous auction house is far from antiquated online at www.christies.com

also houses a comprehensive artist biography list. Don't be put off by the rather intimidating, ugly page design, and the occasional irrelevancies here.

Art, design, architecture and media gateway
adam.ac.uk

This academic site aims to provide students in higher education with access to the highest-quality information on fine art, design, architecture, applied arts (crafts), film studies, and art history.

Art Encyclopedia
www.artcyclopedia.com

With this huge database of over 700 sites, you can find out about over 7500 artists, which are searchable by movement, medium, subject, nationality, or the traditional way – by name. The "Top 30" most popular artist searches are updated monthly. There is also an extensive list of art museums throughout the world, from places as remote as Bermuda and Taiwan.

Art Lover's Guide to Britain and Ireland
www.artguide.org

This guide to the art collections of Great Britain and Ireland contains details of around 2000 "named" artists, more than 650 museums, and a large database of what exhibitions are currently on. There aren't any pictures here (try **www.southern.net/wm** for those), but each artist's entry has a list of venues in the UK exhibiting their work.

Christie's
www.christies.com

The official website of the famous auction house that existed long before the likes of QXL has an auction calendar and a gallery of items, and you can view the sometimes ridiculous sums of money people will pay for old things. You can plan your next purchase or simply save your money and watch live webcasts of the auctions themselves, often at the New York auction house.

An introduction to art
www.southern.net/wm

Art students and amateur enthusiasts alike will enjoy WebMuseum's glossary of artistic movements, a thorough artists index, and list of themes – from Picasso and Cubism to Japanese Momoyama Art. The special exhibitions present very good reproductions of famous artists' paintings, listed by theme. In the past the site has featured the works of Paul Cezanne as well as including an exhibition of the *Très Riches Heures* manuscript.

a

The Louvre
www.louvre.fr

This stylish official site contains a selection of exhibitions with photos and short descriptions, a virtual tour of the museum, and a list of events. You can also buy tickets for entry to the museum from the site, to help you avoid those lengthy queues. Whether you are interested in the ancient Egyptians, 14th-century prints and drawings, or even the history of the Louvre itself you will be satisfied.

Mechanical sculpture theatre
www.cabaret.co.uk

Experience the strange world of mechanical sculpture (automatons). This site is based around contemporary moving models, and the online exhibition gives you some idea of what it is all about. You can order all different kinds of mechanical contraptions from the site, which will be sent out to you wherever you are in the world, and there is a useful education section, which is great for teachers and students alike.

The Metropolitan Museum of Art
www.metmuseum.org

5000 years of art from around the world are displayed in this New York museum, and almost 3500 objects are reproduced here on this site. You can view highlights from the collection of your choice, and by signing the Guestbook you can customize your own online calendar and Met gallery to display only those museum events and works of art that most interest you. Like the real thing, you could spend days here.

Museum of Modern Art
www.moma.org

View a selection of the collection from this New-York based museum, which includes more than 100,000 paintings, sculptures, drawings, and photographs. Films and books can also be found here. There is information about the museum's educational resources that will help you to appreciate and enjoy the works on display, and you can even purchase fashion accessories and furniture from the online store.

Online art gallery
www.artandparcel.com

This online art gallery sells paintings direct from the web page. You can view a directory of artists and see pictures that are listed according to their category. Aspiring artists are also invited to sell their works here. Some artists will work to your commission, and the site boasts examples from over 100 of them.

Site for artists
www.artswire.org

Aiming to bring artists together over the web, this site features links to members' own sites as well as discussion forums, mailing lists, and exhibitions. Weekly news is available directly from the site, and an art-based jobs list (in the US) can also be found here.

The Tate Gallery
www.tate.org.uk

Find out about the four Tate galleries (including the impressive new Tate Modern) and buy prints, slides, and books from the online shop. Even if you don't wish to buy, you can browse plenty of images of paintings, which are all organized by artist and date.

Virtual art gallery
www.art.net

Experience the work of over 100 artists from all over the world at this virtual art gallery. The featured pieces of art range from sculptures to digitally created pictures. Animations, music, and poetry are also available here. Art on the Net includes sites set up by many of the artists involved, so expect a varying degree of quality within them.

Worldwide arts
www.world-arts-resources.com

This all-in-one site tries to cover everything artistic including antiques, dance, opera, and architecture. Even very modern techniques, like Manga cartoons, are covered. It also has an artist portfolio that is changed daily. The massive, searchable database of links to other websites makes World Wide Arts Resources an ideal springboard to other parts of the Internet. Use it to compile a list of your favourite arty sites.

Fashion

The Museum of Costume
www.museumofcostume.co.uk

Anyone interested in the clothes of yesteryear will find the short tour a good introduction to what people were wearing up until the 1960s. Although it offers only a taster of what is available at the museum, you can search the database of 18th-century waistcoats and follow a sound set of links.

Get biographies of all your favourite designers at www.fashion.net

Online fashion magazine
ntouch.linst.ac.uk

Claiming to be the future of fashion magazines, *NTOUCH* is designed and run by the London College of Fashion. You can read about the new wave of supermodels or just find out which trainers are cool this week. The site makes heavy use of Flash and so can be slow to download.

Suppliers' directory
www.whoapparel.co.uk

Who Apparel publishes a directory for suppliers to the fashion industry. Companies are listed in categories such as womenswear, menswear, and services including warehousing facilities. A news service, provided by an external source, has been tailored for people working in the clothes business, although stories from the world's headlines and general business news items are also given.

Vogue magazine
www.vogue.co.uk

Check out the daily fashion news to pick up on what's what in the fashion world. View virtual fashion shows and see the seasonal collections here. You can also see the covers of a selection of past issues, dating back as far as 1946, and view the online archives. Short summaries of what was "in" make for interesting reading, as does "Who's Who", which gives you the low-down on the big fashion names.

You can also buy clothing from the online shop, get your daily horoscope, and also read some of the features that appear in the current month's edition.

The World of Fashion
www.fashion.net

If you really want to know about what is happening in every area of the fashion world, then this US-based site is the place to look. Fashion news is updated daily so you can read up-to-date profiles of the designers, models, stylists etc, watch runway videos, and find out how to get a job in fashion.

Photography

Camera hints and tips
photo.net/photo

If you want to know what sort of camera to buy, where to get it from, and how to take brilliant, colourful photos then try this site. But be aware that the author's language can be colourful too. Gear reviews are included, making your shopping expeditions for camera equipment much, much easier, and handy hints and tips on light and film usage help you take that perfect picture. Once taken, you can post it on the site to be entered for "Photograph of the Week".

Digital photographs
www.zing.com

If you own a digital camera (and if you own a computer, it might make sense to get one), then this site will help you improve those pictures. Follow the online tutorials and, once you are happy, why not store the results online, create your own album of pictures, order prints, or even create your own postcards. If you are confident enough, visit the frame gallery, see others' photos and add your own!

For professionals
www.photodisc.com

Helpful site for the lens professional with almost 100,000 high quality downloadable images from some top photographers. You can buy CDs of stock images in its store. Registration is required to access the full site.

Kodak
www.kodak.co.uk

Kodak's site acts as an introduction to both traditional and newer imaging technologies. You can learn how film processing works and discover what you'll

a

need to create digital pictures you can store on CD or send by email. The "Photonet" service lets friends and relatives see your efforts or order reprints, even from overseas. If you want a more celebrity-oriented approach then try the US site at **www.kodak.com**.

The photographs of Life Magazine
www.pathfinder.com/life

Some of the world's greatest photography has been made for *Life* magazine – and here is a selection for the world to see. It's worth returning on a regular basis to check out the picture of the day and see what was going on in the world on "This Day in Life". You should also take an extended visit to marvel at the 20th-century's best pictures selection, which are each accompanied by an audio commentary from one of the magazine's photographers.

— see also...

As I have shown, there is a wide selection of art galleries available on the Internet, and The Art Canvas (**theartcanvas.com**) can often be a good place to start, with its high quality, scanned images of works from a variety of 19th- and 20th-century painters and sculptors. For paintings and sculptures specifically from the Gothic, Renaissance, and Baroque periods, you should try the Web Gallery of Art (**gallery.euroweb.hu**). Artinfo: From Russia With Art (**www.artinfo.ru**) provides access to information on more than 1000 high-profile Russian artists. The Official Magritte Site (**www.magritte.com**) provides a biography of the artist, as well as books and CD-ROMs to buy. A wider selection of virtual galleries is available from Mark Harden's Artchive (**www.artchive.com**), which also contains extracts of critiques and CD-ROM reviews.

The London National Gallery (**www.nationalgallery.org.uk**) has plenty of information on its collections, as well as an exhibition history and details of those coming up in the next year. It has a job competing with the Fine Arts Museums of San Francisco (**www.thinker.org**), though, which features more than 70,000 images. The Detroit Institute of Arts (**www.dia.org**), one of the largest fine arts museums in the US, has a site featuring information on its collections, video lectures, and a bit of online shopping to boot. For a more European flavour, visit the Uffizi Gallery's official site (**www.uffizi.firenze.it**). Within seconds you can also explore the National Museums of Scotland site (**www.nms.ac.uk**). The Smithsonian American Art Museum (**nmaa-ryder.si.edu**) features art collections, event calendars, and a study centre.

ArtMag (**www.artmag.com**) contains listings of art galleries, artistic events, museums, and photographic galleries all over the world while dedicated photography fans can view the works of a number of skilled photographers at Masters of Photography (**www.masters-of-photography.com**). You should also check out Focus Online (**www.focus-online.com**), a film and digital photography magazine with advice and galleries of work. The strange Secret Garden (**www-personal.umich.edu/~agrxray**) exhibits extraordinary floral radiograph images, where flowers have been photographed using an X-ray machine.

If sculpture's your thing, then check out the International Sculpture Center (**www.sculpture.org**) as it should satisfy your desire for conference listings and details of artists and their works. View a selection of British sculptures at British Contemporary Sculpture (**www.sculpture.org.uk**). Some of the exhibition examples are also for sale. You can buy from the selections of international goods on sale at the Folk Art and Craft Exchange (**www.folkart.com**) too. You can't buy the gargoyles on exhibition at Gargoyles Then and Now (**ils.unc.edu/garg**), but then you probably wouldn't want to. Equally weird is **www.masks.org**, where you can find out about mask-making artists and cultural masks. Art students might enjoy the Art Comics Syndicate (**www.artcomic.com**), with its stylistic cartoons (that would love to be thought of as avant-garde). Frieze (**www.frieze.co.uk**) is a magazine on contemporary art and culture, which includes visual arts, design, film, and fashion – and, strangely enough, horticulture! Traditionalists will feel more at home visiting a tribute site to the graphical satirist William Hogarth at (**www.lamp.ac.uk/hogarth**). You might also appreciate Internet for the Fine Arts (**www.fine-art.com**), where you can browse through virtual art galleries, find out about student organizations, and see the work of some very talented people. Real art swots will love Aesthetics Online (**www.aesthetics-online.org**), complete with articles on aesthetics and art philosophy, theory, and criticism.

Fashion lovers should visit *Elle* Magazine's official site (**www.ellemag.com**), where you can have a look at the famous magazine's worldwide presence. Or, if you fancy buying some fashion, then you should try **www.fashionmall.com**, a US-based fashion shop with some of the top American high street names. Probably one of the most famous websites is **www.boo.com**. This was one of the most famous dotcoms to crash, but it has since been revitalized and Miss Boo is still your host around the shop. Fingers crossed that it succeeds.

Professional and amateur photographers alike can visit any one of Nikon's worldwide sites from its portal at **www.nikon.com**. Once you have all the information to purchase your camera, learn to take better pictures with advice from the professionals at **www.betterphoto.com**.

BOOKS

b) Some of the most successful businesses on the Internet have started off by selling books – the market for the bestsellers is fiercely competitive and shopping around can bring discounts of up to 50 per cent. There are dozens of sites selling books and it would take a book to name them all, but we do list some of the best. The turn of the millennium has seen the first tentative steps towards ebooks (notably by major author Stephen King), by which you download the author's work from the web. There is also plenty of academic information available, from critical works to specialist dictionaries. Rhyming dictionaries may help writers out of a block, while book reviews could tempt you to try using the online shops. Online literature magazines are to be found, as is plenty to encourage younger readers.

Author sites

Agatha Christie
christie.mysterynet.com

The official site of one of the 20th century's most popular writers. It contains lists of her books, plays, and films based on her work. For the avid sleuths, there is the Tuesday Murder Club; every Tuesday "in a cozy English cottage, six friends gather by the hearth and exchange tales of true crime". A must bookmark site for the mystery book lover.

British greats
www.incompetech.com/authors

For those looking for a bluffer's guide to the greats of English literature, you couldn't get a much better start than here. Included are short, pithy biographies of 26 major authors, from Charlotte "Jane Eyre" Brontë to William "The Overanalyzed" Shakespeare. Writers are categorized by colour-coded symbols denoting poets, novelists, playwrights, essayists, and journalists. The biographies have obscure and interesting facts to impress your more literary friends.

Danielle Steel
www.randomhouse.com/features/steel

b

The queen of romantic fiction is an author who takes an active interest in her website. She writes regular letters to her fans, with some quite astounding honesty. There is also a personal scrapbook on the site, the opportunity for visitors to read excerpts from her books, the obligatory, exhaustive bibliography, and a trivia contest too.

Harry Potter
www.bloomsbury.com/harrypotter

The biggest worldwide literary phenomenon of recent years has hundreds of fan sites, but the official one is definitely worth a visit for wannabe Hogwarts students. Playfully interactive (you can enter the site as a muggle and a wizard), there is also an interview with his creator JK Rowling, reviews, and gossip. For those of you who know how, why not scare your friends and send them a howler...

Roald Dahl
www.roalddahlfans.com

The most exhaustive site on the top-selling children's author to be found on the web, this has resources for students, teachers, and fans. It is filled with meticulous biographical information, plot info on all his stories, and movies based on his work. Sadly, excerpts from the man's work are limited, but this site still makes for an excellent read.

The Shakespeare Birthplace Trust
www.shakespeare.org.uk

This site, based around the great bard's historic birthplace in Stratford, is full of biographical detail from Shakespeare's life. Mini online tours are available of the houses in which the playwright lived, together with details for visitors who wish to see them in the flesh. There are several educational resources.

Stephen King
www.stephenking.com

Few famous writers are brave enough to venture onto the web in person. Not so Stephen King. This stylish official site deals with the facts behind the fiction – King answers rumours and criticism, and provides insights into his motivation and influences. Enjoyable, well-written articles will delight aficionados, and may even whet the appetites of newcomers to the man's work. You can also download his e-novel *The Plant*, downloadable in eight installments of between $1 and $2 – worth trying just for the novelty value.

Underground authors of America
www.instantclassics.com

Instant Classics reads pretty much like a treatise on the strange. Art, comics, poetry, fiction, non-fiction, and the general outpourings of American underground culture are jumbled to amusing effect. Links take you to authors' own websites. Note: the site contains some adult-oriented material.

What a tangled web they weave...
www.twbooks.co.uk

An excellent site for lovers of all crime, mystery, and fantastic fiction. Inside the obligatorily creepy design is a huge book section, profiles of over 300 authors, reviews of the latest titles, and essays on mystery fiction.

The world of underground writing
www.levity.com/corduroy

This exquisitely named site, Bohemian Ink, is devoted to "underground writing". A broad range of cult figures is covered with brief biographies, and snippets of the authors' work are included. Every entry comes complete with a raft of links for those keen to shed a little more light on these literary obscurities.

— Browsers

Browsing by genre
www.bookbrowser.com

Stuck for what to read next? BookBrowser makes the task of finding fiction easier by grouping books by genre, identifying the next title in a series you've read, or suggesting a similar or related author. Selections are largely middle-brow US titles, but with over 3000 reviews – and 15 more added each week – you're bound to find something worth looking at.

Texts online
digital.library.upenn.edu/books

Contains links to over 12,000 (mostly academic) titles in all fields, all available as etexts, searchable by author, subject, or title. Foreign titles from countries as far afield as Spain, Czechoslovakia, and Denmark are covered, and the site also

Find out what's new in cult fiction at www.levity.com/corduroy

boasts special features on subjects of interest from women's writing to censorship. This site is hosted by the University of Pennsylvania, and is updated almost daily.

— For book lovers

Directory of antiquarian bookshops and dealers
biblion.co.uk

Biblion is trumpeted as a "bookshop of bookshops": in practice, it's a directory of specialist second-hand and antiquarian book dealers in the UK. This professional-looking site enables you to join as a dealer and search the stock lists of a wide range of participating dealers. Biblion also offers secure online purchasing, so you can get your hands on that hard-to-get title without even leaving home!

The Gutenberg Bible
www.osl.state.or.us/csimages/bible/bible.htm

This site outlines the exhibition of a reproduction of the famous bible printed by Johannes Gutenberg in 1455. Gutenberg is credited as the father of modern printing, and this informative site provides in-depth biographical information, together with sample pages from the book to download and links to other book resources on the web.

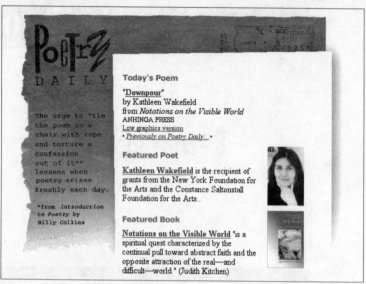

Liven up your day with a piece of poetry from www.poems.com

History of Reading Codes for the Blind
www.nyise.org/blind

The New York Institute for Special Education here provides you with a fascinating insight into books and reading systems that are used by blind readers, from Louis Braille onwards. Hypertext links take you on to illustrated resources on the various systems that are in use around the world. The site is also available to view in large print form.

Keeping the written word
www.pro.gov.uk/preservation/guides

This is an excellent British site that is actually an extension of the Public Records Office. It tells you everything that there is to know about book conservation and also includes articles on English paper with information on writing inks and watermarks. It has a number of Adobe Acrobat files ready for you to download and help preserve your books.

Your daily poetry break
www.poems.com

Need a piece of poetry to liven up your day? This is the perfect site with a great anthology of modern poetry. You can check out the featured poet and journals, or subscribe to the free email newsletter. If your tastes verge on the classical, then try **www.geocities.com/Athens/Delphi/7086/pod.htm**.

— For writers —

Advice for writers
writerswrite.com

b

There are many resources for writers on the web, few of them good. Writers Write avoids the usual plunge into pretentious waffle and provides a wealth of solid advice and resources for aspiring authors. You can also read book excerpts and book reviews. Information is sensibly divided by genres. Unfortunately, most contacts are US-based, but the tutorial sections will provide some useful pointers.

Hints and tips for writers
www.inkspot.com

Inkspot provides expert advice on polishing your prose, both for book publication and for budding writers of etexts. Tips and tutorials are arranged by genre, potential writers can go through the lessons in the workshop, and users can subscribe to the pithy email newsletter, *Inkling*, for regular updates. Inkspot's lively chat forums are a great place for exchanging ideas, too.

Poetry resource
www.poetrykit.org

UK-based site The Poetry Kit is an archive of features, interviews, listings, and links of use to aspiring poets and published writers alike. It also lists the various poetry readings and events going on in countries around the world. Okay, so the features are thin on the ground and it is definitely not the most pretty of sites, but the extensive collection of links makes it the perfect springboard to poetry resources on the web.

Publish Your Own Book
www.iuniverse.com

Get past the slightly self-important and verbose intro and you have a site that lets you publish your own book. The site offers potential publishers information on rights management and website hosting. Their services even include the ebook cover design.

Writing for the Internet
www.ebooknet.com

Under the slogan "Building the eBook community", optimistic eBookNet is dedicated towards the success of the general-purpose Open eBook file standard. It includes in-depth articles not only for readers of ebooks, but it is also aimed at those writing them. The slant of the site is towards encouraging new talent that might otherwise be dissuaded by the cost of traditional publishing. You should also check out Online Originals for a great selection of works only available online. A lively read.

b)

News and reviews

Arts and Letters Daily
www.cybereditions.com/aldaily
With links to high-brow debates on literature, philosophy, and high culture, Arts and Letters Daily has an excellent news resource with links to all the major world broadsheets, magazines, and journals.

BookEnds
www.bookends.co.uk
UK magazine BookEnds is a great place to catch up with popular titles. It's also packed with interesting (and often satirical) spin-off articles on topics relating to featured books, so it's also a leisurely means of keeping track of current affairs. A search engine helps you locate items of interest that you can then buy online. The site offers exclusive fiction from well-known authors, as well as interviews with rising and known stars, reviews, excerpts, and competitions.

The BookSeller
www.thebookseller.co.uk
Book enthusiasts and publishing types alike will want to check out the UK's leading book trade journal. As well as the dry industry-related news, you'll find author profiles and special features, as well as a publishing jobs list, and links to virtually every major publisher website. Handy services such as the twice-yearly "Buyer's Guide" are available to subscribers. An archive allows you to search articles from the magazine dating back to 1995.

Books Unlimited
www.booksunlimited.co.uk
The online book arm of the award-winning *Guardian* newspaper website follows its mother site's lead and so is clean and easy to read. The usual extensive reviews and bestseller lists are here, along with an author database and the chance to read the first chapters of the more literary books on the market. If you don't fancy reading a whole novel, why not glance over the Digested Read – the latest releases condensed into 400 words.

BookWire
www.bookwire.com

This spin-off from the publishing industry is a great place to keep up-to-date with the latest releases. BookWire provides US bestseller listings, as well as news and reviews. Special features provide an informative take on book genres and issues, while famous authors talk you through their picks from the world of literature.

b

Daily Telegraph reviews
www.booksonline.co.uk

Booksonline is a regular online publication from *The Daily Telegraph* stable, incorporating new reviews every day, split into easy-to-navigate categories, plus access to the entire catalogue of reviews published in *The Telegraph* since it went online in 1996.

Newsrack
www.newsrack.com

Skip past the Flash intro movie, not usually associated with this sort of site, and you are faced with an impressive world map. Click on the continent that takes your fancy and search for any and every magazine and newspaper. An excellent resource for any budding journalist.

Publishers Weekly
www.publishersweekly.com

All the latest news reports for publishers and booksellers from the (mainly) US book world are here. Read interviews past and present, and find out when your favourite author will be making an appearance in your town.

Pure Fiction
www.purefiction.com

Recently redesigned, this is a site for book lovers and aspiring writers, and has reviews and writing advice, as well as a writers' showcase. The bookshop contains over 1.2 million titles, so potential writers should not lack inspiration here.

— Online shops

Amazon
www.amazon.com

Probably the most famous site on the web, with mirror sites all over the world (the UK site is found at **www.amazon.co.uk**), it has now expanded into more and more areas – music, auctions, DVDs, computer games, and toys to name but a few. You can read reviews written by other customers, locate every book in print in the US or UK, and have your selected books delivered within a few days. The postage charges unfortunately remove the sweet taste of discounted prices but at least you can shop from your chair – and its customer service is second to none.

Antiquarian bookshop
www.shapero.com

Bernard J Shapero is an online antiquarian bookshop specializing in maps, travel literature, and illustrated and colour plate books. Its services include the ability to order over the Internet, plus regular mailing lists of catalogues and acquisitions via email. Subscribers can submit a detailed account of their interests to pinpoint titles that should interest them quickly.

Book clubs
www.booksdirect.co.uk

If you feel that your interests would be best served by a specialist book club, then try out **www.booksdirect.co.uk**. For example, if you are interested in food, then why not join the Taste Book Club? Or if you are more of a Pratchett fan, then join the Fantasy and Science Fiction Club. Whatever your taste, this site has links to over 20 book clubs, with unbeatable joining offers to entice you to join.

Borders
www.borders.com

Read extracts from the latest bestsellers and learn all about your favourite authors from their interviews. Do you want to know who won the Pulitzer Prizes in 1973? The answers to all similar questions are here, along with the chance to buy books.

Waterstone's
www.waterstones.co.uk

Not quite as all-embracing as Amazon, Waterstone's still encompasses a range of over 1.2 million titles. Best buys here are the front-page bestsellers, with a tempting up to 50 per cent off. Shopping here, like at Amazon, is a simple matter of filling a virtual basket with books and heading for the "checkout". Most books promise to be dispatched within two days. Like Amazon, you can track the status of your ordered goods.

WHSmith
www.whsmith.co.uk

Not just a newsagent and bookshop, WHSmith has really embraced the Internet and turned its site into a place where you can not only spend your money on

Online booksellers dominate the web – and www.borders.com is better than most

books, videos, CDs, and stationery but also search the Internet, look things up in an online encyclopedia, and even sign up for the company's own brand of free Internet access.

— Online texts to download —

Anthologies of English Verse
www.bartleby.com/verse
Project Bartleby is the University of Columbia's etext archive. Here, at BartlebyVerse, you'll find six of the most authoritative anthologies of English verse, including the *Oxford Book of English Verse*, in electronic format. A perfect introduction to poetry.

A world of literature
www.gutenberg.net
This is the last word in electronic books. The US Gutenberg team has been converting texts to electronic formats since 1971, so the library's catalogue is now absolutely vast. Entire, copyright-free book titles are presented – completely free of charge – as text files that can be downloaded and then printed out for your perusal. The titles offered cover fiction and non-fiction alike and are drawn from all over the world.

Penguin have many authors under their wing and plenty of good web stuff. Visit www.penguin.co.uk

Publishers' sites

Dorling Kindersley online
www.dk.com/uk

The company may have been taken over by Pearson media, but the still-adventurous publisher, which was one of the first to venture into computer-based publishing, continues to be a leading web-publishing presence. The site provides much more than online shopping, with plenty of content provided free – one unique feature is the ability to look inside any book before buying.

Harper Collins
www.fireandwater.com

Browse the books published by Harper Collins in dozens of subject areas, read the interviews with their authors, and enter the competitions. The US-based site can be found at **www.harpercollins.com**.

Penguin and Puffin
www.penguin.co.uk

An impressive site, heavily reliant on Flash, it is incredibly high on content, with many well designed mini-sites for its major authors, such as Alex Garland and Nick Hornby. It also includes the Puffin Books (**www.puffin.co.uk**) site, which is a visual treat for kids and provides many fun activities too.

Reader's Digest
www.readersdigest.co.uk
Find all sorts of interesting articles, mildly amusing jokes, and discover the magically abridged world of condensed books that you can buy online. There are also top tips for travel and health, and a prize draw on this publisher's site. You can access other Reader's Digest sites from around the world too.

— Writers' prizes and libraries —

The Booker Prize
www.bookerprize.co.uk
This is the authorized site of the UK's most prestigious literary award. It features lists of previous shortlists and winners, together with details of winners over the last 30 years. A particular highlight is the streaming "RealAudio" recording of the shortlisted authors reading from their work. Reading the quotes from Booker winners and other authors about the award will keep you entertained, and you can also check on last year's bookies' odds.

The British Library
www.bl.uk
Now relocated to London's Euston Road, the British Library has made a determined push towards digital media. And the venerable institution takes its online service very seriously: its book-resource database, BLAISE, contains over 18.5 million entries – and the list is growing all the time. Its new service "Inside" will deliver journals and texts to its users via PDF and other formats – an invaluable tool to researchers. You'll also find details of the Library's collections and special exhibits, as well as information about visiting the library.

Library of Congress
lcweb.loc.gov
This is the fascinating homepage of the US Library of Congress. The site offers beautifully illustrated guides to special exhibits at the Library, plus web-based research materials. Online exhibits on ancient written cultures, from the Dead Sea Scrolls to the Vatican Library, are particularly worth a look.

The New York Public Library
www.nypl.org
Here you can find opening details of all the different branches and details of all the collections. Through the site's online services, US residents can even place

reserves on items of their choice found in the Library's catalogue, as well as review the status of books checked out. The Teenlink takes you to other Internet sites for homework help, sports information, and advice on college and careers.

The Pulitzer Prizes
www.pulitzer.org/navigation/index.html
This is the official site of the world-famous American prizes for journalism, and it features articles on winners as well as a comprehensive archive containing original works – words, pictures, and sound – from previous winners back to 1917. An interesting "History" section details the life of founder Joseph Pulitzer and the development of the prizes.

— see also...

With so many book websites on the Internet, one of the most difficult tasks is simply to decide which ones are actually worth a look: **www.whitbread-bookawards.co.uk** gives you the low-down on which ones impressed the Whitbread judges. High-brow literary review *The Times Literary Supplement* also has its presence on the web at **www.the-tls.co.uk**. Reviews and sample chapters can be accessed at **www.realbooks.com**.

If you get hooked on an author, what then? **www.catharton.com/authors** provides links to sites on many major writers, while Charles Dickens has his own site at **www.geocities.com/Athens/Styx/8490**, as does Sir Arthur Conan-Doyle at **www.sherlock-holmes.co.uk**. For the lovers of sci-fi writer Terry Pratchett, there are numerous sites, including the Discworld Monthly site (**www.ufbs.co.uk/dwm**). The Bronte Parsonage Museum has a website at **www.bronte.org.uk**, where you can read about the three sisters and the inspiration behind classics like *Wuthering Heights*. If poets are your thing, this German-based site on Ted Hughes is one of the best (**www.uni-leipzig.de/~angl/hughes.htm**). Lovers of rhymes, meanwhile, should venture to the Online Dictionary of Rhymes (**rhyme.lycos.com**) to release their inner poet. They might soon join the 2.4 million poets reputed to be contained at **www.poetry.com**, although, if a browser, just stick to the 100 greatest poems.

But what of lesser-known figures? Read their words in webzines like **www.zetnet.co.uk/oigs/gazet**. Or perhaps you should get involved yourself? Don't be shy – submit you own work to **www.oneofus.co.uk**, to Maybe, Later **www.illyria.com/webzine.html**, or to the more high-minded **trace.ntu.ac.uk/**. And from the obscure to the unintelligible, dedicated lovers of the beat generation should make a beeline for **www.charm.net/~brooklyn/LitKicks.html**.

The online bookshops are phenomenal, and the competition means that there are a lot of them out there... Here are just some of them, all with their own merits: **www.bol.com**, **www.barnesandnoble.com**, **www.thebookpeople.com**, and **www.alphabetstreet.co.uk**. More academic books can be found at **www.blackwells.co.uk**. Most of these will draw a blank if a book's out of print but that's not a problem for The BookFinder General. You can visit him at **www.nwnet.co.uk/BFG/about.htm**.

b

Soon, though, books won't just go out of print. According to some people, there will be no print at all – which is where sites like **www.openebook.org** and **eserver.org** all come in, spreading the gospel of non-print. And owners of palmtop computers can even download etext-reading software from **www.mobipocket.com**.

Print may not yet be history, but there's certainly some history behind it. See it at **www.sc.edu/library/spcoll/sccoll/renprint/renprint.html**. And if that whets your appetite to discover more of the forgotten art of bookbinding, seek good advice from **www.stemnet.nf.ca/~barobert/bindery/index1**. Of course, some books don't die without a fight – **www.ala.org/bbooks** commemorates titles and authors past and present that have fallen victim to the censor. Publisher Random House showcases its own banned titles from history at **www.randomhouse.com/books/bannedbooks**. The rogue's gallery includes *Huckleberry Finn*, would you believe?

COMPUTERS

A very large chunk of the world wide web is devoted to computers because the Internet was originally the domain of the nerd and, also, because it is the ideal way to share computer-oriented knowledge and files. You will find technical help, free programs and utilities to make your computer work better, and low-cost add-ons from the many online shops. You won't have to be a genius to understand much of the available data, though, because a large part of the information is aimed at less experienced users. But if you want to get techie, you can find things that will really challenge your brain and make you spend far too much time away from your family...

— Computer reference sites —

All your questions answered
www.experts-exchange.com

Don't suffer the frustrations of a broken computer, erratic printer, or a wonky word processor. Quiz the experts available at this site, or browse through the answers to other people's queries. The site works on a points system. The longer you are a (free) member, the more points you have and the more difficult and frequent your questions are allowed to be. Earn extra points by answering other people's questions. The most popular topics are listed on the front page.

Computer graphics programs and techniques
www.pcartist.com

Whether you want to know what computer graphics programs to use, or which compression techniques are best for web graphics, this site should help you out. There are reviews of all the major graphics tools that you might need to use on the web, from Dreamweaver to Paintshop Pro. There is a good mix of easy ("What are vector graphics?") and hard ("The lowdown on cgi") articles, but all of them

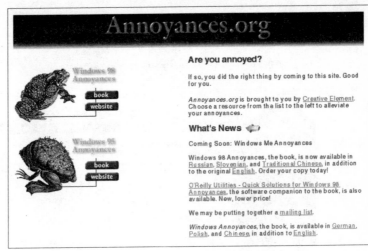

Get relief from the frustrations of your computer at www.annoyances.org

are really just introductions to their subjects. Read everything on this site and then follow the supplied links in order to become an expert on computer design.

The Computer History Museum Site
www.computerhistory.org

Follow the thrilling (sometimes) history of computers, robots, and the Internet, with the well constructed and colourful timelines within this site. The museum itself is based in California, but here you can view its online archives and exhibits. Do beware of the online photo collection, however – it frequently crashes.

Computer support site
www.annoyances.org

You will find so much information about optimizing and fixing your Windows software here that you'll probably not bother with any other Internet offerings – and that includes Microsoft's technical support section. The Annoyances site includes help on Windows 95, 98, and 2000. Book versions of the help given are available, with titles covering Office 97 and other Microsoft programs.

Computing dictionary
www.webopedia.com

The Webopedia is an online dictionary of computing and Internet terms, and very useful it is too if you want to understand any of the technical websites that abound. You can educate yourself by traversing the categories and finding the meaning to such terms as BLOB, nibble, and FAQ.

Computer geeks will be kept goggle happy at www.geek.com

For all techies, geeks, and nerds
www.geek.com

As if the Internet didn't have enough nerdy websites, Geek.com is dedicated to those who spend a large amount of time online, can program a VCR without the manual, and would only consider using PCs they'd built themselves. A technical glossary will help you through the tough times, and there are hints on the technical necessities to consider when buying a laptop or PC. Tips, tricks, and technology news all adds up to a winning result for nerds everywhere.

Internet etiquette (netiquette)
www.albion.com/netiquette/

The Internet is a wonderful resource allowing everyone equal access to each other's opinions. However, sadly not everyone is equally as nice and touchy individuals can become offensive if you display what they consider to be bad Internet manners. Avoid nasty emails by reading the Netiquette Home Page and following its advice.

New Information Society Initiative
www.ukonlineforbusiness.gov.uk

Small businesses can get advice on how to use technology effectively to compete in their particular market. Find your nearest ISI Centre and organize an appointment, browse through the free booklets (in Adobe Acrobat format), and read case studies of competitors who have already taken the plunge into the 21st century. For the serious there is an outline of the UK Government's Policy for the Information Age too.

Online dictionary of computing
www.foldoc.org
This site enables you to search for the meanings of the immense number of often baffling computing terms there are out there. Links to other sites are included in the relevant places, making this an ideal resource for learning about computing. If you find yourself returning frequently, which, let's face it is quite likely as it is so useful, consider downloading the text version of the site to your PC to save your phone bill.

Using the web anonymously
www.anonymizer.com
I'm sure you have nothing to hide, but there is a principle behind using the Internet anonymously and this site goes some way towards letting you visit websites without giving away too much about yourself. All you need to do is visit the Anonymizer and enter another website's address on its page. You'll then be completely secret and safe thereon in when you are exploring the wonders of the Internet.

— Hardware —

Getting the best out of your PC
www.hardwarecentral.com
If you want to get every last drop of performance out of your PC then follow the advice on this site to fully optimize your system. The extensive forums should answer any questions about your desktop PC that you might have. There is extensive advice on overclocking, a technique that can be used to turbo-charge your PC's processor.

Guide to hardware
www.tomshardware.com
If you'd like to become more familiar with the contents of your PC then read the German doctor Tom Pabst's findings. He regularly puts the latest hardware through performance tests and offers his comments in no uncertain terms. With his help, you'll become a PC guru in no time.

— Literature/articles

Computer Buyer Magazine
www.computerbuyer.co.uk

The online presence of the UK magazine is packed with reviews of the latest PCs, hardware, and software, and is an indispensable site for anyone wanting to buy a PC or upgrade an existing model. The Top 50 award (based on opinion) ensures that the equipment listings are always up-to-date. The daily news service and an active chat forum make this an essential visit.

Finding technical books
www.oreilly.com

For details of some of the most useful and technical computer books, try the site of the book publisher O'Reilly & Associates. If you want to find a book about simply using the Internet, or writing a letter using a word processor, though, look elsewhere. Only hardcore nerds wanting to learn about HTML, Perl, and Linux need apply – and if you are feeling extra lucky, then why not ask Tim O'Reilly a question, although you should make sure it is complex enough.

Maximum PC Network
www.maximumpc.com

Home of the US *Maximum PC* magazine, this mini network of technical sites aims to educate wannabe nerds in the ways of building fast PCs, creating home networks, and running performance benchmark tests. *Maximum PC* magazine's own website features reviews, too, and news for the technically inclined, and you can take part in the online auctions to sell your old stuff and upgrade.

News For Nerds
www.slashdot.org

This is a great place to visit if you want the latest computer-based news. The scope of this site isn't limited to computers, though. World issues, comics, music, and games are all covered. Anyone is allowed to submit articles, so if you have an opinion or specialist knowledge of Linux then let them know.

News on technology
www.theregister.co.uk

The Register is an online technology newspaper that is full of tasty gossip, supposition, and speculation. It's frequently right, too. This site is a must for the budding techie entrepreneur. Visit The Register regularly if you want to feel

www.theregister.co.uk is a site with no thrills but mountains of information

yourself at the heart of the so-called "IT industry", although to get the real experience you should actually spend a few hours in the pub first...

Ziff Davis: reviews and advice
www.zdnet.com

Hardware and software reviews, hints, tips, and help – it's all published on ZDNet, the enormous website run by computer publishing monster Ziff Davis. The websites of all Ziff's computer magazines are available at a click, although much of their content has already been absorbed into the main site.

— Major manufacturers —

Advanced Micro Devices
www.amd.com

Intel's main rival in the PC processor market publishes here details of its new products, benchmark results of its performance, and offers software to make certain programs run faster if you have an AMD chip in your machine.

Apple Computer
www.apple.com

Learn all about Apple's home computers, including the resurgent Imac, the software you can run on them, and download updates to the Mac operating systems. You can also read the latest news about technical developments, find out where you can buy a computer, and learn how to fix problems as they occur.

Dell Computer
www.dell.co.uk

Buy a PC from one of the most successful manufacturers in the world today direct from their site. You can choose a base model and then customize it to suit your needs, adding more memory, bigger hard disks, or a better monitor, and the price changes are reflected. If you want to talk through your choices with a sales person just enter your phone number during office hours and they will call you back.

IBM
www.ibm.com

The original PC manufacturer is still going strong, and its website contains details of the current ranges of computers. You can customize their configurations, if you know what you are doing, then buy the products online. Even if you're not sure how much RAM you'll need, or how large your monitor should be, the online help aims to guide you through the purchasing process.

Intel
www.intel.com

Check out Intel's latest PC processors, home networking hardware, and digital cameras. There are press releases published online as well as very detailed technical information about the company's different microchip products. A buyer's guide aims to help you choose the specific processor you should have in your PC. They also have an impressive line in streaming media.

Microsoft
www.microsoft.com

Find out about the latest software products from arguably the world's most successful software publisher (the UK site is at **www.microsoft.com/uk**). The technical support section is second to none. If you have a problem with the software on your PC (and let's face it, most of it will be Microsoft software) check here first, before calling your computer's manufacturer and spending hours on a phone line talking to teenage techies. US residents can buy Microsoft products from this website.

Palm
www.palm.com

Lovers of handheld gadgets, such as the executive's current fave, the Palm Pilot, should browse this site. Get help with which type of Palm organizer you might need, and the various, often expensive, peripherals that go with them. The site has mirror sites all over the world, so it is easier to see which products are available in your particular market.

Psion
www.psion.com
Home to the little pocket computers, beloved of nerds and well-paid businessmen the world over. Although you can't buy items like the Series 5mx and Revo here, there is a large database of re-sellers who will be able to provide you with one.

— Search sites

AltaVista
www.altavista.co.uk
One of the best search engines on the Internet, AltaVista offers varying levels of searching, which differ from its rivals — you can search by region, or by type of media (image, video, sounds). The most basic screen will get you started, though you will need to learn how to narrow down your search (see pages 14-16). If you aren't sure what you're looking for, browse the categories.

Ask Jeeves
www.ask.co.uk
This web search engine doesn't ask its users to scramble around with complicated forms and database languages. Instead, you pose questions in plain English and the resulting lists of sites are supplied in the form of answers, rather than meaningless web addresses and page titles.

Best use of search engines
searchenginewatch.com
After reading the handy notes in the introduction to this guide, learn how to use Internet search engines to their maximum efficiency, whether you are looking for sites you need or are trying to get your own ones noticed. There are lists of specialist engines that concentrate on certain types of page or file, such as MP3 music files, and reviews that evaluate just how good they are.

Dogpile
www.dogpile.com
Probably the best of the metasearch engines, the very simple interface hides a complex search. Like most search engines, it is best for making specific searches,

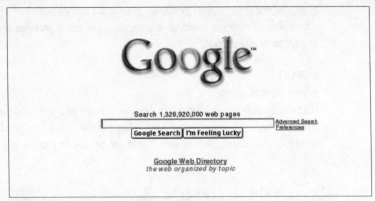

Appearances are deceptive – simply the best search engine on the net is www.google.com

otherwise you might end up barking up the wrong tree. It has a huge directory and you can localize in various ways, by type of media or even to find jobs.

Excite
www.excite.com
Search the entire Internet, or localized areas of it, using this well designed search engine. You can restrict searches to sites in the UK, Europe (or alternatively use **www.excite.co.uk**), or plain news sites. There are also categories of sites to browse through, if you're not quite sure what you're looking for. News headlines and stock quotes are included to encourage you to return frequently. You can even get WAP content, as well as text message to mobile phones.

Freeserve
www.freeserve.co.uk
The Internet Service Provider that changed the face of Internet access in the UK has a generally helpful website that offers a web searching facility, news headlines, auctions, and a shortcut to the Scoot business search engine. If you want to create professional web pages you'll find an Internet domain registration service, and there are plenty of adverts to entice your money away.

Ghost Sites
www.disobey.com/ghostsites
Discover the fascinating world of the dead website. Ghost Sites searches for other sites that haven't seen an update in a long time, possibly because of a failed business or a loss of interest from the original author. Humorous reviews then follow, with awards for the least useful or most abandoned and marks (in the form of ghosts) out of five for each site.

Google
www.google.com

Giving the appearance of just about the simplest web page you can imagine, this site's minimal design belies the powerful search engine that lies at its core. Enter a search phrase and you have two options – "Google Search" will give you the lists of results or try "I'm Feeling Lucky," which will take you straight to the first on the list.

HotBot
www.hotbot.com

Both a web directory and search engine, Hotbot offers a few interesting features such as the ability to create a list and then search that same list for other keywords. This could help the less experienced Internet explorers to refine their web searches, although it has to be said that sites like AltaVista are generally still more powerful in the long run. This site also has the almost obligatory free web access. Worth checking out.

Infospace
www.infospace.com

This web directory has an interesting feature in the shape of special software you download and customize to provide an Internet experience designed around your specific interests and, possibly, business needs wherever you are in the world. The Yellow Pages business finding service works in the US, Canada, and UK thanks to regionalized versions of the site.

Lycos
www.lycos.co.uk

This Internet search engine distinguishes itself by providing "webguides". These are small groups of related sites, which are sometimes accompanied by articles. The overall theme could be privacy on the Internet, tax advice, or surviving as a student. Inexperienced web users, particularly those in the UK in some instances, will find this a handy way to start exploring the Internet. It also happens to be home to one of the most extensive mp3 search engines available at the moment (mp3.lycos.com).

SeniorSearch UK
www.seniorsearch.com

This is a comprehensive directory of links of interest to older web users. SeniorSearch is far from being as exhaustive as regular services like Yahoo! or AltaVista, and the site lacks a keyword search – but resources are more likely to suit the specific needs of senior citizens.

Webring
www.webring.org

Communities and organizations on the Internet are no less "real" than their non-virtual counterparts. Directories like Webring enable you to locate people on the web with whom you share common interests. The site provides categorized links to web rings – groups of sites linked by a common theme – and the sites are navigable from one to the next. If you have your own website, this is an invaluable way of increasing traffic to it.

Yahoo!
www.yahoo.com

This top searchable web directory beats most others hands down, with its comprehensive coverage of almost every area of the web. There are also other features, including news headlines, TV listings, and sections dedicated to health, movies, and local events – they have their information "fed" from a number of reliable external sources (Reuters among them) to ensure its high quality. Available in many regionalized flavours, people from China to Sweden will be able to feel at home on the Internet (the UK version is found at **uk.yahoo.com**). Its other features are too numerous to mention – go see for yourself. Needless to say, this should be one of your first stops on the web – not for nothing is it the world's most popular site.

— Software and downloads —

All about drivers
www.driverguide.com

If something within your PC used to work and it has now started failing, then you'll probably need a device driver (software that talks to printers, scanners etc for the uninitiated). DriverGuide lets members download drivers, as well as access chat forums aimed at helping locate software for discontinued hardware. You can help others too, by sending in the drivers for your own gadgets via email.

Computer Net
www.cnet.com

A truly huge site that includes its own download site, **www.download.com**, where you can get all the drivers and software that you might need. You can read, post, and answer questions in the help forum, find out the latest software prices and the latest techie news and share prices as well. Mirror sites can be found all over the world.

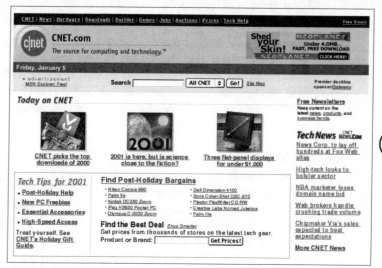

Find out about the latest software and download what you need at www.cnet.com

Computer programming
www.progsharehouse.com

This resource for computer programmers contains tutorials, articles, FAQs, and codes that can be used in your own software. Just about every programming language under the sun is included, as well as some unearthly ones too! Articles from seasoned, and sometimes embittered, programmers can be eye-opening.

Drivers, hardware, news, and reviews
www.windrivers.com

More than just a place to download hardware drivers for your PC's bits and pieces, Windrivers collates help and news bulletins from other websites and even publishes some reviews under the guise of **www.winreviews.com**. The most ingenious part of this site is that you can search for any piece of hardware, even if you only know its FCCID code (printed on almost every piece of electronics in the world). It even has a FTSE-type table showing the latest prices for pieces of hardware, and shows the fluctuation in price.

Free software
www.shareware.com

Download all the free software your computer and your spare time can handle from this well-respected and easy-to-use site (it is part of **www.cnet.com**). It caters for most common types of computer, including Windows PCs and Mac computers – you can search through a quarter of a million shareware files.

More free software
www.winfiles.com

No matter what you want to use your PC for, someone will have written a free or nearly free program to help you. Winfiles is a massive, easy-to-use archive containing software, neatly organized into different categories, such as email updates, Windows shareware, and bugs and fixes. So if you want to mount a web cam in your garden pond or create your own home network then this is the place to try first.

Privacy/Encryption software – PGP
www.pgpi.com

Read about and download some of the most powerful and controversial encryption software available. Its strength rivals anything available to the military and, as a result, it has been the centre of legal action in the States. If you have something to hide, or wish to exercise your rights to privacy, start using PGP (Pretty Good Privacy) – it's a lot easier to use now than it used to be.

— Stores ——————————————

Buy discounted goods
www.buy.com

Computer hardware and software can be bought here at discounted prices – digital imagery, networking, and other peripherals are all catered for. You can also track your orders. Look out for the excellent buy.com vouchers that are often offered at other sites (spend £20, get £10 off is just one good example).

Dabs Direct
www.dabs.com

Dabs Direct is the place to buy the bits and pieces you'll need to upgrade your PC. There is more than just memory and hard disks in the online catalogue though. There are branded PCs from all the big names as well as printers, monitors, and software. Web orders have free delivery to UK addresses, and you can track your goods to see if they have come into stock, been sent out, or are temporarily unavailable. Note: it will not deliver outside the European Union.

Insight
www.insight.com

Whether you live in the US, UK, Canada, or Germany, Insight provides an excellent outlet for all things Mac- or PC-based. The prices have traditionally been very competitive, besides which it is always easy to shop around online. Delivery is free for orders made over the web and you can save a price quote for three days if you're not ready to make a decision straight away.

The Outpost
www.outpost.com
Outpost will sell you anything to do with PCs or Macs, networking, software, and home electronics. Although based in the US, the company will ship internationally for a very low charge. The "TruePrice" feature, where prices quoted are what you pay (ie inclusive of domestic taxes), is useful and should be universally adopted.

— Web page construction help —

Creating a successful web page
www.anybrowser.org
Anybrowser is another great site for website authors to add to their list of favourites. For the technical reasons explained on the site, not every computer reads web pages in the same way. Follow the advice supplied and your pages will be universally readable – well, nearly. And if you are forever frustrated by websites designed only for specific browsers that you don't have, then join the Campaign for a Non-Browser Specific www.

Creating and developing your website
www.wdvl.com
If you're interested in writing your own web pages, and want your efforts to be available to everyone on the Internet, you should read what this site has to say. The Web Developer's Virtual Library starts at the beginning and takes you right through to very advanced topics, providing something for everyone. If you are writing a small homepage or creating a killer commercial site come here regularly. Exhaust yourself and take yourself through the Top 100 tutorials. There is a great "History of the Internet" section, too.

Monkey around with your site
www.webmonkey.com
This arm of the Wired website is an essential bookmark for those who want to learn how to create their own pages. Some of the best designers have donated their time to put together tutorials that are easy to follow and are annotated with pictures that show you exactly what to do. The makers of the site have done their best to demystify the complexities of webpage design.

Why learn the difficult stuff when www.moonfruit.com will create your pages for you?

Moonfruit
www.moonfruit.com

This award-winning site will create the most amazing websites for you using the latest Flash technology. Use its online tools to create an impressively visual multimedia site. You can publish your CV online or, if you want to draw attention to the local rugby team, this is the place to come.

Running your own website
www.webdevelopersjournal.com

The Web Developer's Journal aims to take some of the pain out of administering your newly created website and is neatly divided into different sections, for suits (businessmen), ponytails (designers), and propheads (programmers).

Spice up your web pages
www.jalfrezi.com

A sizzling hot site that teaches all you need to know about html, all explained in a simple and concise way. If you get stuck on your html tags, there is a handy A–Z toolbar to find out what each tag does. There are also explanations of tables, forms, frames, stylesheets, and more. There are several mirror sites too.

Up-to-the-minute articles about the web
webreview.com

Once you've decided to create your own website, and realized that you'll need to know at least a bit about HTML to get the results you want, you absolutely must visit WebReview. There are articles on all the subjects you don't yet realize you'll find interesting. See what's there now and, when you want to do something clever, you'll remember where to go for help.

For computer game sites see Games, pages 119–121.

— see also...

As you can imagine there are still hundreds more computer news sites on the world wide web, so if the ones listed earlier do not suit your needs then try one of the following – **www.brillscontent.com**, the attractive and informative **www.thestandard.com**, **www.linux.org**, and Tucows (**www.tucows.com**), which also offers games and music to download.

The first Internet shops sold computer gear, and this tradition continues with Computer Warehouse (**www.computerwarehouse. co.uk**), where you'll find printer cartridges, extra disks, and other bits and pieces at competitive prices. Crucial Technology (**www.crucial.com**) will also be happy to do business with you, provided you only want to buy computer memory at ridiculously low prices. These stores will all undercut each other with certain products. You can never have enough online shops on your list. Make sure you add SMC Direct (**www.smcdirect.com**), Software Paradise (**www.softwareparadise.co.uk**), Software Warehouse (**www.software-warehouse.co.uk**), Tech Direct (**www.techdirect.co.uk**), and Watford Electronics (**www.watford.co.uk**). PC World (**www.pcworld.co.uk**) is also worth a look, if only to verify buys from other places as bargains.

For advice on what you should spend your money on in these places, make use of the educated opinions of computer magazine websites. *Computer Shopper* (**www.computershopper.co.uk**) is one of the biggest PC magazines, while computer magazine publisher VNU's site (**www.vnunet.com**) offers news, reviews, and comment – some of which is valid. PC Pro (**www.pcpro.co.uk**) is aimed at the "high end" of the market. Future Net (**www.futurenet.com**) is home to many popular computer and technology-led magazines, including *PC Plus*, *Amiga Format*, and *PlayStation Power*.

In the market for a new computer? Try a range of manufacturers' sites, and then check out the reviews with your favourite computer magazine's website (**www.comp-buyer.co.uk**) and purchase online. Compaq (**www.compaq.com**) is one of the world's most important computer manufacturers. Mesh (**www.meshplc.co.uk**), Evesham Micros (**www.evesham.com**), and Elonex (**www.elonex.co.uk**) aren't as well known, but will often offer better value for money when buying a computer for home use or for a small business. Dan (**www.dan.co.uk**) is a leading PC manufacturer, complete with online showroom and unusual-looking computers, while giants Time (**www.timecomputers.co.uk**) and Tiny (**www.tiny.com**) are always ready to offer some interesting deals. Big players also worth a mention include Hewlett-Packard (**www.hewlett-packard.co.uk** and **www.hp.com**), Gateway 2000 (**www.gateway.com**), NEC Direct (**www.nec-online.co.uk**), Fujitsu PC Corp (**www.fujitsu-pc.com**), and Viglen (**www.viglen.co.uk**).

Inevitably something will go wrong with your PC at some point. You should check out Computer Incident Advisory Capability (**www.ciac.org**) to learn how to detect hoax email alerts and Symantec's AntiVirus Research Center (**www.symantec.com/avcenter**) for information on real threats. When everything has been sorted out, relax by playing a few games. Find out which ones are the best at PC Zone (**www.pczone.co.uk**).

Finally, once online, you will already have an extensive list of search engines to find whatever it is that you want to locate, but there are also many search and metasearch engines that you should try out – **www.highway61.com**, **www.metacrawler.com** and **www.go.com** are just three others to try if you cannot find what you want from those listed earlier in the chapter.

EDUCATION

Students, teachers, and parents alike can find a wealth of information on the Internet. Homework can be made much easier by searching online encyclopedias (see pages 245–249) and trying online tutorials, while parents can find out how to help educate from home. There are ideas and lesson plans for the wired-in teacher, and tailored news for those with an interest in the latest UK government reforms. The amount of help for those in higher education is staggering, with advice ranging from coursework to CV writing and job applications. There are puzzles for geniuses, help for those with special needs, and adult education resources. And there are even sites for the youngest of children, providing educational games.

— Alternative teaching sites —

Home tutoring
learninfreedom.org

This site advocates giving students the choice to use teachers and schools voluntarily when required. It explores the issues surrounding teaching children in their homes rather than in a recognized classroom, and what taking on that responsibility means. There are college ratings, including details on which ones have accepted home-tutored students, and numerous articles – some including anti-school quotes from the likes of Albert Einstein and George Bernard Shaw. A booklist and resources guide will also help steer you in the right direction.

Introduction to home schooling
www.homeschool.com

Providing a thorough look at teaching a child from home, this informative site includes the "Ten Most Important Things To Know About Homeschooling", a list of useful reference books, and online courses – including a "click learning" section for children. A resource guide to curricula and other commercial products, as well as a handful of interviews and articles, completes this introductory site.

Steiner Waldorf Schools Fellowship UK
www.steinerwaldorf.org.uk

Find out all about this alternative method of teaching, and browse the directory of schools in the UK and Eire that offer it. There is also a list of kindergartens and, for American readers, an alternative site at **www.awsna.org** provides a similar service for those that are living in the US, Mexico, and Canada. Further links list worldwide schools.

For graduates

Jobs and career fairs in America
www.jobweb.org

The site of the National Association of Colleges and Employers has news for both job seekers and employment professionals in the US, publishing a calendar of careers events fairs. The news is almost entirely optimistic, but that's hardly surprising – graduates won't want to feel more insecure than they already do. In any case, there are dozens of articles to help the recently graduated find their place in the job world.

MBA and postgraduate guide
www.merlinfalcon.co.uk

Locate a university that provides the MBA course you're interested in from a worldwide database. Courses are listed by country and can be broken down into full-time, part-time, or distance learning. A postgraduate guide includes diplomas, masters degrees, certificates, and PGCEs available in the UK and Ireland. There are no design frills to Merlin Falcon's site, but it does provide all the information that you could possibly be looking for.

Vital information for all graduates
www.prospects.csu.ac.uk

So utterly useful; if UK graduates only ever bother with one site after finishing their exams this should be it. There are available jobs listings, vacancies for graduates of the coming year, job-seeking strategies, and free downloadable software to help with filling in a standard application form. "Prospects Direct" is a great system that automatically searches for the kind of job you are after and sends you email messages when it finds ones that match your criteria.

Teenagers can get help with stressful exams at www.a-levels.co.uk

For students

Advice from other young people
www.infoyouth.com
If you've decided to go for higher education, go straight into employment, or would prefer to take some time off to think about it all, spend a little of that revision time reading the sound advice contained on this site. InfoYouth is "made by young people – for young people".

A-Levels
www.a-levels.co.uk
Easy to navigate, this site cuts to the chase for teenagers in the final throws of their secondary school education. It lists texts that are relevant in most subjects and, of course, gives students the chance to buy the books. Contact addresses and emails for the various (confusing) exam boards are also listed, and advice is offered on taking a gap year.

Discount booking service for ELT students (UK)
www.gouk.com
Aimed at international students studying in the UK, this site offers information about the available schools and colleges. It operates a free, discount booking scheme, and also features tourist information for that popular between-lectures time. There is general advice on how the Brits live, and an accommodation list.

Guide to everything a student needs
www.bigwideworld.com

Aimed largely at the teenage student population, hence the hipper than normal page design, this site offers guides to universities, colleges, and careers, as well as the lighter subjects in life. There are areas where you can find out about choosing a bank account, where to go travelling, and what films are worth watching. The latest gadgets and gizmos are reviewed and a set of links provides access to online dictionaries and helpful government websites.

Information for students of disability services
www.abilityinfo.com

The information on this site is aimed at students and professionals studying or working in this field of expertize. There is a news ticker that can push the latest headlines onto your screen, job listings, and a bookshop. Discussion forums are also provided, and there are loads of links to a whole range of other sites.

Letts Education Guides
www.letts-education.com

Letts, makers of the highly respected revision guides, has moved online and has something educational for everyone, ranging from reception to Higher Education. The site has a breakdown of each age group and answers all your questions. Curious about what is expected at Key Stage 3? This site will answer your questions – and will, of course, sell you their guides as well.

National Union of Students
www.nus.org.uk

The colourful site of the NUS is never going to be as "hip" as some of the other less institutional student sites, but it is a font of information with the latest news, advice, useful links, and most importantly, lots of discounts and special offers.

Online student magazine
www.juiced.co.uk

Juiced is a youth electronic magazine published on the Internet by the Electronic *Telegraph*, and contains film, music, sport articles, horoscopes, and news. There are also sections on travel and, more importantly, careers. Special offers and competitions are listed for use in that rare student commodity – leisure time.

Open University
www.open.ac.uk

Discover which of the enormous number of available courses suit you best and reserve yourself a place. You can also find out which of those late night "Learning

Zone" programmes will appeal to you, and order a copy of the listings if you wish to browse offline. You can find out what the Open University has to offer in your area as well.

Studying worldwide
www.studylink.com
StudyLink publishes CD-ROM directories of so-called learning opportunities in both the UK and Australia. There are directories of courses for school leavers, and business/management and postgraduate programmes around the world. A special post-grad site regularly features "schools", meaning "universities".

Universities and Colleges Admissions Service
www.ucas.ac.uk
If you want to go to a UK university or college this is the organization to apply through. This site offers advice to UK and international applicants, mature students, and even referees. There are tips on filling in your application form, and financial advice is offered with information on how to apply for help.

The Year In Industry (UK)
www.yini.org.uk
It may be slow and unnecessarily flash, but The Year In Industry site aims to help talented students into industrial placements during their gap year at university. Graduate opportunities are listed alongside information for students, parents, and teachers. Case studies aim to encourage students along this path.

— For teachers and parents —

Catholic Teachers Gazette
www.cartrefc.demon.co.uk
Choose between a Flash and non-Flash offering from the publishers of the free newsletter of the same name. The latest job vacancies are available in schools from state primary, middle, and secondary levels, as well as independent schools. Administration vacancies are also listed, and details of the Saint for the week are available here too.

Department for Education and Employment
www.dfee.gov.uk
Get the news hot off the government's press, complete with spin. More importantly, there is a quite comprehensive online database of DfEE circulars and

Teachers and parents alike can learn from the informative www.topmarks.co.uk

publications, which is ever expanding. The Department runs an electronic communications service, which can alert you by email whenever a new document is posted on the site. There are links aimed at young people and job seekers.

Educate the Children
www.educate.org.uk

Educate the Children covers the whole of the National Curriculum for primary education – it has over 2500 lesson plans, worksheets, and articles available to download (in the PDF format). The site also gives advice on assessments, and provides pictures and suggestions for lessons. The Teacher Forum is a web-based affair, and includes a staff-room area where gossip and complaints are welcome. Subscribe to the informative email newsletter. The Parent Zone helps Primary school parents understand their child's education and gives activity suggestions.

Education Unlimited
www.educationunlimited.co.uk

The Guardian newspaper's educational supplement features stories for students and those working in the academic world. Issues such as national debates, new curriculum, and the latest spoutings of parliament are all covered, next to university league tables and special reports on, among other things, teachers' pay.

European schools network
www.en.eun.org

The European Schoolnet (EUN) has been designed to help school networks all over Europe work effectively together, sharing ideas and projects. Of particular interest is the section that looks at combining the Internet with education, especially within lessons in primary and secondary education. Help is available online for teachers wishing to explore this new(ish) technology.

Parents Online
www.parents.org.uk

Designed to help parents with children of primary school age, this site contains articles on government policies, book reviews, readers' letters, and a weekly activity idea. There are sections on education, health, leisure, and an Ask an Expert forum. If you have Adobe Acrobat you can even download sample pages from home learning books. There is a Free Ads column for grown-out-of clothes.

Teachers' Library of Resources
www.teacherslibrary.org.uk

This excellent collection of links, articles, and worksheets will be a welcome aid to any teacher or parent who needs a bit of help explaining terms such as carbon dating or homeostasis. Each article, whether it is on site or linked from another, is rated by level (eg GCSE, A-Level, Key Stages 1–3).

Times Educational Supplement
www.tes.co.uk

Take part in heated debates in the virtual staff room, choose from lists of schools with websites, and peruse the online job vacancies in the teaching world. The links are a good mixture of official UK government curriculum and policy ones, as well as academic study-based offerings. Read some of the latest extracts from this newspaper supplement online as well. There is a separate site for Scotland: **www.tes.co.uk/scotland/news**.

Top Marks
www.topmarks.co.uk

A site for teachers and parents alike – for parents it has articles and features by practising teachers to help with education. There is also the UK Tour guide, which gives teachers the opportunity to publish their pupils' work about their local area. The search engine allows you to search the site for relevant articles in subject areas, from science to the classics. It even gives you the particular audience (Key Stage etc). A must see site.

Up My Street
www.upmystreet.co.uk

If you really want to find out the truth about your local area, or an area that you are possibly about to move into, then this is the site to check out – and it does cover local schools. It gives the highest scoring schools in the area, and also has a table of the results within the schools in the area, with average results and much, much more.

Intelligence sites

American IQ Test
www.iqtest.com
Take a free, timed, IQ test and, if you want deep analysis, spend a few dollars and receive a report. Unfortunately this one is for Americans only – unless you feel you are particularly familiar with quarters, cents, and dimes. Do you dare risk your self confidence?

Exercise your brain
www.mindtools.com
Get your brain into ship shape with the online tutorials at MindTools. You can also "plan and live an excellent life" with a piece of shareware software, and read self-help articles on planning skills, improving your memory, learning time management, as well as learning how to manage stress effectively. I can personally recommend this last chapter, especially to any authors out there that are under the pressure of deadlines…

Mensa International
www.mensa.org
Learn about this famous organization for clever people and take an interactive test online, which sadly won't count as an official admission test. The benefits and details of membership to Mensa groups worldwide are listed, as well as ways for "Mensans" to communicate, including email and Internet news groups but, strangely, not telepathy.

Online business courses
www.headlight.com
Sign up to a host of business-based online courses on subjects ranging from computer systems administration to brainstorming and promoting creative thinking. There are over 3000 courses to choose from here. There is a small selection of free beginner-level courses to introduce you to the system too. You can also take an assessment so Headlight can ensure that you're not thrown in too deep with any course that you choose to take up. This site is well worth a visit if you are looking to expand your business knowledge.

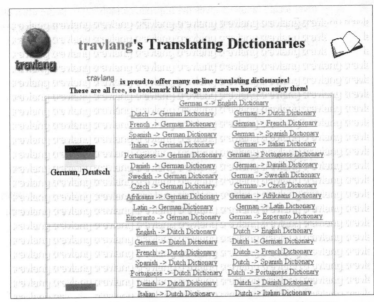

Dictionaries are just one of the handy tools for learning languages at www.travlang.com

— Language sites —

Bilingual Research Journal
brj.asu.edu

Concerning itself with issues surrounding bilingual classrooms and teaching, this online journal offers practical information as well as research articles that could prove useful for those studying this area as an academic subject. There are also book reviews and case studies, available online or as downloadable files in Adobe Acrobat. The site itself can be adapted to suit your computer, with a choice of two versions – text-only or graphics – and two formats. Archives allow you to access back issues, although you can also order the paper version online.

Language database for teachers and students
www.travlang.com

Interested in learning a new language, or are you just wanting to brush up on old skills? Travlang is an essential language resource for both students and teachers alike, featuring free translation dictionaries for 24 languages including German, Spanish, Norwegian, and Czech. For example, there are English-French, French-English, French-German, and German-Afrikaans versions. Amazing. Brush up on your foreign language skills with a quick lesson in the basics such as numbers, shopping, and directions. A pronunciation guide will also help you on your way. The site provides travel information and facilities. And subscribe to the "Word of the Day" email to receive and learn a new foreign word each day.

Learning

BBC Schools Online
www.bbc.co.uk/education/schools
This site has a healthy mixture of education news, learning resources for primary and secondary level students, and a special "Home Learning" section that will help keep teachers and scholars in touch with their jobs/studies. There is also a guide to the best education websites which, although incomparable to the excellent book you're now reading, is still very handy.

Campaign for Learning
www.campaign-for-learning.org.uk
Promoting the worthy ideal that we should all be learning away to our brain's content, Campaign for Learning is a charitable organization that publishes details of awareness days and articles discussing the issues surrounding education of the masses – impressive names, including Education Secretary David Blunkett have been drafted in to get the message across. The National Learning Forum has a discussion page here, but you'll have to join the NLF first to be able to join in.

Database for teachers, students, and parents
www.schoolzone.co.uk
Teachers, students, and parents should benefit from this site, which contains thousands of links to hundreds of subjects. They vary from Welsh resources to the weather and climate, and all are to be found on other websites. However, the links have been selected by teachers, so you should be able to trust them.

Educational exhibitions
learningcurve.pro.gov.uk
Part of the Public Record Office (**www.pro.gov.uk**), this site displays a large number of educational exhibitions, including ones that were made for the Millennium celebrations. There is information on the Domesday Book and a discussion of 19th-century political change, covering subjects such as white slavery, the luddites, and the suffragettes. The excellent "Snapshots" section takes a look at moments from history based on sources from the National Archive.

Educational Web Adventures
www.eduweb.com
Skip the long Flash intro and access a large number of interactive educational web games, exploring the worlds of art, science, and history, which includes a simulation where you try to run a community-based ecotourism project. Eduweb actually writes these mini-sites for educational institutions so the links are external, but if you want it to produce something similar for use in your school, their rates and contact details are available.

Interactive learning
www.sparkisland.co.uk
This is a brand new interactive learning site, based around the fictitious Spark Island, which relies heavily on Flash, with a lot of curriculum-led activities for primary school children. Special characters lead the children through the site – it can be confusing, but given that the site is relatively new, it is likely that these problems will be ironed out.

Learning to use the web
www.dreamscape.com/frankvad
Jump straight to the Virtual Internet Tours, where you will find a basic introduction to the web, or, alternatively, use one of the categorized links to over 50 Internet search engines to find what you are looking for on the Internet. Be warned, though. You'll have to negotiate an extremely annoying commercial each time you try a new site.

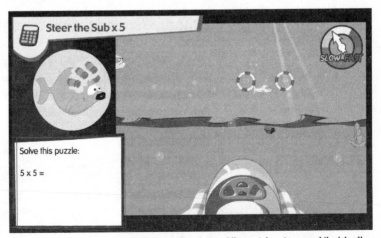

www.sparkisland.co.uk is a great interactive site – learn while you take a tour round the island!

Lessons online
www.learn.com

Enrol in a few online courses (what they call the Instant Learning system – 80 per cent faster than normal courses) from an almost surreally varied list and change your life. For example, you can learn and remember the Ten Commandments, change a flat tyre, or make a Japanese-style sponge cake. There is no doubt that you will find a course that is tailor-made for you. You do need to join to access the lessons, but membership is free.

National Grid For Learning
www.ngfl.gov.uk

You can join discussions with teachers and other education professionals on all manner of educational subjects, but best of all you'll find here some well organized links to, and summaries of, important but often quite well hidden sites that may be of help to your lessons or studies. For example, there are a few governmental sites worth checking out, and the museums and libraries are also a worthy inclusion, as well as links to sites for Higher Education.

Online educational encyclopedia
www.spartacus.schoolnet.co.uk

Approved by both the US Education Department and the UK's National Grid For Learning, the Spartacus Educational Home Page provides an Internet encyclopedia that spans the Norman Conquest through to the Vietnam War, via the emancipation of women and the slave trade. (American history from 1840–1960 gets special treatment.) Articles are accompanied by great illustrations.

PLAY – Project Literacy Among Youth
www.kidsplay.org

Raising children's awareness of the media and advertising is the name of the game here. The hope is that teachers will educate younger members of society to evaluate the ever-present constructs of newspapers, TV, and other forms and not accept them entirely on face value. Just what our cynical youth needs…

Mathematics sites

Geometry Center
www.geom.umn.edu

This maths research and education centre has a number of useful and fun puzzles and tools. The graphics archive has 3D images, fractals, and tiling puzzles while the web applications include a rainbow builder and an advanced curve calculator. Geometry formulae and facts are available, too, along with some free, maths-based software.

Mathematics made fun
www.c3.lanl.gov/mega-math

This site helps teachers and parents turn crusty old maths concepts into colourful, fun stories and projects. The Hotel Infinity is a story that explains (sort of) the paradox of infinite numbers, there is an introduction to the problems in map colouring, and a play that challenges the reader to apply logical analysis. Print some of these out and annoy your kids.

Maths Net
www.anglia.co.uk/education/mathsnet/

This excellent site is updated daily. It includes interactive puzzles, many of them Flash-based (and therefore more fun). It also explains spreadsheets, graphs, and even fractal zooms and has a huge resource centre. You can also follow the Maths Net Trail where you surf the Net to find the answers to questions it poses to you and build up your score – this is a riveting way to learn about Maths. Show this site to your children!

— School revision

GCSE answers to Maths and English
www.gcse.com

The plain design of the site belies the useful information contained within. Ideal for revising/panicking students, model answers are provided for both English and Maths GCSEs (roughly Grade 10 in the US). There are also resources for GCSE sciences. Contact details of the UK examining boards are provided. You can buy past papers from them but why not ask your teachers for the free ones your school can supply? You may, however, wish to buy the help notes that are available from the online bookshop.

SAT Math
www.satmath.com

This excellent site for students in the US provides online tutoring on math- and SAT-related questions and topics. There are interactive lessons and quizzes, but best of all is the built-in analyzer that provides students with the chance to see exactly which areas they need to improve in the most. Membership does cost

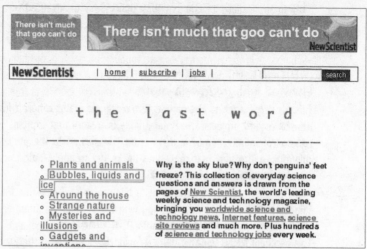

The *New Scientist* provides answers to all kinds of scientific phenomena at www.last-word.com

although you will receive an individual study plan and an interactive CD of math tests 1 and 2. Alternatively you can email your query to the support section for free and receive an answer within 24 hours.

Science sites

All your science questions answered
www.madsci.org

If you have a scientific question, post it here and one of the "collective cranium" will answer you. Past postings have solicited some very in-depth and serious, but clear, explanations. The "Random Knowledge Generator" can find a few assorted examples for you, so you can see what sort of questions are being answered before posting one of your own.

CHEMystery: An Interactive Guide To Chemistry
library.advanced.org/3659

This "virtual chemistry textbook" is aimed at US high school chemistry students, although its depth is roughly equivalent to the UK chemistry GCSE. For example, you can learn about mixtures, compounds, and states of matter. This all makes the site a good starting place for revision for US and UK students alike. They also have a brand new Physics site entitled Think Fizzle, which can be accessed at **(library.thinkquest.org/16600)**.

Design and Technology Education Index
www.technologyindex.com

This rather garish site is aimed at teachers and students of design and technology subjects, with departments covering robotics, electronics, mechanisms (including a moving Tyrannosaurus Rex kit), and graphics (or technical drawing). You can buy isometric templates, electric motor generators, and copies of Robot Science and Technology magazine. In fact, there is a lot of robotics stuff here, the coolest being the Cybug.

NASA
www.nasa.gov

This extensive site nearly demands a book to itself. Follow the Mars Pathfinder mission, find out what is happening with the Mir space station, and read about how to become an astronaut for real. A shuttle schedule and countdown is available for future launches. With its own "NASA Education Programs", this could be a potentially great teaching aid.

New Scientist's help page
www.last-word.com

The New Scientist has this great offshoot site that explains all things scientific in a language that children can easily understand. The archive contains 600 questions on scientific phenomena, with answers provided by the readers – this is a perfect place to find out the answers to difficult questions.

Pupil Researcher Initiative
www.shu.ac.uk/pri/

Encouraging communication between scientists and schools, and with an aim to make GCSE and Standard Grade science "more real, more relevant, and more motivating for pupils", the PRI also hopes to involve schools with each other to undertake science projects. There is information about their scheme on the site, as well as an article that describes the skills that are necessary in order to write technical reports.

Science directory
www.scicentral.com

This comprehensive web science directory is aimed at professional scientists from a large number of disciplines. There are categories for biological, health, engineering, physical, chemical, and earth and space sciences, as well as a dedicated policy and ethics section. The online news stories are drawn from various respected sources. You can also customize your own science news alerts from the site.

—Social sciences sites

Anthropology and the origins of mankind
www.geocities.com/Athens/Acropolis/5579/TA.html

If you can negotiate the fussy design of this anthropology site, you'll discover a really good set of articles about human evolution, a glossary, and, oddly, some blank world maps. You can use these to record site locations of digs or other projects and discoveries. A "Know Your Bones" lesson and very relevant links to other sites make this an engrossing place to visit. Try out the pleasantly titled "Name That Skull" to see how well you know animal heads.

Encyclopedia of Philosophy
www.utm.edu/research/iep

This Spartan-looking affair contains some serious, classical philosophical texts in a number of formats so that you can download them. There is also a timeline, outlining the different schools of ideas throughout the ages. A list of keywords is provided, and the search facility makes the database instantly accessible.

Environmental issues and information
www.envirolink.org

The EnviroLink Network is, it claims, one of the world's largest environmental information "clearing houses". An online library is stocked with activist resources, information on nuclear issues, and links to government agency sites and other organizations. There is also a large section on sustainable business, including a specialist bookstore. A mailing list, which is how this site originally started, is available. (For other environmental sites see "The Natural World", pages 214–218).

History database
www.historychannel.com

The search facility on this site makes isolating a specific historic moment a piece of cake. So if you can't quite remember what year one of the space shuttles crashed, and it's not on the timeline provided, you can dial the details up. There is a "This Day In History" page and video clips for those special sporting moments. If you fancy yourself as the new AJP Taylor, have a go at the History IQ quiz.

Sociology
www.geocities.com/CollegePark/Quad/5889

SocioRealm is an excellent, high-gloss site bringing together information from diverse disciplines such as sociology and criminology, and aiming it at a general

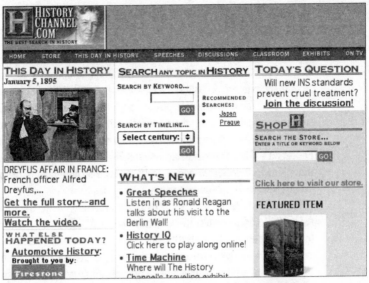

Find out what happened on this day in history every day at www.historychannel.com

audience. You'll also find in-depth discussion of the work of luminaries such as Durkheim, Marx, and Weber – names that will strike fear in the heart of many an undergraduate – together with rated links to other resources on the various subject matters.

Statistical Abstract of the US
www.census.gov/statab/www

This is a slightly dull but extremely useful site. It has gathered together a vast number of statistics on social and economic conditions in the US, including state rankings. One section can present you with the various figures on health, employment, and social welfare "in brief". However, throughout the rest of the site, you will have to use Adobe Acrobat to access all the other figures that it offers to you.

The world around us
www.worldbank.org

Get a better understanding of the world that is around us, particularly in terms of developing countries, and make and maintain links to schools from all over the earth. The data section has plenty of in-depth information and statistics on subjects including AIDS, food, pollution, and urbanization. The World Bank Group also welcomes articles that are submitted by students on the subject of sustainable developments.

— see also... —

Whether you are a student, teacher, or concerned parent, there are an enormous amount of relevant websites. Parents will find the DfEE School and College Performance Tables (**www.dfee.gov.uk/perform.htm**) of interest, as it allows you to judge the performance of your child's school. You can also check up on the guardians of the UK educational system by visiting the Office for Standards in Education – Ofsted (**www.ofsted.gov.uk**). The illustrated guide to every school in the UK, which includes exam results and inspection reports, is available at SchoolsNet (**www.schoolsnet.com**).

Younger students will find essential revision help at Project GCSE (**www.projectgcse.co.uk**). Geographers will find Geological Maps on the Web (**geomaps.geo.ukans.edu**) a handy place for project material. And Maths students will find **www.calculator.com** useful as well.

If you need a bit of competition to get you stimulated, try the American Mock Trial Association (**www.collegemocktrial.org**), where American students can engage in a simulation of the US' fine tradition of litigation. Less specific, but no less cut-throat, are the National Academic Quiz Tournaments (**www.naqt.com**).

Learn Plus (**www.learnplus.com**) at the moment gives online lessons in Spanish and German, although other courses are planned for the future. Perseus Project (**perseus.csad.ox.ac.uk**) will help you discover the history of the ancient world with this art, archaeology, and teaching resource, while Study Web's (**www.studyweb.com**) education-led web directory provides links to educational sites, including reference, teaching resources, and even mental health.

Teachers are equally well catered for. Education Week (**www.edweek.org**) has news, special reports, and extracted articles from the US magazine of the same name, and the Society for Promoting Christian Knowledge (see "Society, Politics, and Religion", page 264) has set up a new site with assembly material for primary schools at **www.assemblies.org.uk**. The British Association for Open Learning (**www.baol.co.uk**) promotes distance learning, and provides an online journal covering technical issues and coverage of the education industry. English teachers and students will find the articles and links at EFLWEB (**www.eflweb.com**) invaluable. Keep an eye on the National Curriculum by regularly visiting the Qualifications and Curriculum Authority (**www.qca.org.uk**). The Reading Online (**www.readingonline.org**) electronic journal of the International Reading Association aims to keep professional educators up-to-date with current developments too. The Bilingualism, Languages, and Education Network (**www.rmplc.co.uk/orgs/blen**) provides news and education resources for teaching English as a second language.

Preparing for university? The US site Education Training service (**www.ets.org**) is the gateway to information about college and graduate school. Find out about two of the world's most famous learning institutions – University of Cambridge (**www.cam.ac.uk**) and University of Oxford (**www.ox.ac.uk**) or, if you are in the US, visit Harvard University at **www.harvard.edu** or Yale University at **www.yale.edu**. SearchGate (**www.searchgate.co.uk**) provides everything a conscientious student could want, including guides to courses, colleges, shows, and student issues. A more fun site can be found at Student UK (**www.studentuk.co.uk**), which has lots of advice and entertainment news too. After the fun, though, you'll need to think about employment. College Grad Job Hunter (**www.collegegrad.com**) will help you have something to do (and hopefully some money to spend) after leaving college. Jobtrak (**www.jobtrak.com**) will try to locate the job that suits your interests, and will also post your CV to attract potential employers, while the University of London Careers Service (**www.careers.lon.ac.uk**) provides help to anyone studying at an institution affiliated to the University. Anyone can use Monster campus (**campus.monster.com**), though, to get expert career advice before it's too late. If you are currently working and want to find out about evening courses in London, then **www.floodlight.co.uk** is your best bet, with **www.oncourse.co.uk** helping you further afield.

And finally, what about those old school chums you've lost touch with? Ask yourself if there is a reason for this and, if you still want to re-establish contact, visit UK Alumni (**www.alumni.net**), which provides a directory of the people who have bothered to register.

ENTERTAINMENT

The entertainment industry is big money so it's no surprise that there are a huge number of sites vying to supply you with the ultimate in TV, film, and music services. You'll find TV listings, film guides, equipment reviews, and, of course, shops where you can buy all of these things. We have included other fun things in this category, like theme parks, toy shops, and sites for sci-fi fans. However, if you are looking for much more detailed sites about the music world then you will find them listed in their own, dedicated Music section (see pages 197–210). Books have also been given their own chapter (see pages 36–49).

— Cartoons and comics ——

Aardman Animation
www.aardman.com
This is the home of Peter Lord and Nick Parks and the award-winning *Wallace and Grommit/Chicken Run* team. You can watch animated clips from your favourites, including the whole of Creature Comforts and Morph. Catch up on their latest news or send an electronic postcard.

Animation World Network
www.awn.com
If you foster a serious interest in animation, this is the place to come for a world view. There are profiles of artists, articles on animation technologies, and information on commercial studios and film distributors. Multiple magazines and email newsletters are available, and there are sections for job-seeking animators.

Comics galore
www.marvel.com
This is the electronic home of cult classics such as the *X-Men* and *Spiderman*. Updated every two or three days, Marvel's website is full of new comic content.

Wallace and Gromit and Morph can be found at the excellent site, www.aardman.com

There is also a free-subscription chat forum and resources, as well as a comprehensively stocked online shop. This is a must for comic lovers.

Comic shop online
www.comicshack.uk.com

The Comic Shack provides a list of over 30,000 titles, from *The Incredible Hulk* to *Batman* – all available on its website. Graded according to the condition they are in, you can either buy from or sell to the site. A "Wanted" section tells you which copies of what comic they are looking for in particular at any given time. The London-based shop's owners are real devotees of comics and graphic novels, and promise that all titles are shipped speedily to each of their customers with reasonable postage charges.

Creating your own cartoons
www.spirit.com.au/~pat

PAT's Cartoon Pages include a good introduction to drawing cartoons called "The Cartoonist's Fountain of Knowledge". There are tips and techniques (that you can add to yourself) and cartoon-style fonts to save you time. There are also plenty of links to interesting discussion forums and articles on diverse subjects including propaganda and visual studies. There are also details of cartoon clubs and galleries around the world. A special section on using computers to create cartoons will interest cyber-toonists.

Find out all you want to know about the latest DVD film releases at www.dvdworld.co.uk

Directory of cartoonists
www.pipemedia.net/cartoons

If you need a cartoon drawn for your local newsletter, headed notepaper, or promotional material then pay a visit to The Cartoonists' Guild online directory. Cartoonists are categorized, so whether you need a caricature or a web page illustration you'll be able to locate an appropriate person.

For all sci-fi comic fans
www.fandomshop.com

American site Fandom is probably the finest place to get hold of comics and comic memorabilia and merchandise on the Internet, as well as toys and videos. Goods are arranged (helpfully) by price or by publisher. Prices are in dollars, and delivery from the States to elsewhere may take a while, but the selection is unrivalled.

Stay Tooned
www.staytooned.com

Get previews of and read the background news to animations, festivals, and artist profiles contained in Stay Tooned. Short films (cartoon sushi) are reviewed, and a "Site of the Month" should keep those with a cult interest in this subject happy.

View popular comics
www.comics.com

Probably the most sought-after comic address on the web, United Media's comic collection includes office geek Dilbert, the famous Peanuts strip, as well as newspaper regulars Garfield and Peanuts (all of these have their own sites – www.dilbert.com, www.snoopy.com etc). Images are presented at fairly decent quality, and you'll find a 30-day archive for each strip. And, of course, United Media has not missed the opportunity to offer books for sale.

— Electronic equipment —————

Dixons
www.dixons.co.uk

The high-street electronics chain has its own online presence, from which you can buy the usual selection of cameras, binoculars, computers, and games. You can find out where your nearest store is located and consult a buyer's guide that explains home cinema and the fundamentals of the many other gadgets and accessories available to purchase.

DVD World
www.dvdworld.co.uk

An excellent site, with lots of great DVD films and player offers, not to mention a Playstation 2 section. The simple, uncluttered design makes the site easy to navigate and its goodies very tempting to buy.

Gadgets galore
www.firebox.com

This site could also be called "where men buy stuff". It is the supreme site for buying gadgets – a site to suit mostly upwardly young mobile males who desperately want a new electrical toy to play with during rush hour. As if to push the point home, the site is split into categories like "Boys Toys", "Expensive Stuff", and "Gadgets". From ice shot glasses to £36,000+ powerboats, this site has something for every man.

Home entertainment gadgets and systems
www.home-entertainment.co.uk

Find out about the latest gadgets that will change your world forever (in your spare time, at least). If you have yet to catch up with the DVD revolution, or want to know which particular subwoofers are the best, then check out the reviews section. If you are not sure what you should purchase, then go to the useful buyer's guide section. All the latest developments in home entertainment systems are announced on this site, and you can also buy older technology in the classified section.

Home entertainment magazine site
www.homecinemachoice.com

Home Cinema Choice Online has published reviews of equipment, answers to DVD questions, and a decent number of ways to "hack" your DVD player to be able to play differently regionalized disks. Sometimes these include using soldering irons and so are only suitable for experts or the foolhardy.

Quality Electrical Goods
www.qed-uk.com

Not the prettiest of sites, but one of the best for buying electrical goods in the UK. Its delivery service is impeccable and more to the point is free (for goods over £100). You may not be able to access your account details, and it is frustrating having to fill in your details each time, but for these prices it is worth it.

— Events

Festivals database
www.festivals.com

Whether your idea of bliss is to chill out to the smell of incense while having your palm read, or you prefer to partake in the World Championship Duck Calling Contest, you'll find details of hundreds of festivals and events all over the world at this site. Browse through categories or search for your favourite subject.

Miss Universe
www.missuniverse.com

Home of Miss USA and Miss Teen USA as well as Miss Universe, this site offers information about the contenders, lists success stories, and covers the history of the pageants. Do visit if you are interested in this sort of thing.

Night-Out Magazine
www.night-out.co.uk

This entertainment guide contains a magazine with listings of new clubs and a small photo gallery of parties in clubs. The most useful part is the venue directory, which lists clubs all over the country, and will keep you informed of special events.

Plan It For Kids
www.planit4kids.co.uk

If you are stuck as to how to entertain your demanding children, then visit this site. Simply select the area (or country) that you want and it will make some

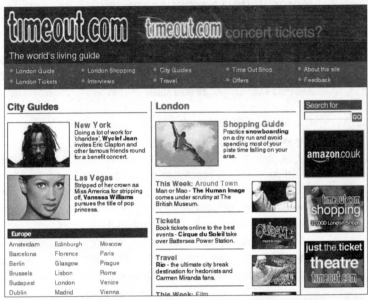

New York, Paris, London... find out what is happening in the world's cities at www.timeout.com

suggestions to keep the whole family happy, from museums and galleries to theatres, shows, and other activities. The colourful **www.kidsevents.co.uk** is definitely also worth a visit.

Time Out
www.timeout.com

Based on the magazine of the same name, this site give you details of the clubs, bars, galleries, restaurants, museums, and music venues in all the world's major cities. Events to come are reviewed, along with venue information and admission prices. You can also learn about the world of fame from the celebrity interviews that have appeared in the magazine over the last 30 years.

Worldwide Events Guide
www.whatsonwhen.com

This is an attractive site, colour coded for ease of use, that tells you what is going on in each major city all over the world. The permutations of categories – that allows you to search by theme or by country, just take your pick – means that you can either find out what is happening in the city you want to visit, or just browse to find something interesting. The site also offers flights, accommodation, insurance, and other travel services, making this site a future serious rival to **www.timeout.com**.

World Wide Events
wwevents.com

Aiming to help you enjoy (or even avoid) major events around the world, this excellent resource lets you choose the country and then the region to find out where and when a specific show is running. You can also submit your own event, or one you've heard of, to the listings.

— Films —————————————

All about movies
www.hollywood.com

The strength of this film site, and the reason it is included here along with several other possibly better ones, is that it has an excellent multimedia section where you can choose a film from the menu and select from images, trailers, video footage, and notes. Beware of the intrusive adverts.

British Academy of Film and Television Arts
www.bafta.org

Find out which films, TV programmes, and interactive entertainments are in the running for the next awards ceremony. You can see who was nominated and won last year, and find out about this month's events programme of film screenings and workshops. A press release area lets you in on the official line that is fed to entertainment journalists, although you will miss out on the boozy lunches of course.

Empire online
www.empireonline.co.uk

Read the latest entertainment news and buy videos, DVDs, and books from the online shop. Box office figures are available and, just so you know what you're missing, the contents of the paper version of the magazine is listed. You can also watch trailers from forthcoming films.

Entertainment reviews
www.sceneone.co.uk

Spanning the most popular forms of live and recorded entertainment (cinema, TV, radio, music, theatre, gigs, and comedy), Scene One's database contains reviews of films, videos, plays, and singles. It also injects some of its own opinion on these subjects, but leave these alone as the summaries of what the papers say are actually far more interesting.

Film personalities
www.filmunlimited.co.uk

Coming from *The Guardian* and *The Observer,* Film Unlimited offers insights into the world of the most important or interesting actors, producers, and those other individuals involved in enticing us into stuffy cinemas. Video releases, an A–Z of British personalities, and a mood-matcher section that chooses a film for your current state of mind makes this a must-see site.

Film plots, images, and reviews
www.darkhorizons.com

Are you after images, clips, and reviews of the latest blockbusters? You won't be disappointed with the spookily named Dark Horizons site. Films of the year are organized along with their plot lines, cast details, and links to trailers and other resources, while a "News And Rumours" section should keep you bang up-to-date with the world of Hollywood. You can also check out episode guides to your old cult TV favourites.

Film previews, listings, and merchandise
www.popcorn.co.uk

Recently revamped, this site enables you to read previews of the next best film releases, find out what is screening at your local cinema in the UK, and view trailers that you can download directly. You can also order video and DVD titles, and buy pieces of film merchandise direct from Popcorn. There are competition prizes for those who want to save their cash too.

Film reviews and news
www.thereelsite.com

This highly opinionated film review site also publishes some often speculative news on the film business. If you want to know more details about *The Blair Witch Project 5* (or whatever), or think that the *Terminator* sequels 3 and 4 will just "suck" if Mr Schwarzenegger isn't involved in them, then why not try The Reel Site out for yourself.

Internet Movie Database
www.imdb.com

Containing probably the most comprehensive list of films in the world, the Internet Movie Database lets you search through actors, directors, and genres. What's more, its rating system is based on your views, not the critics. It is ideal for solving those trivial arguments about who played who in what movie, and provides an unbiased view in disputes over which video to rent on a Saturday night. The UK site can be found at **uk.imdb.com**.

— Jokes

Joke database
www.lotsofjokes.com
This is a huge database of jokes, some clean but most are likely to offend someone. There are rude song lyrics, oxymorons, and lists of things not to say to "her when she's pregnant" or "a-naked-man". There are some funny jokes, but it'll take some exploration to find them. As, no doubt, the actress said to the bishop.

Online comedy publication
www.netfunny.com
Originating from an Internet news group rec.humor.funny, this website has a large archive of jokes and provides random chuckles, lists of favourites, as well as a selection of the best jokes posted onto the site. To get the most out of the site you'll need special software, but there's plenty to keep the unadventurous happy.

— Magic sites

Introduction to the world of magic
www.allmagicguide.com
There are loads of links here to different magic sites, including ones where they give the game away, and the site also features step-by-step instructions on how to perform. There are also book and video reviews, and a list of dealers. Learn a few tricks from here and one of the exclusive clubs might take you on...

The Magic Circle
www.themagiccircle.co.uk
Find out a limited amount about this famously low-key magician's society, and apply for an application form. As a mere member of the public you'll be restricted to a limited photo gallery and a history of the club, but should you be allowed to join you'll be privy to the "Members Area". It also includes information about public shows and forthcoming events.

The Society of American Magicians
www.magicsam.com
Download details of how to join this old society for conjurers from a very "corporate" and uninviting website. For example, you can buy SAM luggage tags

and read about the conventions and magic shows to come, but if you want to learn how to do tricks – forget it! However, there are links to members' websites, some of which have archives of tricks. Become a member and get the M-U-M magazine, which will keep you up-to-date on lectures, performances, and news.

— Movies and TV

Entertainment Online
www.eonline.com

This good, all round entertainment site covers movies, music, and TV, with features on the latest blockbuster films, this week's favourite actors, and a section containing games and quizzes. E! Online also includes gossip on which projects celebrities are currently involved in, and transcripts of online chat interviews.

New films and reviews
www.aint-it-cool-news.com

Written by self-proclaimed film nerd Harry Jay Knowles, Ain't It Cool News is THE film site to read if you want to know what films are coming up and, more importantly, if they're any good. His film reviews are so spot on that producers invite the guy to pre-previews. Like films? Visit here.

Rotten Tomatoes
www.rottentomatoes.com

This US-based site will give you the critical lowdown on all the latest films. It has a vast review database, taken from newspaper and website sources. It then accumulates the reviews and gives them a rating (either fresh or rotten). Subscribe to the weekly newsletter to find what has been said about the latest US releases. It has great news and gossip areas as well – one of the best.

Shaken, not Stirred
www.jamesbond.com

As befits the dashing 007, the official site is flashy and suave. Catch up with the latest news about the next Bond film (due late 2001), watch the trailers, and see the posters as and when they are ready.

Star Wars
www.theforce.net

Don't head to the lacklustre official *Star Wars* site (**www.starwars.com**), go here for all the information you might need on George Lucas's epic series of films. All

THE FORCE.NET PRESENTS
FANFILMS.C⊙M

FANFILMS · FILMMAKING · NEWS · COMMUNITY

galaxyfaraway.com

HOME
ABOUT
CONTACT
ADD A FILM

TFN Main

FANFILMS
New Films
All Films
Search Films

CATEGORY
Short Films
Animation
Trailers
Music Videos
FX Projects
Coming Soon

FILMMAKING
General
FAQ
Preproduction
Production

NOW SHOWING

BAD DUDES STRIKE BACK

View Film:
Flash Film
Flash Trailer
Download movie file for viewing
at any time.
Windows – baddudes.exe
Macintosh – baddudes.hqx
Story
Dude Studios and TheForce.Net is proud to present
The Bad Dudes Strike Back, the anticipated
sequel to **Star Dudes**.

Running Time:
5:00 / 1.2 MB
00:35 / 268 KB

A Word From The Director

Star Wars lovers will be in heaven at www.theforce.net – all news, however trivial, is listed here

the insider knowledge that you might need about the next two *Star Wars* films, the first of which is currently being filmed. And you cannot leave this site without watching Star Dudes and The Bad Dude Strikes Back – two hilarious Flash animated movies condensing the first two *Star Wars* films into about four minutes each (if you can't find them easily go to **theforce.net/theater/animation**).

The world of Disney
www.justdisney.com
This isn't an official Disney site, but is still packed with in-depth information about the company's history, as well as that of the man himself. There are pictures, quotes, and sounds, while the links section caters for visitors providing access to review and guide sites. The fascinating-sounding secret Club 33 is mentioned, too.

Music, sound, and video

Blackstar videos and DVDs
www.blackstar.co.uk
One of the very best places to buy your European videos and DVDs, Black Star will hunt down rare titles for you, pre-order near future releases, and the site

offers most items at a discount. Pre-ordering gets some serious money off, and the postage is free. Their loyalty scheme is called Star e-wards, which allows you to spend over a certain amount and then get anything from a free video to a DVD-player.

British Video Association
www.bva.org.uk

Find out about up-and-coming releases and read in-depth about the video industry at the site of the organization that is concerned with representing video publishers. There are also links to some of the major players in the industry, including regulatory bodies. You can find out where the law stands on tape and disk copying, as well as visit the British Board of Film Classification for news on recent decisions.

CDs over the net
www.cdnow.com

Aside from selling music CDs and movies on DVD and video, the US-based CDNOW has innovated a way to provide music that you pay for and then download straight to your computer over the Internet. You can also buy custom-made CDs here that contain just the tracks that you want from any number of albums (these can be shipped all the way to Europe, though is often expensive to do this). There are also interviews with various artists on the site to keep you up-to-date with the music world.

DVD Town
www.dvdtown.com

One of the best of many, many sites, DVD Town has all the normal features that you would expect, but possibly the most innovative is its rating system pop-up on the main featured titles on the home page. Marks out of ten are given for each DVD – for sound quality, picture quality, entertainment, and extra features (that appear nowadays on almost all DVDs). What's more you can personalize the site to your own tastes.

HMV
www.hmv.co.uk

This high street music store provides a very useable Internet version of itself, which is organized into musical categories, with separate sections for games, DVD, video, and spoken word tapes and CDs. You can find out here when releases are due out and how much they'll cost you. It's a shame that you can't pre-order on the site, but the low prices (well, less than the prices in its shops anyway) should soften this blow...

After Phil or Bootsy Collins? You can find music, videos and more at www.towerrecords.com

Music, video, book, and games shop
www.101cd.com

You can never have enough music and video shops on your list of favourite sites. Try 101cd.com when shopping around, and compare its often surprisingly low prices with other online stores, though the focus is more on the mainstream. You can also choose from a large catalogue of books and computer games.

Online store
www.jungle.com

This online store stocks music, computer games, computers, and software, and movies in both VHS and DVD format that it can send to you wherever you are. When it began, the site came under heavy criticism for its slow customer service, but it has since become one of the best and quickest sites to buy from, helped by the easy, and fun, navigation. It also provides an email service that you can call on any phone and have your messages read to you by a computer. Prices include VAT and delivery is free.

Tower Records
www.towerrecords.com

Much improved in recent months, this popular record shop's online effort features articles as well as the usual shopping areas. You can customize your own CD and download music from the site, as well as browse through the video, DVD, and book departments. A slightly lighter UK version of the store is available at **uk.towerrecords.com**.

Sci-fi sites

The Borg Collective
www.theborgcollective.com
Make sure you have time to spare before visiting this *Star Trek* fan site. Not only is there a huge amount of information through which to navigate, but the large graphics also make the site extremely slow to download. You can send Internet greeting cards from the site, learn about the Borg's history, read various character profiles, and play a game of *Star Trek* trivia. You can also visit the official site at **www.startrek.com**.

Sad Geezer's Guide to Cult TV Science Fiction
www.sadgeezer.com
Fans of *Red Dwarf*, *LEXX*, and *The Hitch-Hikers Guide To The Galaxy* will have fun here at this aptly designed site. There are episode guides to these, and other, TV shows, as well as tests to make sure that you really know your science fiction facts. Links to similar sites are available on the site, and these are packed with so much detail that you won't even need to watch the programmes... A must-see site for science fiction fans.

A world of science fiction
www.scifigate.com
Written especially for hardcore science fiction fans, the site rates some very specific sites based on sci-fi, fantasy, and horror TV programmes such as *Xena: Warrior Princess*, *Stargate SG-1*, and *Doctor Who*. Readers can also send in their own ideas for future series of popular programmes such as *Buffy The Vampire Slayer*. And of course, you can read the transcripts and episode guides for all the TV shows.

The X-Files
www.thex-files.com
Explore the archives of the official *X-Files* website and uncover past episodes. You may not find definitive answers to all the mysteries but you might be able to dig out a few clues. The vault contains a huge amount of merchandise that you can spend your cash on too.

Luvviness abounds at www.theatrenet.co.uk – find out all about plays in the West End and afar

Theatre

News, reviews, and tickets
www.theatrenet.co.uk
Join TheatreNet's ShowSavers club and you can make savings when attending shows both in and out of London. Hotel rooms, merchandise, and books are also in the list of special offers. The site also offers the latest theatre news – all the major shows have their own well-designed mini sites within the larger whole.

Playbill online
www.playbill.com
Check out the listings of the newest Broadway, and off-Broadway, shows. The categories include London and US national tours, and you can buy your tickets online. There are articles and interviews, as well as links to gift shops. Fancy treading the boards yourself? The casting section may help.

The Royal Shakespeare Company
www.rsc.org.uk
Find out what the next performances from the company will be, where the venues are, and the tour dates. You can also buy gifts, books, and other Shakespearean

bits and pieces from the online shop, and a separate box office section will gladly sell you tickets for any of the up-and-coming shows online.

—Theme parks

Alton Towers
www.alton-towers.co.uk
Find out about the rides, prices, and facilities at one of the UK's most popular theme parks on this brilliantly designed site. You can take a 360-degree panoramic view of some of the hotel rooms directly from your screen, and tickets are available to buy during the park's open season. If you need scaring, you can find out details of the latest big ride, including the Hex, which shakes the screen when your cursor goes over it!

Chessington World of Adventures
www.chessington.co.uk
Do a quick reconnaissance of this UK theme park using the online map and you can hopefully avoid the big queues or losing your kids when you are actually there. Zoom in to find out about each ride. The "Thrillometer Readings" and height restrictions should also help you to avoid disappointments when you visit the park. It also includes opening times, directions, prices, and booking details.

Disney online
www.disneyinternational.com
The official Disney website has information on its CD-ROM games, films, cartoons, musicals, and videos. However, you can also find out about the Disneyland resorts in the US and Paris. While you're waiting to visit you can keep the kids occupied with the online animated stories and games.

See also "Universal Studios" in Travel, page 295.

— Treading the boards

Database for dancers
www.danceservice.co.uk
Aimed at professional dancers, as well as appreciative audience members, Danceservice UK provides regionalized news, class resources for students and

teachers, and interviews with experienced dancers. A contacts list will prove handy to both pros and novices. The authors claim that this is the only database with such a wide range of links.

Salsa

www.salsabeat.freeserve.co.uk

Stay up-to-date with the increasingly popular UK salsa. Find out when special events are to take place, download salsa tunes, and get the low-down on various salsa bands. There are also links to similar sites all over the UK and the world, so this is worth a visit even for those not living in the Big Smoke.

Showbiz kids

www.startips.com

If you want to put your son or daughter on the stage, follow the advice offered by this Hollywood site, which is aimed at helping parents promote their children as young stars. It includes tips on getting started and signing with an agent, as well as the best ways to present photo CVs.

— TV, radio, and ads —

The Advertising Standards Authority

www.asa.org.uk

You might wonder why you would visit a dry-sounding site like this. However, there is much entertainment to be had in reading about the latest ASA adjudications. You can find out which ads have received complaints and what the ASA recommends as a result.

BBC TV

www.beeb.com

Beeb.com is the British Broadcasting Corporation's "fun", and now commercial, site, with big colourful logos instead of "boring" headlines. You can find your way directly to *Top of the Pops*, *Top Gear*, and *Gardeners' World* from here, while books and videos are available to buy. It is separate from the BBC's licence-funded business, so the adverts don't denote a licence fee reduction, sadly.

Coronation Street

www.coronationstreet.co.uk

Pop into the Rovers Return to take an "exclusive" look behind the scenes of this long-running UK soap, have a go in the competitions and win yourself Corrie memorabilia, and download images to decorate your computer with. You can also chat with the stars, follow the video diary, and watch the interviews provided.

Eastenders
www.bbc.co.uk/eastenders
If you find yourself at a loose end between episodes of this soap, you can spend time recalling some of the exploits of "Ricky!", sour Pauline, or Dirty Den. Take a tour of Walford, express your opinions (remember, it's not real!), and catch up on the storyline, if you cannot wait for the Sunday omnibus.

Episode guides
epguides.com
This remarkable set of episode guides (some of which have plot summaries and guest stars), covers US TV series as diverse as *Jeeves and Wooster*, *Ally McBeal*, *King of the Hill*, and *Manimal*. Cast lists are linked to the Internet Movie Database site (**www.imdb.com**) so you can visit there to find out what else your favourite TV star has been in.

Fox
www.fox.com
The mother site of *The Simpsons* hosts a lot more than our yellow friends. The site is huge, with features on all its hit shows including *Ally McBeal*, *The X-Files*, and *King of the Hill*. Simply scroll down the right-hand menu and take your choice. It also has TV listings for the US.

Golden oldies
www.spudtv.com
Couch potatoes rejoice. This is the site for you. There are features on interesting, and sometimes a little off-the-wall, themes. Old shows are revisited and good, bad, and undeservedly popular programmes are highlighted. The resident TV Historian is available to take your TV trivia questions.

Independent Television Commission
www.itc.org.uk
Has digital TV passed you by already? Catch up with the introduction and technical appraisal published on the ITC's site. You can also read about which UK TV stations are in trouble for breaching the code of conduct, and which Channel 4 documentaries have allegedly misled viewers. For those that are particularly interested you can also find out how the ITC regulates programmes, advertising, and sponsorship, and can follow complaints that have been made against programmes in the past.

Online TV Guide (US)
www.tvguide.com

This US TV guide publishes programme listings for all the cable, broadcast, and satellite channels. You enter your zip code or choose your time zone and it works out what's available in your area. Catch up on the soaps – any questions you have about them can be answered by "The Expert". News and gossip is readily available here, and a chat forum is provided to fill in time between episodes of *The Simpsons*.

TV Century 21: The Gerry Anderson Home Page
tv21.simplenet.com

Dedicated to the producer of shows such as *Torchy the Battery Boy*, *Fireball XL5*, *Thunderbirds*, and *Captain Scarlet and The Mysterons*, this site has news, and almost too much detail on the models used in his programmes. Interviews with all the personalities involved in the shows are also included. Get those sought-after pieces in the trading zone.

The UK Tuner
urn.su.nottingham.ac.uk/tuner

Do you fancy turning your computer and Internet connection into a radio? Find out where you can "tune in" at this large list of online radio stations, TV shows, and one-off broadcasts (webcasts). The sites are listed in two main categories – RealAudio and Windows Media Player. Links are also provided for those of you who don't have these programs.

Unmissable TV
www.unmissabletv.co.uk

This site ensures that TV really is unmissable, allowing you to search for the times of all your favourite shows – you can narrow down your search by choosing your region, and whether you want to look on terrestrial or cable TV. You can also spend time reading up on the latest gossip and previews of upcoming shows on the box.

What's on? The Toob!
www.thetoob.com

Visit this site to locate Internet "events", which could be anything from short films stored as archives to live broadcasts of music or chat. There are also computer-based technical help clips, short videos on health issues, and links to news sites that use live and stored audio and video stories. This is definitely an interesting site to look around.

See also the "Radio" and "TV" sections in News, beginning pages 236 and 238.

The goggle-eyed should visit www.unmissabletv.co.uk for the latest on soaps, dramas, and more.

— see also... —

Science Fiction sites are a dime a dozen, but you could be in heaven at **www.scifi.com**, which has all the news that you could possibly want. Fans of the nihilistic 70s sci-fi show, *Space:1999,* will be happy at **www.space1999.net**.

One strong characteristic of the Internet is the presence of personal tributes to favourite films, stars, and even cartoons. The Big List of Movie Mistakes (**www.movie-mistakes.com**) dissects famous films and ruins them all for you, pointing out filming mistakes that are so obvious once you know they're there – they have a Top 25 and, would you know, the most expensive, *Titanic,* is at the top. Another great way to spoil a film is to visit the Movie-A-Minute site (**www.rinkworks.com/movieaminute**), where you'll find ultra-compressed summaries of popular movies. For those who already know what they are getting (in far too much detail), there are pages devoted to films such as *Star Wars* (www.geocities.com/Area51/Rampart/2720/starwarsthewebring.html). Going back in time, you'll find dedications to silent movies at The Silents Majority (**www.mdle.com/ClassicFilms**) while homage is paid to yesterday's Hollywood stars at Bombshells (**www.bombshells.com**). As for the Oscars, find out all you want to know about the ultimate movie prizes at **www.oscar.org**.

Today's stars are definitely of the animated variety. Say hello to the online presences of the cult cartoon *South Park* at South Park Central (**www.totalsouthpark.com**). The latter is found in the UK on Channel 4, and so is one of hundreds of shows featured on the site (**www.channel4.com**). As you'd expect, *The Simpsons* (**www.fox.com/thesimpsons**) are also connected, even providing a free Internet access service to those in the US. If "Cow and Chicken" and "I am Weasel" mean anything to you, Spumco's Wonderful World of Cartoons (**www.spumco.com**) will sate your cravings for disturbing children's cartoons. For more of roughly the same, try Nickelodeon (for UK residents at **www.nicktv.co.uk** or for those in the US at **www.nicktv.com**) but you'll only "get" the site if you regularly tune into this children's TV channel. Most people will 'get' the Cartoon Network site (**www.cartoon-network.co.uk**) as it is the home of the marvellous Scooby Doo (and Shaggy too). For classic comic lovers, visit the colourful *Beano* website (**www.beano.co.uk**) to see Dennis the Menace and other old favourites. *Viz* (**www.viz.co.uk**), on the other hand, tends to appeal to the ruder person, as shown by the Roger Mellie Profanisaurus, the definitive reference guide to sexual euphemisms.

Other cult-viewing essential sites include the *League of Gentlemen* (**www.leagueofgentlemen.co.uk**) – a local site for local people. And for the lovers of the doll world, visit **www.barbie.com** for a surreal online experience. For those keen on the online TV experience go to **www.virtuetv.com** to watch concerts, music videos, interviews, live sport, and short films on your computer.

There are absolutely hundreds of sites from which you can buy your goods to watch the entertainment that is detailed in this chapter – some of the best of the rest happen to be Empire Direct (**www.empiredirect.co.uk**), Unbeatable (**www.unbeatable.co.uk**), and Richer Sounds (**www.richersounds.com**). All are in competition with each other, which means that prices are often much lower than on the high street.

Alternatively, do you want to know what all those couch potatoes at home are watching? Try the Broadcasters' Audience Research Board (**www.barb.co.uk**) to find out how many people share your taste in soap operas, using the data from this audience analysis site. If you want to consult British TV episode guides have a look at **www.phill.co.uk**.

There are also various quiz sites like Trivia Bytes (**www.triviabytes.com**), where you can take part in the online trivia quizzes, using sound and other multimedia elements as questions. For the ultimate challenge, why not visit *Who Wants To Be A Millionaire?* (**www.phone-a-friend.com**) though unfortunately you won't actually win any money at all. Assuming you haven't been a successful participant there, you might want to resort to UK Free Stuff (**www.ukfreestuff.net**), which will find the free things in life for you – but only if you live in the UK of course.

Find out what's around the corner in the world of entertainment with sites like **www.dvhs.co.uk**, where the new digital video tape format that will no doubt revolutionize our lives is outlined. Technology-based TV programme *Tomorrow's World* (**www.bbc.co.uk/tw**) should also keep you up-to-date with the latest innovations – even if they never actually materialize in the real world.

e

FOOD AND DRINK

Your taste buds will doubtless be tickled by the tempting array of recipes, luxurious items, and exotic cocktails detailed on these foody websites. You will also find information on GM foods, fast food outlets in your area, and cuisine from around the world. Whether your interest lies in basic home cooking or creating a killer Thai banquet you will find hundreds of different options, plus advice on what to drink with your chosen feast. You'll be making space by the toaster for your PC in no time.

f

— Drink

All about tea
www.teacouncil.co.uk
Discover those elusive tea facts including the average daily consumption per person, what percentage of the UK population are avid tea drinkers, and what the future holds for the tea market. A directory of suppliers, importers, and other specialized services is available, as is an overview of the history of the drink.

Beer and where to drink it
www.goodguides.com/pubs/search.asp
Not really feted for its cuisine, the British do excel at a good pub and this site has them all. You can search by region, but not just for what alcohol each pub serves. For every one they tell you whether it serves food, has accommodation, and its general value. The pub descriptions are detailed and informative.

Cocktail party planner
www.hotwired.com/cocktail
Browse the archives of cocktail recipes or use the pain-free "Virtual Blender". Once you have specified one or more ingredients, it will search for you, and then pinpoint the recipes that you should like. Or, even easier, just go to the Drink of the Week (hic…) to find a recipe to try out. The party planning page will help you keep record of all those important planning points: the number of people you're

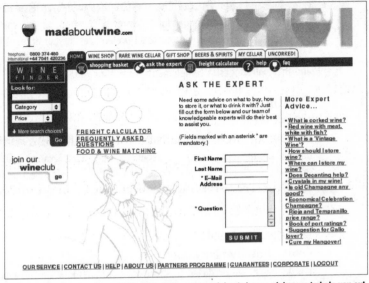

madaboutwine.com

telephone 0800 374 400
international +44 7041 420236

HOME | WINE SHOP | RARE WINE CELLAR | GIFT SHOP | BEERS & SPIRITS | MY CELLAR | UNCORKED!

shopping basket   ask the expert   freight calculator   ? help   faq

WINE FINDER

Look for:

Category

Price

More search choices?   Go

join our **wine**club   go

FREIGHT CALCULATOR
FREQUENTLY ASKED QUESTIONS
FOOD & WINE MATCHING

ASK THE EXPERT

Need some advice on what to buy, how to store it, or what to drink it with? Just fill out the form below and our team of knowledgeable experts will do their best to assist you.

(Fields marked with an asterisk * are mandatory.)

First Name

Last Name

* E-Mail Address

* Question

SUBMIT

More Expert Advice...

• What is corked wine?
• Red wine with meat, white with fish?
• What is a 'Vintage Wine'?
• How should I store wine?
• Where can I store my wine?
• Does Decanting help?
• Crystals in my wine!
• Is old Champagne any good?
• Economical Celebration Champagne?
• Rioja and Tempranillo price range?
• Book of port ratings?
• Suggestion for Gallo lover?
• Cure my Hangover!

OUR SERVICE | CONTACT US | HELP | ABOUT US | PARTNERS PROGRAMME | GUARANTEES | CORPORATE | LOGOUT

If you fancy buying your favourite tipple in bulk, www.madaboutwine.co.uk is sure to help you out

having around for your party, what glasses you have to use for the event, the time of day it is to be held at, and how formal you intend the event to be.

Cocktail recipes
www.cocktail.com

Access a massive database of cocktail recipes, submit your own speciality, and read a few book reviews. The editorial section might be a little stronger than some of the drinks, but we're all entitled to our opinions. The shopping section just links you to other sites selling cigars, gourmet food, and booze.

Learn more about wine
www.winespectator.com

Learn to be a wine buff and put your lesser friends to shame when the next bottle is cracked open. Features include an interactive tasting, a database containing wine reviews, and a worldwide wine retailer directory. The library will take you through the basics of wine appreciation. To get the most from this site you'll need to subscribe for a fee, although a cheaper trial is available.

Mad About Wine
www.madaboutwine.co.uk

This excellent site entices you to stock up your cellar with a variety of wines. There is no snobbery here – the wines vary from the cheap and cheerful to the more expensive and rarer vintages. The site promises to deliver its readily available wines within five days, longer for the rarer tipples. You can ask the experts for advice and can even put your personal preferences in your account through the "My Cellar" area. You can also tell their experts what you are having for dinner and they will suggest a complementary wine for you.

Oddbins
www.oddbins.co.uk

Avoid the sly smiles when you fail to pronounce posh wines correctly by buying directly off the web, using the services of the award winning Oddbins wine merchant. You'll find special offers, a "Fizz Finder" to help select a nice bottle of bubbly, and a no-nonsense (well, nearly) guide to the gassy wine. Free delivery if you order 12 bottles or more.

Whisky in depth
www.scotchwhisky.com

Whisky lovers are predicted to spend far too much time on this highly detailed effort of a website. The "Malt Whisky File" is a searchable database that asks you to express your tastes in order to tell you what your perfect dram is. Pour yourself a glass and settle down to learn how whisky is made, the regional differences, and just about anything else you'll ever want to know.

The world of beer
www.breworld.com

Keep up-to-date with what's happening in the world of beer – including how to make your own. Find out about beery events and discover the best places in London and other major cities to visit for a good pint. A discussion forum offers a chance to ask questions and help others, and a good selection of recipes will keep you locked in the garage "working" for some time. The list of equipment and ingredients suppliers can only act as encouragement.

— Luxury food

Cheeses from around the world
www.wgx.com/cheesenet

Refer to the "World Cheese Index" to find how fatty each cheese is, where it comes from, and which wines are likely to best accompany a snack. You can find out how cheese is made, and even ask "Dr Cheese" any cheese-related questions that you think of.

Dean and Deluca
www.deananddeluca.com

The famous New York deli store has its own immaculately designed website. The site sells delectable looking food, from tupelo honey to foie gras, kitchenware, and corporate gifts (but be warned that it is all very expensive). You can also request their catalogue in order to salivate over the goods on offer, but only if you live in the USA, unfortunately.

Fortnum and Mason
www.fortnumandmason.co.uk

This most prestigious of grocers, famous for its luxury goods and hampers, offers a tastefully designed online shopping service within its beautiful site. This is complemented by a smattering of recipes and short pieces on cigars, wine, and cheese, as well as other elegantly unhealthy pursuits. And they say that you can't buy class...

Gastronomic Delights
www.morel.co.uk

Another site offering fine food that it will deliver to all over the world too. The company was founded in the early 19th century and has always supplied the finest quality products – so if you feel like splashing out on a hand-painted box of champagne fizz truffles or a seasonal hamper, then it is very easy to order them from this site.

Gourmet Francais
www.gourmet2000.co.uk

Order the finest ingredients for your gourmet creations from this continental online grocery store. There are all sorts of interesting products on offer – from wild mushrooms and truffles to emu pate. There is also a small selection of organic, British, and Italian food.

Online chocolate shop
www.chocexpress.com

Send your loved one, or potential loved one, a box of chocolates or sweets (and even the occasional bottle of bubbly) by way of this online gift shop – it is a free service throughout the UK. Enrolling someone ensures that they will receive monthly packages of chocolates to scoff. A scoring card for them to fill in will helpfully steer future selections towards their specific tastes. ChocExpress also runs a chocolate tasting club – wonderful. What the ensuing weight gain on both sides will do for your budding relationship is another matter completely of course. But isn't it worth it to be able to buy chocolate on tap?

Recipes

All about cheese
www.ilovecheese.com

The ultimate site devoted to cheese, I Love Cheese is both amusing (just check out the 1950s-style images) and informative. This site will find the perfect cheese for your tastes and offer recipe ideas. Do you consider meltability when you visit the shops? Well, then. The site is run by the American Dairy Association and offers a free bi-monthly email newsletter.

Barbecue hints and tips
www.barbecuen.com

Give your summer barbecue a boost by following some of the tips and recipes provided here. You can find out what the perfect cooking temperature is, what utensils you'll need, and how to achieve that unique smoky taste without the accompanying charring. An online store is also available.

Food and Drink
www.bbc.co.uk/foodanddrink

Check out the latest recipes featured on TV, and remind yourself of the drinks that Jilly and Oz bang on about most eloquently. Unfortunately we are not treated to transcripts of their opinions, but you will get a rough idea of the prices, which are probably more informative.

Ideas for meals
www.mealsforyou.com

Come here not just for recipes, but complete meal plans. The recipes are listed by ingredients as well as the dietary requirements they fulfil. You can store the recipes that you like in your online cookbook. You can use Meals for You to choose an entire menu quickly. It will show you exactly how long the meal will take to prepare, and how good (or fun) it will be for you. Measurement units are available in US, British, metric, and antipodean.

Internet Chef
www.ichef.com

Full of handy tips and good advice, Ichef is one of the best culinary websites around at the moment. For example, if you cannot follow the written recipe, why not watch the video of the meal being cooked – ingenious (though don't try and cook at the same time as watching). The recipe categories scroll down the page

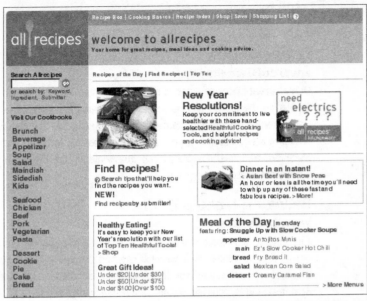

Impress all your friends and cook something up from what is on offer at www.allrecipes.com

forever so that you will never need to be short of delicious meals for guests or family again. Their spotlight on particular food items changes regularly, so if you are wondering what to do with those green beans in the larder, this site will enlighten you and give you plenty of mouthwatering ideas.

Recipe network
www.allrecipes.com

This is the ultimate resource for all home-based chefs. The site acts as a gateway to a number of its own other sites, which include **Cakerecipe.com**, **Cookierecipe.com**, **Pierecipe.com**, and **Christmasrecipe.com**. There is, of course, a reason behind this well-organized philanthropy. An online cookery store, **Culinarystore.com**, sells a large range of kitchen equipment and, of course, is just one click away…

Star Chefs
www.starchefs.com

Don't be put off by the home page and the poor navigation to be found here, as it is still a site worth visiting. Where it differs from the many other food and drink sites is its section on celebrity chefs, which includes biographies, recipes from them, and interviews. There are also numerous features and articles on all types of food and drink.

Reviews

Coffee Review

www.coffeereview.com

Overwhelmed by the selection of coffees in the supermarket? The why not let the experts do the tasting for you, once you've read about how to interpret their tasting results. Different types of coffee bean, with details about their country of origin, are listed. Categories include espressos, dark roasts, and organics to name but a few. US residents can buy some of the reviewed products at **www.greatcoffee.com**.

Eating in – and out

www.taste.co.uk

This new site has been brought to the public jointly by Sainsbury's and Carlton. It has all the information that you will need on culinary entertaining as well as details of where to eat out. The categories to be found on the site include recipes, wine, restaurants, entertaining, and, interestingly, organics. You can also find out what's currently on the Carlton Food Network, and learn about its various chefs and presenters.

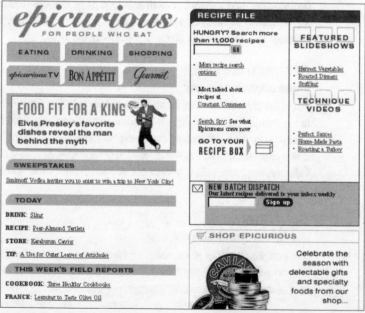

No food lover with an internet connection should forget to visit www.epicurious.com

Zagat's restaurant reviews
www.zagat.com

At this site you can find more than 20,000 reviews and ratings of restaurants that can be found in the US, London, Paris, Toronto, and Vancouver. Categorized by Zagat ratings, cuisine, cost, or location, the paths to find the restaurant of your choice are easy to follow. Once found you can pull up a handy map telling you how to get there. It also gives you a chance to vote on your favourite venue.

— Safety and other issues —

Everything about food
www.epicurious.com

Whether you want a hand equipping your new kitchen, have forgotten how to mix a Singapore Sling, or want to mellow the taste of garlic then this site will suit. There are a staggering 11,000 recipes here to choose from you, if you so desire. In fact, there are so many articles that once tried, no other food site will satisfy.

Food safety and preservation
www.foodpres.com

If you are not quite sure how long that cheese has been lurking at the back of the fridge, how do you find out if it's still safe to eat? The advice on this site will help, although its main emphasis is on food preservation.

The Vegan Society
www.vegansociety.com

Find out what it means to choose a vegan lifestyle, and use the information sheets to learn about staying healthy while eschewing animal products. You can locate vegan cookery courses, discover the truth about diabetes and other disorders, and find out what kinds of alcoholic beverage are "safe". You may be surprised…

The Vegetarian Resource Group
www.vrg.org

Maybe you are trying to raise a vegan family, or want to know where to buy specialist vegetarian goods. Is kosher gelatine vegan? This site will give advice and explain things that the most fastidious veggie might be unsure about. Vegetarian teenagers have a section all to themselves, with help on how to reassure worried parents that they won't break in the next gust of wind.

See also "Food and Drug Administration" in Health, page 145.

— Supermarkets —————

Jewel-Osco
www.jewelosco.com
Browse this US food store by category and pick up the latest bargains from your armchair. Place your orders online for pickup at your local store and search the menu database for ideas on turning your goods into great-tasting meals.

Sainsbury's
www.sainsburys.co.uk
Work out what you can make from the ingredients already in the larder, or get some more food in by shopping online. Sainsbury's runs a home delivery grocery service that costs £5 each time (it's called Sainsbury's to You). It has links to its banking service as well, and you can build up your recipes from the site (there are over 4,000 to choose from).

Tesco
www.tesco.co.uk
Tesco's online shopping service is available to a growing number of households throughout the UK – and this is the place to access it. It no longer offers just food supplies, but will also deliver sofas, TVs, fridges, and crates of wine. It is certainly easier to navigate this simple and effectively designed site than to push a wonky trolley along countless busy aisles.

— World foods and restaurants —

Curry info and shopping
www.curryhouse.co.uk
All you'll ever need to know about curry making is contained in The Curry House's electronic pages. You can also order specialist ingredients from the Chilli Willie Spice Emporium and learn about the potentially life-saving gadget called the CurrySafe, which stops your takeaway curry tipping over in the car!

Taste of Ireland
www.tasteofireland.com
Find guides to restaurants in Ireland, food shops where you can buy classically Irish fare (smoked salmon and cheese, it appears!) online, and a recipe book containing traditional dishes. Most of the site's efforts are directed at the

restaurant guide, which has detailed listings including sample menus and the occasional featured recipe.

US restaurant reviews

www.eathere.com

Imagine the scene – you are on a trans-US car journey and you're starting to flag, but which roadside diner should you opt for? If you've planned properly you'll have read the reviews on this site and know where to go for the best hamburgers. Places are also rated on how kid-friendly, smoker-tolerant, and alcoholic they are.

— see also...

There are plenty of websites that offer recipes from all over the world. Global Gourmet (**www.globalgourmet.com**) is a long-established site that features various delightful cuisines of countries from all over the world. Asia Cuisine (**www.asiacuisine.com.sg**) offers a full Asian culinary experience, with information on kitchen design and recipes. For a more limited range of recipes and ingredients that are popular in Thai restaurants, try Thai Cuisine (**www.thaicuisine.com**). A veritable feast of recipes for lovers of Indian food, as well as shopping tips and references, may be found at **www.daawat.com** and Indian Recipes (**www.indianrecipes.com**).

Eat Germany (**www.eat-germany.net**) is not a suggestion but rather a comprehensive guide to restaurants across Germany, Switzerland, and Austria by state and city – click on the US flag in the left-hand menu for the English language version. Try Epicuria – Le Serveur de la Gastronomie Francaise (**www.epicuria.fr/anglais**) for information on regional French products and recipes, and order delicious products from the online shop of the Italian delicatessen Valvona and Crolla (based in Scotland) at **valvonacrolla.com**. For French dessert and side dish recipes visit Le Cuisine de Veronique (**cooking-french.com**).

The Global Gourmet (**foodwine.com**) is similar to World Series Baseball in that it's not very global and only America takes part. Nevertheless, there is some interesting information, wine reviews, and recipes. Other good American food sites include Webicurean (**www.webicurean.com**) and The Searchable Online Archive of Recipes (**soar.berkeley.edu**). A good example of a regional US food site can be found at Foodstop (**www.foodstop.com**), which takes you on a gourmet tour of New Orleans. For a more personal viewpoint, check out **www.gastronomer.com** with guidance on eating and, amusingly, advice for young men on dining for young ladies.

Fast food is everywhere, and that includes on the web. Burger King (**www.burgerking.co.uk**), McDonald's (**www.mcdonalds.com**), Domino's (**www.dominos.co.uk**), and Wendy's Restaurant (**www.wendys.com**) can all be found online. Before visiting any of these restaurants, check out Food Finder (**www.olen.com/food**), an American nutrition guide for some of the best known restaurant chains in the world. The truth revealed!

Maybe you're trying to cut down on burger sessions. Try Cyberdiet (**www.cyberdiet.com**) for recipes, food facts, exercise plans, assessments, and motivation for a healthier lifestyle. Get back to basics with the Wheat Foods Council (**www.wheatfoods.org**), which provides nutritional information, news, discussion, and recipes for grain foods. And if you are worried about genetically modified food, hopefully the issues will be cleared up for you at **gmworld.newscientist.com**.

Vegetarians are well catered for on the web, as proved by the excellent Living and Raw Foods (**www.living-foods.com**), a site dedicated to providing comprehensive information on vegetarian food as well as recipes. Meat Stinks (**www.meatstinks.com**) is a bit less subtle, outlining the effects of using meat for food on the environment and our health. Tarla Dalal (**www.tarladalal.com**) is a good source of vegetarian recipes from around the world. Political veggies should visit the Vegetarian Society of the UK (**www.vegsoc.org**), which features vegetarian news, as well as recipes and online shopping facilities. Discussions are held at Veggie Life (**www.veggielife.com**), where the forum is accompanied by recipes, press articles, and an online shopping mall.

Expand your drinking horizons at the Joy of Sake (**www.joyofsake.com**), which provides product information on Japanese rice wine. Wines and Food from France (**www.frenchwinesfood.com**) carries some good basic information on French wines, as well as interesting recipes and the low-down on cheeses, while **www.winedine.co.uk** is an online magazine for lovers of, unsurprisingly, wine and food. Or if you just want wine, then check out the great deals on cases at Virgin Wines (**www.virginwines.com**).

GAMES

What the web doesn't "know" about computer games just isn't
worth knowing. You'll find reviews, walkthroughs, cheat codes,
and pictures of games that aren't even finished yet. If staring at
a screen isn't your cup of tea, you'll be pleased to hear that there
is also a huge amount of coverage provided by the Internet on
board and card games. Resolve poker disputes with rules guides
and buy the latest *Star Wars* version of Monopoly to keep the
family happy. There are cerebral sites for chess players, too many
places for people interested in role-playing games, and plenty of
online shops that will sell you anything from a PlayStation 2 to
a set of dice.

g

— Computer games —

All about games
www.gamespot.co.uk

GameSpot deals with computer games for the PC, Nintendo 64, Dreamcast, and
PlayStation. There are reviews, strategy courses, news items, and features on
games developments, hardware upgrades, and game artificial intelligence.
Previews of up-and-coming games are also published regularly, and there is a
calendar of approximate release dates for those long-awaited games, including
an already impressive array of Playstation 2 reviews. Cheat codes are provided,
too, for those who can't win fair and square.

Dreamcast
www.dreamcastmag.co.uk

Get the inside information on this games console. There are previews and reviews
of the latest games, and news stories covering almost all things Dreamcast. The
site can give advice if you have trouble getting through any game. You'll have to
visit **www.sega.com** for help connecting to the Internet and other technical
support issues, though, unless you want to rely on the chat forum.

Hardcore gamers will have all their needs supplied at www.gameplay.com

GameBoy hints and tips
www.gbstation.com

Find out which are the essential GameBoy games and seek help on the chat forums, or just go straight to the cheats section. Release dates for the next load of games are available, and you can aspire to new hardware too by reading the mini reviews.

Gameplay
www.gameplay.com

Brilliantly designed, you can play, shop, or read the magazine and its games reviews that the site is based on. You can play online games for prizes as well as buy DVD films. Wireplay is the free online games service – just download the software and play. There are lots of demos, patches, and more – in fact, everything that you would want from an online gaming environment. You can even gameplay through your WAP phone.

Inside Mac Games
www.insidemacgames.com

As with many computer games sites, Inside Mac Games errs on the technical side, assuming that you know what an Unreal Tourney and MacMAME is. If you are in the market for such a site, you should visit this one. It's got all the news, the usual reviews, sneak previews, and some interesting views in the chat forum.

Kids' games
www.surfmonkey.com
Go on a voyage to the deep sea or a virtual trip to the desert, vote for your favourite pop star or get a sneaky preview of the newest Muppets movie. Designed to be a safe and fun place for kids to play online, this site offers a special web browser that keeps nasty Internet pages at bay, gives info to parents, and also provides great online games. The shop's stock includes toys, video games, and sports gear, and a chat forum lets kids run up their parents' phone bills.

UK Gaming
www.ukgames.com
Not as pretty as other sites, however, you are almost guaranteed to find out about every game released here. The home page shows the release dates of all the latest games, and sells them at discount prices. Cheats, charts, demos, and discussion groups can all be found here too.

— News and software

g

The Adrenaline Vault
www.avault.com
Read the latest news about up-and-coming computer games and download software fixes for the ones you bought last weekend but cannot finish (because of the software bugs). You can check out the demos, or get patches to improve your gameplay with your current games. You'll also find cheats and hints for those games that seem impossible to finish.

PC games news and updates
www.bluesnews.com
For real PC gamers who know their TNT2 from their MODs, this techie website publishes the latest news (updated daily) on 3D games, including software updates, as well as features on optimizing your mouse (really) and where the next network game party is happening. There are links to similar sites, God help us.

PlayStation
www.absolute-playstation.com
Claiming to undergo updates three times a day (you're never going to visit that often, now are you?), Absolute PlayStation offers a seriously large archive of games reviews, previews, and tips. You can choose to find out what is new either in the US or Europe.

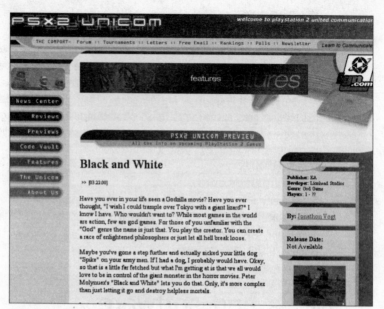

Hints, tips, and reviews for Playstation 2 games can be found at www.psx2unicom.com

PlayStation2 in depth
www.psx2unicom.com

Find out everything there is to know about the PlayStation2, including cheat codes, game guides, previews, and anything else fellow gamers are willing to discuss on the busy chat forum. This effort was outstanding long before the console was released and has continued to be so.

— Old favourites —

Action Man
www.actionman.com

The classic "boys" toy has undergone something of a renaissance in recent years, as the home page reflects with dozens of countries to choose from! You can buy your Action Mans here etc, and there is a collectors' section as well.

British Chess Federation
www.bcf.ndirect.co.uk

This most uncomplicated of sites contains a huge amount of information, including details about local UK clubs, tournaments, and news articles from the national press. National Club Championship rules are published, as is the monthly newsletter. There are no playing tips, which is extremely disappointing, although a few links may take you to sites where you can play the game.

Foosball/Table football
www.foosball.com

Refine your table football technique with the library of tutorial images and movies, learn the official rules inside and out, discover trickshots, and even discover the history of the game that revolutionized sixth form common rooms absolutely everywhere.

The Game Report Online
www.gamereport.com

This is the online version of a quarterly magazine by the same name. It concentrates on card, dice, and board games, and reviews the latest arrivals. The site has a partnership with an online games shop and hosts games auctions too. Extracts from the paper magazine are sometimes published online too. Leave your comments on its various news features.

Mr Potato Head
www.mrpotatohead.com

Nearly everyone has had a Mr Potato Head so he needs no introduction. Follow his life, using the "Tater Timeline" and the scrapbook, or just visit the fun corner and, among other things, construct your own spud head online.

North American Tiddlywinks Association
www.tiddlywinks.org

You'll be eating, sleeping, and drinking tiddlywinks by the time you've finished absorbing the information held on this wink-flicking site. You can learn the rules, advanced strategies, and how to talk like a bona fide winker. There are international tournaments to take part in too, details of which are all here. So get practising!

— Online games and puzzles —

Board games and mental skill exercises
www.msoworld.com

Providing coverage of the Mind Sports Olympiad as well as a set of message boards for like-brained people to chat, this site is a hub of cranial activity. There is a free puzzle section where you can download favourites such as Tic-Tac-Toe or

Draughts, and new puzzles are posted on the site every day, and there is also an area where you can play games online. There is a host of IQ tests and a massive network of links to other "mind sports sites" too.

Family favourites
www.hasbrointeractive.com

Home of an extraordinary range of family game favourites that include Monopoly, Scrabble, The Game of Life, and Risk, Hasbro's site also provides free online games that you can play right from your web browser program. So now you can easily play Atari classics like Frogger, Missile Command, and Centipede.

Gamesville – bingo and other games
www.gamesville.lycos.com

Play multi-player, online games such as bingo, pop trivia quizzes, and American football pools, and you may even win prizes or cash (the site says that they give out over $300,000 per month in cash and prizes). These games are free to join in with. Just make sure that you carefully read all the small print on the site and also check that gambling is legal in your country/state before you start playing any of the gambling games.

Lexigrams
lexigrams.com

This site is a bit disturbing if you don't understand what a lexigram is, and, as no online dictionaries or encyclopedias I've found provide adequate explanation, I'm afraid you're on your own! Suffice to say, you'll only enjoy Lexigrams if you like clever word play. Very weird place (that's one).

Playnet
www.playnet.com

Register here and begin online gaming – you can win prizes at games like Wild Card (find out the rules on the site!) as well as the chat forums. All game types are covered, from RPG to shoot-em-ups.

Stan Lee Media
www.stanlee.net

A veritable feast of online entertainment is available at this award-winning site. Ensure that Flash is installed on your machine and enter the various areas where you can watch "web-isodes" of online animated cartoons, including the 7th Portal and The Drifter, and then play online games associated with the various shows. If you like the look of the impressive content, then eulogize over it with others in the community area.

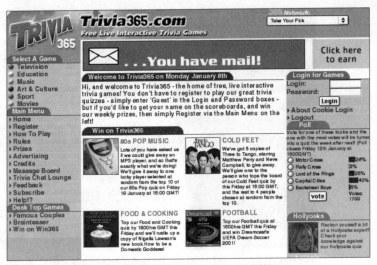

Test your wits and win prizes on the interactive games at www.trivia365.com

Telegraph Premier League
www.telegraphpremierleague.com

Play *The Daily Telegraph's* online fantasy football game at this site and have all the information that you need at your fingertips. You can set up any number of teams here and log on as regularly as you like to administer to them. Give the game a try, and then compete against the hundreds of other bored managers out there...

Trivia challenges
www.trivia365.com

Become an expert at pub quizzes, or one of the world's biggest bores, by playing the online trivia games on offer at Planet Trivia. Categories include television, music, sport, and movies and, if you register, there are opportunities to win cash prizes. And if you regularly top the scoreboards you also stand to win "unique prizes", whatever they are.

Trivial Pursuit
www.trivialpursuit.com

Discover the multitude of versions of this popular game, as well as its origins. An online version is available, where you play against other people for prizes. Downloading the necessary file may take a long time, but if you're going to play a whole Triv game over the Internet then this won't bother you will it? As long as you have unmetered access of course...

STORES GAMES BOOKS MAGAZINES ONLINE PLAY EVENTS COMPANY INTERNATIONAL

Budding Merlins should find all the info they need at www.wizards.com

Word games and puzzles
www.thinks.com

This is an odd, mixed-up site that offers "brain games, puzzles, and pastimes". It actually contains a large number of links disguised as content. However, there is a good section on words and wordplay, a plethora of online web games, and some interesting fractal images and generated music.

For other mind tests see "Intelligence Sites" in Education, page 74.

Role-playing games

Fantasy games
www.games-workshop.com
Official home of the Warhammer role-playing games and many other fantasy pursuits, Games Workshop publishes sets of rules and special offers. You can also browse through a few of the countless Citadel miniature figurines available. The UK version is available at **www.games-workshop.co.uk**.

Online multiplayer game world
www.avalon-rpg.com
Avalon is an online game, the likes of which many of us just don't have time to encounter. It is a multi-player role-playing game that runs in real time and works

in an evolving online world where your actions could, theoretically, affect every other player. You can read the histories of other players' endeavours if you can't actually be bothered to play yourself.

Role Playing Game Association
rpga.ukonline.co.uk

A seemingly unlimited number of fantasy resources are available here for the dedicated avoider of reality if you live in the UK, Eire, or South Africa. Computer software can generate characters for a number of games, automatic dice rolling can be done online, and there are links to dark corners – where the arcane art of putting capes on and running around with rubber swords in groups is published.

Wizards of the Coast
www.wizards.com

If the games Dungeons & Dragons, Magic: The Gathering, or Pokemon (the card game) mean anything to you, you'll know that Wizards of the Coast publishes them all, along with stacks of others. Each game has its own area, sometimes providing such things as (free) character sheets and attributes, and the latest must-have add-ons (not free).

g

— Rules and information —

Card games
www.pagat.com

If you can't remember what beats a straight flush in poker, or what happens when it's the banker's turn in Pontoon, this is the place to seek help. It is an utterly comprehensive guide to card game rules and links to frequently asked questions.

Gambling emagazine
www.gamemasteronline.com

Thoroughly digest the "Casino Survival Guide", where you can learn which games pose the least disadvantages and consult the online adviser to get clued up with the hot tips for playing many card games including video poker, craps, and blackjack. There is also a special report on Internet gambling using online casinos.

Gaming dictionary
www.gamedictionary.com

This online dictionary is not just restricted to computer gaming terminology – some of the terms are indeed generic to computers or the Internet – but the main thrust is to explain the repeated jargon that crops up on almost every gaming website. It's good news that this site exists, because anyone who claims to know about trilinear filtering is either downright lying or just won't spare the time to explain it to you.

Scrabble
www.scrabble.com

Anything from the basics right up to "weird words" that you can use to get rid of those pesky letters is included on this site, along with hints and tips, history, competitions, and some winning ways from the world's top Scrabble players. There is also a children's area for all you younger fans, with various other games to expand your minds with.

War games forum
www.wargames.co.uk

This is a terrifyingly comprehensive site, devoted to little metal and plastic models used in war games. You can find businesses that will paint them for you, discover new ranges of figures, and use the searchable index of the *Miniature Wargames* magazine. There's much more than just this, though. Why not go and see the site for yourself?

— Toy histories and collectibles —

Arcade games archive
www.gamearchive.com

If you have a thing for the arcade games of old (ie from around 1976) then this enormous archive of what I can only call "stuff" will doubtless satisfy. The electric wiring for many different pinball machines is documented, pre-production sketches from famous arcade favourites are included here, and there are answers to technical questions that normal people just don't ask. Sound interesting? Then visit it yourself and find out more.

Fast food toy collectibles
www.thetoyzone.com

Aimed at those who collect the toys you get at fast food outlets, The Toy Zone has sections covering Beanie Babies, Dalmatians, and Happy Meals, as well as publishing a McFAQ (frequently asked questions about McDonald's). A special kid's page (aren't they all?) lists what toys will be appearing at your local burger bar each month.

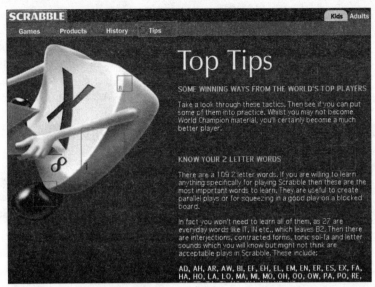

Get a list of those useful two-letter words, in any language, at www.scrabble.com

For all toy enthusiasts

www.toy.co.uk

This site provides a service enabling toy collectors to find new things to fill their spare rooms with. Essentially the site contains some very handy links to toy museums, magazines, and books. A chat forum is available for collectors to haggle on, and a list of essential toys is provided for the astute purchaser. Promised soon are online shopping, toy reviews, and worldwide contacts.

History of Home Video Games

www.videogames.org

This site is a directory of video game sites that have been categorized in an original way – by the year the games were released. And the dates go right back. For example, if you remember playing a tennis-style game back in 1975 you'll find that Atari Pong was the one, and there's all sorts of interesting details about each video game available here for your perusal.

Star Wars figures

www.rebelscum.com

The one-stop-shop for *Star Wars* figure collectors, Rebelscum also looks closely at other action figures, Lego, and other collectors' collections. You can find out about custom figures, too, and view some film scenes re-enacted with these toys, possibly by people with far too much time on their hands.

Toy collecting
www.toymania.com

If you collect toys, particularly Star Wars, X-Men and Pokemon, this is a good place to find out who wants to buy, and when the next collectors' fairs are running. Serious collectors should pay particular attention to the bootleg area, where details of fake merchandise are published. You can also find out where to buy such stuff if you collect the fakes!

Toys R Us
www.toysrus.co.uk

Avoid dragging mewling children around shops crowded with other people's brats by doing your shopping at this impressive online toy shop. There are also links to toy manufacturers so that you can check out the latest train sets or Barbie dolls. Strangely, you can buy mobile phones here too.

See also "Collections" in Hobbies, pages 152–154.

 # see also...

One of the very first "practical" uses of the Internet was to provide access to games, and this fine tradition continues today. There are online magazines such as PC Gamer Online (**www.pcgamer.com**), which provides news of the latest computer game titles. There is always plenty of opinion on the web, and Game Over Online Magazine (**www.game-over.net**) publishes alternative previews, reviews, and games' cheats. Some people prefer to play games on console systems like Sega, Playstation 2, and Dreamcast. If you are one of those then look to websites such as Console Domain (**www.consoledomain.com**), Daily Radar (**www.dailyradar.com**), and Dreamcast.net (**www.dreamcast.net**) for information on the latest games. Games Domain (**www.gamesdomain.co.uk**) will appeal to those PC games players who want to know how to beat popular titles and find out what everyone else is buying. Similarly, Gamer Zone (**www.gamerzone.com**) will appeal to owners of PCs and consoles games, providing a forum to swap tips with other players. PC games are big business. If you get stuck, make sure you get your money's worth by visiting the game's own website for hints, tips, and cheats. Here are a few suppliers and game sites to get you started...

Activision (**www.activision.com**) is the home of many popular PC, Mac, and console games, including the Quake range of titles. Stomped.com (**www.stomped.com**) covers all-things Quake, including weird add-ons developed by other players, and the other tournament games, including Unreal. Eidos Interactive (**www.eidosinteractive.com**) is a leading creator of PC games providing forums, clubs, and demos. Epic Games (**www.epicgames.com**) is the place to go for the great Quake-pretender, Unreal, and Unreal Tournament – if you want to play other players online, then go to either **www.mplayer.com** or **www.heat.net**, though those outside the US might experience slow gaming. Visit iD Software (**www.idsoftware.com**) to find the source of all today's 3D first person kill-'em-up games. Gamers.org (**www.gamers.org**) is holding the torch for the classic 3D game Doom, with extra levels to download and links to modern 3D games' sites.

Windows manufacturer Microsoft also makes games, the details of which may be found at **www.microsoft.com/games**, and includes **www.zone.com**. It also gives some valuable information for its various consoles, like the Sidewinder, which are used with many PC games. Novalogic (**www.novalogic.com**) is the place to find updates for a good many military simulation games, while Sierra UK (**www.sierra-online.co.uk**) will also be of assistance should you own Homeworld, or any of its other groundbreaking efforts. Not all computer games use 3D graphics. Fantasy Futures (**www.funbets.com**) provides a range of share dealing games. On a more traditional note, the Domino Games site (**www.gamecabinet.com/rules/DominoGames.html**) provides all the dominos rules you can handle. Or did you ever love drawing with your Etch A Sketch (**www.etch-a-sketch.com**)? Alternatively, are you a loner who loves playing solitaire (**www.solitairegames.com**)?

g

The Internet is games heaven for those with the console. Game Pro is a must for the hardcore gamer, with tips for Playstation, Nintendo, Dreamcast, and PC Games. Daily Radar (**www.dailyradar.com**) is also another very good site.

Playing games needn't be a solitary affair. Family Game Night (**www.familygamenight.com**), run by Hasbro, contains explanations of games and guides for popular family games such as Monopoly. You can find people to play Internet games with at Access Denied (**www.accessdenied.net**). Excite Games (**www.excite.com/games**) features online board, card, word, and arcade games. You can use the rules here for fun in the living room too. Those in need of strategy, and possibly the odd orc or two, will find plenty of websites to plunder. Gameworld (**www.gameworld.com**) features live role-playing games and other online adventures. Visit a virtual web world, complete with 3D graphics, at Nowhere (**imagiware.com/nowhere**).

HEALTH

Whether you are looking after your family's health, would like to try some alternative therapies, or just want to keep fit, there is an abundance of help and advice waiting for you online. You'll find special diets, information about drugs, literature on sex education, and calculators that will help you assess how healthy you really are. And because the Internet is more interactive than a leaflet from your GP's surgery, you can ask questions and research areas as much and as deeply as you want, until you feel much more in control of your own health.

— Alternative therapies —

Align your biorhythms
www.facade.com/biorhythm

Need to keep in tune with your energies? This online engine will plot the interactions of your physical, emotional, and intellectual biorhythms when you enter your birth details. Other parts of the site provide advice and guidance.

Alternative Medicine magazine
www.alternativemedicine.com

This regular online magazine is a digest of all things offbeat. Holistic practices can be found here alongside reflexology and nutrition therapies. For those willing to suspend their disbelief, this US magazine is well worth the subscription fee.

British Medical Acupuncture Society
www.medical-acupuncture.co.uk

This UK site aims to promote the ancient Chinese practice of acupuncture, but it is also up-to-the-minute with the latest reviews of acupuncture-related software. As well as this it includes details of meetings and courses for practitioners. Downloadable PDF documents provide information and advice on the whole subject, and a search engine helps you find and identify qualified practitioners in

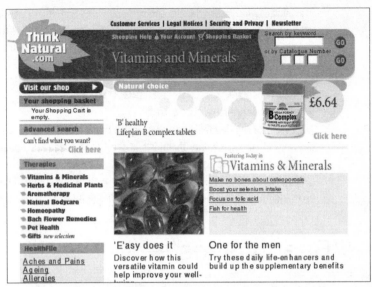

Get advice on everything from insect bites to depression at www.thinknatural.com

your area. Those interested in learning more about acupuncture for themselves can find details of courses listed here, too. A thoroughly useful site.

Homeopathy
www.homeopathyhome.com

Make this site your first port of call for queries about the world of homeopathy. Here you'll find frequently updated news on this popular branch of alternative medicine, details of forthcoming educational courses and seminars, together with bookshop links of various nationalities, enabling you to buy titles on the topic over the Internet. Online chat and message boards let you swap views and experience with like-minded users.

National Federation of Spiritual Healers
www.nfsh.org.uk

This UK body promotes healing by prayer or meditation. Its site provides a crash course in the practice, and provides a service to find a willing healer in your area. It even extols the virtues of "distant healing" over the Internet.

Natural health info and shop
www.thinknatural.com

Find out what herbs and oils will help with insect bites, rashes, and the menopause, as well as learning about homeopathy and natural bodycare. A shop is available, which sells vitamins, aromatherapy oils, and other items to keep you young and happy. If you need to alleviate depression and allergies then look no further – those are just two of the areas that this site has items available to help you with. You can also select gifts for your friends and family.

UK directory of alternative therapy centres
www.synergy-health.co.uk
Aside from selling decidedly non-prescription remedies, Synergy provides a useful directory of complementary therapists in the UK. The regularly updated "Health News" provides some useful pointers towards alternative health, and the site's listings let you know what's going on in your area. A prescription drug database gives information on side effects and drugs that don't mix.

— Beauty sites

All your questions answered
www.makeupdiva.com
This site is basically a straightforward question and answer session on all aspects of beauty. It covers health and beauty regimes for skin and hair, too. You can subscribe to the free "Ask Diva" weekly email, but if you can't find what you're looking for in the archive, fire off a question to the Diva yourself. A link to the **MakeoverStudio.com** enables you to submit your photograph for a free makeover – go for it, girls!

Beauty consultancy for aesthetic surgery
www.wlbeauty.com
This painfully pink website, Wendy Lewis & Co, dishes out well-meaning beauty advice on cajoling back into shape those wrinkles, bags, and body parts that migrate as we grow older. Any questions, then ask the pleasantly named Beauty Junkie. And if that doesn't work, Wendy's got plenty of links to a surgeon who can, with consultations in London and New York…

Colour Cosmetics
www.cosmeticscolour.com
This cosmetics company's home site provides hints on covering a multitude of beauty sins, as well as offering the chance to become a Colour Cosmetics beauty representative. The free "Online makeover" offered by the site is less exciting than it sounds – you provide a profile of your skin, eyes, and so on, and it will suggest a make-up colour scheme.

Create your perfect look
www.pinkparis.com

It seems like candy pink has become the favourite colour for beauty sites on the web. Lurid design aside, this glitzy American site provides down-to-earth beauty tips for that "perfect" look. Hair and cosmetics are considered in some depth, and the frequently asked questions list reads like a beautician's agony column. You can even download videos that help you attempt to be at your best, once you've downloaded the software...

— Dental health —————————

American Dental Association
www.ada.org

This site offers information and resources for patients and dental professionals. There are details about dental treatments and diseases, along with a guide to dental benefits and a directory that will help you find a dentist in your area.

British Dental Association
www.bda-dentistry.org.uk

The BDA's online presence is aimed both at practitioners and patients. The "Dentists" section offers support for professionals, while the "Public" section provides articles on aspects of dentistry for general readers. A handy directory also helps users locate a dentist in their area.

A guide to dental healthcare
www.jnjoralhealth.com

This site from healthcare firm Johnson & Johnson provides basic dental health and hygiene advice to kids via some colourful cartoon characters. The site provides an easy step-by-step guide on how to brush teeth. Interactive diagrams help parents and kids alike learn a little dental terminology.

— Disorders and illnesses —————

All about the heart
www.heartpoint.com

Everything you didn't know, and probably didn't want to, about the human heart and its frequently found conditions may be found here. There are health tips to

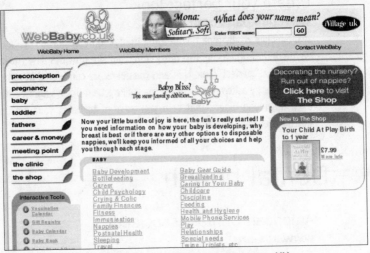

www.webbaby.co.uk is full of practical suggestions for bringing up your child

keep your ticker in top shape, nutritional guides – including lots of nutritious recipes – and an editorial page where professionals give their views on developments in healthcare.

Allergies
www.allergy-info.com

There is advice on all sorts of allergies and how to treat them available on this US site. You can even check the daily pollen levels in your area.

Macmillan Cancer Relief
www.macmillan.org.uk

Macmillan nurses form part of the backbone of cancer care in the UK. The home pages of Macmillan Cancer Relief help put patients in touch with the resources in their area, and also provide online access to various self-help publications such as The Cancer Guide. There's also some worthwhile advice to sufferers on the various benefits they're entitled to, and details on how you can support the charity.

Marie Curie
www.mariecurie.org.uk

The excellent site of UK cancer care charity, the Marie Curie foundation, is a superb source of information for sufferers, carers, and those wishing to make a donation. This well designed site hosts information on fund-raising events, Marie Curie campaigns, and news about care and treatments. The "Day in the Life" column written by a Marie Curie nurse is worth a special look.

Mental health issues
www.mentalhealth.com

This Canadian site draws together a range of resources on mental health issues. A list of conditions is available, with definitions for both North American and European physicians, and an excellent and informative encyclopedia of the most popular psychiatric medications. It also outlines treatment plans and provides diagnostic tests.

Migraine Action Association
www.migraine.org.uk

The UK site of charity Migraine Action aims to increase awareness of this common but debilitating condition. Here, you'll find information on symptoms, as well as help and support contacts for sufferers. The site also features a brief discussion of treatments for migraines, and lists the common migraine triggers such as stress, environmental factors, and certain foods. The site provides an online facility for subscribing to the organization and a list of clinics.

Schizophrenia
www.openthedoors.com

A friendly site, accessible in five European languages, that seeks to demystify this misunderstood disorder. There is information for professionals and for families with schizophrenics, and a place where personal stories can be submitted.

— Family health

Baby info on the web
www.webbaby.co.uk

Here is a wealth of information about babies. A clinic offers medical advice and help on recognizing dangerous toys, while the online shop sells bedding, safety equipment, and other essentials. There is even an advice section for fathers. An online baby photo album lets you see your little darling while at the office.

Family issues and advice
www.thefamilycorner.com

This online counselling site hands out some useful, practical advice on home and parenting issues from household budgeting to divorce. Articles are sensitive and well pitched for the average reader – unusually for this type of site on the Internet, Family Corner (largely) avoids lapsing into psychobabble. Join the community boards and chat with other parents about childrens' issues.

For all parents-to-be
www.babyworld.co.uk

Baby World provides tons of useful information for mothers- and fathers-to-be, with in-depth articles on pregnancy and child health. Even legal issues surrounding childcare are given a thorough airing. You can put any burning questions to professionals, such as a midwife, a doctor, and a fertility expert. Registration is free, and enables you to chat with others sharing the experience of parenthood with an area for birth stories and baby diaries.

Grandparenting
www.cyberparent.com/gran

Leaving aside a bit of schmaltzy self-promotion on its introductory page, Grandparents' Web provides a sensible insight to the world of grandparenting. This site doesn't flinch from tackling thornier issues such as marital break-up or discipline, and offers excellent tips on making the most of the time spent looking after grandchildren.

Happy Families
www.happyfamilies.com

If your home life drives you nuts, why not stay sane by swapping anecdotes with like-minded types on the Internet? Happy Families is a site devoted to looking at the lighter side of family life, with users posting stories and advice. You can even swap stories about pets. Other resources include light-hearted epostcards, which you can send to friends and relatives.

Health in focus (netmag)
www.healthinfocus.co.uk

A wealth of health can be found at this site, with innumerable categories, covering just about every aspect of looking after yourself and your family. Essential facts, guides to healthy living, health care for your home. Tell the site your ailment, and it will give you all the information you need to make your suffering more bearable. There is a list of patient support groups as well.

Fitness

Aerobics
www.turnstep.com

Turnstep is a page of frequently asked questions containing information drawn from Usenet forums on aerobics. Recent changes include a complete overhaul of the "pattern" search engine (that's the aerobics steps, to you and me), which now searches from a library of more than 6000 moves. Beginners might like to start by making selections from the most recent 50 steps that can be found on the opening page.

All you need to know about yoga
www.yogasite.com

The Yoga Site takes a more hands-on approach to exercise. It offers instruction on postures, as well as links to other sites of yogic note that are to be found on the Internet. So if you're brave (or flexible) enough to attempt such specialities as the "cobra" or the "downward facing dog", then you'll find all you need to get started at this useful site.

American Heart Association magazine
www.justmove.org

Just Move is an upbeat online magazine from the American Heart Association. Judging by its youthful tone, its aim is to stamp out the risk of heart attack before it sets in. Practical advice abounds on getting out and about, and, above all, getting yourself fit. Well worth a peek for Internet-obsessed couch potatoes who need a bit of exercise!

Fun & Fitness
www.fun-and-fitness.com

This highly illustrated US site offers a user-friendly way for you to get fit. It is organized by zones, which each concentrate on muscle fitness and nutrition. Exercises are prescribed for each set of muscles, and these are presented in simple point-by-point text. The "Nutrition Zone" provides information on different food types, an explanation of metabolism, and can also recommend a personal diet and exercise combination for you. The "Fun Zone" has a quiz for you to see how well you've paid attention to the details given on the site. If you want a more traditional guide to improving fitness, then why not browse the Fitness Bookshelf to see what is available there.

Get fit the cool way
www.phys.com

This is a suave website with fitness, nutrition, and weight loss advice. Practical articles (such as how to make the best of dining out), "body" calculators, and quizzes make this a more interactive site than many other sites of this ilk. You can also "Go for a Goal" – like getting a six-pack. All the pages and categories are well illustrated and make this an excellent all-round health site. Well worth a visit if your aim is to get fit.

Great alternatives to dieting
www.allhealth.com/neversaydiet

Didn't you just know dieting was a bad idea? This site puts the kibosh on plans of cutting down, suggesting you switch your plans to maintaining mental health, and offering gentle ways to exercise for those who are ill or just don't have the time to go down to the gym. This page from **AllHealth.com** provides a good deal of support on the psychological and emotional aspects of weight loss too.

Online Health and Fitness Network
www.efit.com

This site is a wealth of information for would-be exercise fanatics. The site boasts a massive quantity of superlative content; special features examine topical health issues, complete with video clips (efit TV it's called). Membership is free, and entitles users to a free customized fitness program.

The world of yoga
www.yoyoga.com

For those taking a (slightly) less active approach to fitness, the Yoyoga site promotes a holistic approach to getting in shape. Soothing words from celebrities, recipes for healthy eating, and some thought on the philosophy that lies behind this Eastern art are the order of the day here.

h

— Information and advice —

All you need to know about health
www.healthy.net

Arranged around a virtual "map" of health resources, this site covers all aspects of health, providing access to information and self-diagnosis tools, as well as general advice about how to keep yourself in tip-top condition. The style may be a bit fusty, but that's because it's aimed partially at professionals. In fact, the site provides access to Medline, the international medicine and pharmacy database. Articles up to 1997 can be downloaded for free.

ASH – Action on Smoking and Health
www.ash.org.uk

ASH has been well known for badgering smokers into giving up for years. Its online presence provides more of the same, plus advice and support on combating those cravings. More interestingly, ASH lifts the lid on a few things the tobacco industry has tried to keep quiet.

Home | Boards | Quizzes | About Us | Privacy | Feedback | Membercenter

how do I become a digital diva ?

Made especially for women in the UK

iVillage
allHealth
.com

You are here: allHealth > Never Say Diet

Never Say Diet

FIND IT

☉ on allHealth.com
○ on iVillage.com
○ on the Web

WHAT IS YOUR HEALTH CONCERN?

Choose a topic

Daily Health Tip

HEALTH TOOLS
Search Medline

The Never Say Diet Center is not about traditional dieting; it's about new ways of thinking about food, exercise and self-image. We at allHealth understand that many obstacles -- from existing medical conditions, to an already jam-packed schedule, to poor self-esteem -- can stand in the way of our commitment to getting and staying healthy. And we understand that no one can do it alone -- everyone needs support. You'll find it all in the Never Say Diet

NSD Departments
100+ Club
Battle the Bulge
A Few to Lose
Keeping It Off
Putting It On
NSD Home

TAKE THE

www.allhealth.com/neversaydiet gives you new ideas about food and health

British Medical Journal
www.bmj.com

The Electronic *British Medical Journal* features articles about the latest research and discoveries in the medical world from the paper version, as well as listings of jobs, courses, and careers. There is a searchable archive, a debating forum, and a letters page, too, and you can arrange for articles to be emailed straight to you hot off the press.

Drug abuse
www.trashed.co.uk

The Health Education Authority's stylish and hip site Trashed is all about substance abuse, with each drug's origins, their components and effects, and how the law deals with them. More streetwise types can search for drug information by typing street slang names for drugs into the site search engine.

First aid
www.parasolemt.com.au

Okay, so in a medical emergency you won't have time to log onto the Internet to find out what to do, but if you spend a few minutes on this excellent website every week then you'll be able to react more effectively if something nasty does happen. The subjects covered include how to deal with the traumas as well as the first aid training.

Feeling depressed about relationships? Join others online to talk about it at www.breakupgirl.com

Health advice
www.healthanswers.com

If the number of sites in the US is anything to go by, health advice is big business. HealthAnswers is one of the best around, with basic diagnostic tools, health advice, a decent database of drugs, and even its own radio. Other resources include a "Body Mass Index Calculator" to keep tabs on your tum.

Healthcare issues
www.healthbond.com

US site HealthBond provides up-to-date information to businesses about policies and issues affecting healthcare, but it's also useful for patients to browse. It includes news on major political and legal stories in medicine, plus an interactive polling of users on important topics.

Information for all patients
www.patient.co.uk

Patient UK is a thorough primer on getting the best out of health services in Britain. This well designed site includes a glossary of medical terms, information on, and links to, NHS services, health events, and details of patients' rights. A link to the Scoot business directory enables you to locate doctors in your area.

Live more healthily
www.adam.com

Learn how to live a healthier, and therefore longer, life with the advice from this site. You can ask the experts questions that you could never bring yourself to pose to your own GP, or just browse through the illustrated health encyclopedia and of course buy the goods on offer. Just make sure that you don't contract a good dose of paranoia while visiting the site...

Lovelife advice
www.breakupgirl.com

Alternative super-heroine Breakup Girl has been there. However depressed, however desperate, however ditched you've felt – she knows how you feel. The site provides uplifting but tongue-in-cheek advice about splitting up, emotional stress, and even comes complete with a bite-sized read-it-at-work version. Fire in a question, or simply laugh with (or at) others, and the celebrity gossip is bound to cheer you up!

Medical info links
www.healthgate.co.uk

The Healthgate site has a wealth of links to various other places that provide descriptions of drugs, give nutrition advice, and deal with women's, men's, and old age issues etc. You can also link to beauty shops, as well as those that supply medicine and vitamins and minerals. And if you have a friend or relative that is ill, you can send them a get well card from the site.

NHS Direct: health info and advice
www.nhsdirect.nhs.uk

Part of New Labour's strategy for cutting waiting lists, NHS Direct aims to get people out of GP's waiting rooms by providing basic diagnoses over the phone or online. There are over 200 audioclips available here too, if you feel reassured by a friendly authoritative voice. Advice is given by trained nurses, and the topics covered are all basic ailments. There's also useful information on getting the best from NHS services.

Online Medical Dictionary
www.graylab.ac.uk/omd/index.html

Online cancer research body CancerWEB provides a patient-friendly glossary of medical terms, covering a broad sweep of disciplines. Words can be searched for alphabetically or by subject, and updates let users know about any recent entries and amendments. Word lists are long, though, so they may take time to download on your machine.

Private healthcare
www.privatehealth.co.uk

Going by the dubious acronym PHUK, Public Health UK provides a database of private healthcare resources in the UK online. There is guidance about using private care facilities, getting health insurance, as well as useful hospital and doctor finders. The site also features a database of over 7000 nursing homes.

Terrence Higgins Trust
www.tht.org.uk

The Terrence Higgins Trust is one of the organizations at the forefront of AIDS awareness in the UK. Its online home provides advice to sufferers about treatments, legal issues, and other concerns, and it is aimed at gay and heterosexual people alike. The Trust provides one-to-one support via its helpline number. You can also make a donation, or even become a volunteer yourself.

Women's Health
www.bbc.co.uk/health/womens

This is part of the excellent BBC Online Health site aimed specifically at tackling female health issues. Easily digestible articles cover topics from osteoporosis to breast cancer, to the trials of cellulite and sexual health. You can "Ask the Doctor", with responses posted daily. The site even supplies links to pages on medically minded TV programmes such as *Casualty*.

h

— Interactive sites ——————

NOVA Online: Electric Heart
www.pbs.org/wgbh/nova/eheart

Find out all about the human heart, courtesy of this TV programme's website. There is an annotated, animated map of the organ, a list of "amazing" facts, and even a virtual operating theatre where you can perform a heart operation – if you don't mind downloading a few files first.

Visible Human Project
www.nlm.nih.gov/research/visible/visible_human.html

This is a groundbreaking project that involves slicing a male and female body into very thin slices (up to 1mm thick) for use in medical research. You can read about the project here, and find links to related projects that have used the data, as well as learn to create your own interesting 3D images and movies using the images supplied by the project.

— Nutrition ————————————

Ask the Dietitian
www.dietitian.com

This is a question and answer-driven site that covers all aspects of food, cooking, and nutrition. It also provides extensive material on eating disorders. The friendly, agony-aunt style enables Ask the Dietitian to tackle extremely thorny issues in a sensitive manner. The detailed articles are cross-referenced with hypertext links.

Cyberdieting
www.cyberdiet.com

If you are serious about going on a diet, then this site will answer all your questions and worries. There are categories on Self Assessment, Nutrition, and Exercise and Fitness, and live chat forums where you can talk with others, and get answers to your questions from professionals.

Nutrition
www.mynutrition.co.uk

Beautifully designed and easy to navigate, you can find out everything to do with healthy food, eating, and supplements. Free consultation is available. The latest news and health library is supplied by Patrick Holford, a leading nutritionist.

h

— Pharmaceuticals ————————

Database of pharmaceuticals
www.rxlist.com

Here a database of currently prescribed pharmaceuticals allows users to access the official US government-approved patient information on any of the listed drugs, including prescription information and details of any known side-effects. You can also check out the parent site **www.healthcentral.com**.

Food and Drug Administration
www.fda.gov

This friendly looking website is the home page of the US government's Food and Drug Administration, the regulatory body that approves drugs for prescription in the USA. It contains an exhaustive database of pharmaceuticals and cosmetics, the latest news on medical drugs, as well as advice on buying drugs safely online.

Psychology

Psychology explored
www.psychology.com

This decidedly California-speaking online journal doesn't talk an awful lot of science – it's mostly aimed at punters wanting to improve their lives. There are plenty of online psychometric and personality tests here to scare yourself with, and the chance to ask a therapist a couple of your burning questions. There is also a link to Amazon that enables the fraught to buy books that'll sort them out. This is indeed a worthwhile place to call in... but don't take it all too seriously.

The technology behind psychology
www.victoriapoint.com/catalyst.htm

This is an online journal examining psychology in the modern world – with specific reference to computers. Articles outline the good and bad in technology, covering topics from pathological Internet use to the benefits of using computers to analyze patient behaviour. The social effects of new technologies are discussed in some depth.

Sexual matters

Health awareness
www.intelihealth.com

This is a good-looking and informative general health site from North America's Johns Hopkins University, which is divided into "zones" for easy navigation. Special features cover some topics in depth; and the site is particularly good on sexual health subjects, such as HIV and AIDS. Other "Featured Health Areas" include arthritis, diabetes, and pregnancy. There are useful links to other healthcare resources. It is worth having a look at the Flu-o-meter, which tells you which States are suffering the most.

Marie Stopes International
www.mariestopes.org.uk

Marie Stopes' pioneering birth control clinics provide advice and information to both men and women on issues from contraception and sterilization to abortion. Here you'll also find details of the location of local centres. There is no one-to-one online advice, but the site's services are growing all the time.

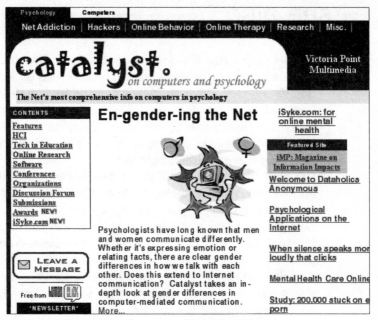

www.victoriapoint.com/catalyst.htm examines all facets of psychology

Sexual freedom issues
mail.bris.ac.uk/~plmlp/normal.html

Stridently political – and mischievously titled – page arguing the case for sexual freedom. Covers homosexuality, pornography, celibacy, and disability, as well as other areas considered outside the sexual "mainstream". Topics are discussed seriously but the content can be explicit, so be warned!

Teenage health issues
www.iwannaknow.org

The web is an ideal medium for you to learn about issues, such as sex, that are too embarrassing to ask parents or friends about. Advice here from the American Social Health Association can seem uncompromisingly explicit, but it's necessarily so. Sound and reassuring.

Viagra
www.viagra.com

Viagra hit the headlines as a "miracle" cure for impotence, but this coverage was quickly followed by scare stories about the drug's less-wanted (and less-publicized) side effects. This site, created by drug manufacturer Pfizer, provides the official line – and addresses a number of the allegations.

— see also... —

There are a huge number of sites on the net with advice on staying fit and healthy. For starters, a trip to the online chemist's at **www.boots.co.uk** may be in order. Or you could consult the medical reference site at **MedicineNet.com** (**www.medicinenet.com**) for their advice and a store selling non-prescription medicines and beauty products. Those undecided about parenting can get their facts straight at **www.ippf.org**. Couples considering help with fertility can find mutual support at **www.fertilethoughts.net**.

Of course, the happy arrival's only the first of your worries. As well as talking you through pregnancy, **www.thebabiesplanet.com** will help mums and dads through the early days after the birth, too, though try to ignore the terrible music on the home page! Dads even have their own channel on **www.iparenting.com**. For advice on common ailments for kids then look up **www.kidshealth.org**. Kids can get medical advice for themselves at **www.brainpop.com**, which has lots of movies to maintain their interest. But make sure your mothers and fathers take good care of themselves, too: **www.bewell.com** should help you do just that. Disorders and illness, unfortunately, befall many a person, and you will find excellent advice on the world wide web, including information on AIDS (**www.hivpositive.com**) and on lesser ailments such as Eczema (**www.eczema.org**), while **www.mentalhealth.net** has an extensive list of mental health professionals.

Some people say that if you look good, you'll feel good. And a quick trip to **www.lorealparisusa.com** should sort you out for health and beauty tips. Of course, if you're desperate (and rich) enough, **www.cosmetic.org** can advise on the latest in cosmetic surgery. More natural solutions to health issues can be pinpointed at **www.acupuncture.com**. For definitive guidance on alternative therapies, consult NOAH at **www.noah-health.org**.

One tragic fact of growing up in this current age is the risk of getting involved with drugs and **www.geocities.com/SouthBeach/Cove/8430/drugs.html** will help educate young adults and parents about the dangers.

Of course, you'd be better off never getting sick in the first place and the web can help you nip those symptoms in the bud. Try **www.discoveryhealth.com**, **www.thedailyapple.com**, or **www.pdr.net/gettingwell** for size. It pays to live well, too, and you can fight the flab at **www.slimming-world.co.uk** or **www.shapeup.org**. Men wanting to toughen up their torso can head to **www.menshealth.co.uk** for tips. Those who'd prefer to stay less paranoid about their physique should try **www.bodypositive.com**. And for the follically challenged among us, visit **www.regaine.co.uk** for the latest in miracle treatments for hair. And find out whether you are sleeping properly or not at the online health magazine site Doctor Koop (**www.doctorkoop.net**).

But there's only so much you can do for yourself and sometimes you'll need to call in the professionals. In the UK, that's the British Medical Association. You'll find its website at **web.bma.org.uk**. BUPA, Britain's largest private healthcare provider can be found at **www.bupa.co.uk**. The latest information on nursing can be found at **www.nursing-standard.co.uk**. Help and advice on nursing in a crisis are on the web at **www.emergency-nurse.com**.

h

HOBBIES

No matter what your hobby or interest, someone else who shares your passion will have created a website dedicated to your favourite pastime. The most popular activities, including driving, crafts, and collecting are admirably catered for online, more often by amateur than professional sites, while there are thousands of more esoteric sites out there. You can live vicariously through the experiences of other hobbyists, pick up hints and tips on how to spend your free time more efficiently, and even brighten up your computer with related pictures, icons, and screensavers. If your hobby is not listed among those here, then put your hobby into a search engine – you can almost guarantee that you will find a relevant site out there...

— Animals

All things aquatic
www.aqualink.com
If you keep, or would like to build and maintain, an aquarium, the information on this site could prove invaluable for you. AquaLink covers tropical fish from fresh water and marine environments, and its online store should be able to provide for all your specialist needs. An online disease diagnoser could help to save your fishies' lives at some point in the future.

Birding on the web
www.birder.com
Use this site to find out the best places to go bird watching, receive alerts when rare birds have been spotted all over the world, and browse the "Geographical Birding Guide" to find area guide books written by local residents. There are links to images, bird songs, and games, too. (For bird organizations, see "The Natural World", pages 211-225.)

Lennie the Dog, Goldie the Fish, and others give you a wealth of pet advice at www.petsource.com

Choosing and caring for your pet
www.petsource.com

If your pet has just eaten something dodgy, or been involved in a motor accident, use the first aid information on PetSource's site to ensure you give it the best possible chance of recovery. There is also plenty of general health advice and a survey to help you choose the best type of pet for your lifestyle, with cartoon characters (Lennie the Dog and Garbo the Cat for starters) to direct you through their areas of the site.

The Complete Hamster Site
www.hamsters.co.uk

Hamster fans can find out everything they need to know about looking after the different varieties of these fluffy rodents. There is a chat forum, lists of approved books and care products, and a few images of hamsters for you.

Dog lovers
www.howtoloveyourdog.com

Take a tour with three lovable looking hounds and find out all you need to know to get the best of canine companionship. Find out what it costs to have a dog, what their needs are, basic training, and, if you feel they are far enough under your control, why not learn how to teach them a few tricks. It is best to avoid the dog poetry section, though.

Serious collectors can bid on items worldwide at www.icollector.com

UK Animal Rescuers
www.animalrescuers.co.uk

This small but handy site lists most of the animal charities and organizations you're likely to need if you have an animal in trouble. There are "Lost and Found" notices, and links to animal rights activist groups, although there appears to be no political preaching on this site.

— Collections —

Clarice Cliff – Art Deco ceramics
www.claricecliff.co.uk

Collectors of Clarice Cliff pottery can use this site's services to get a valuation for insurance purposes, view available items in the classified ads, and offer their own pieces for sale. "The Guide to Shapes" should help you date your favourite pieces. Unfortunately a silly design element makes this site slow and a touch irritating.

Collecting coins
www.coin-universe.com

Calculate the value of your coin collections, learn how to differentiate your annealing from your basal state, and locate coin auctions. Coin Universe includes articles related to coinage, both ancient and contemporary, and a coin guide, which sadly seems preoccupied only with US coins. This site is part of the Collectors Universe empire, found at **collectors.com**. For international coins, try **www.currencyuniverse.com**.

Directory of dealers and retailers
www.collectiques.co.uk

If you are a collector, whether of barometers or Beanie Babies, Collectiques' large online directory of dealers and retailers should help you to acquire more stuff. You can also buy tomorrow's antiques from the site, such as a Noddy Toyland Car or a model of the Millennium Dome. The "Library", containing "The Hallmark Database" and articles on antique collecting, adds value to an already extremely useful website.

Internet Collector
www.icollector.com

Trust me when I say that every form of collectible item is available for auction at this site. The site acts as a portal to the world's auction houses, and allows you to bid on any item you want. Subscribe to the "My Agent" service, which will search the auction houses for the items you want and send you the results by email. The site is very easy to navigate and is a must see if you are serious about collecting.

Pokemon Cards
www.pokemon-trade.com

The playground craze has naturally transferred online, and includes all the information needed to trade Pokemon and Digimon cards successfully, including prices, strategy, the various cards, and news links. There are also areas for the next new crazes, Dragon Ball and Monster Rancher.

Scrapbook ideas
www.scrapbookideas.com

If your idea of fun on a wet weekend is to attend to your scrapbook, you might pick up a few handy tips from this site. There is a discussion forum where "scrappers" swap ideas, and competitions where the best page layouts are rewarded with points – which can then be used to win prizes or the coveted title of "ScrapExpert".

Stamp collecting
www.bl.uk/collections/philatelic

The British Library's website contains a rather sparse philatelic section, which has details of its stamp collections, speckled with a few close-up photos of old specimens. Researchers wanting to drop in will find the contact details handy, as well as details of the Library's services, including photography and maps.

Stamp info and services
www.wardrop.co.uk

Stamp collectors will be over the moon when they see the wealth of information available here. There are details about philatelic software, including databases of stamp analyzing programs and virtual albums. Wadrop's "Philately Online" will help you find a trading site, request an insurance quote for your collection, and seek out a local stamp club.

Toy soldier collections
www.williamking.com

Serious toy soldier collectors can subscribe to William King Military Miniatures to receive notification when new model sets are released, or just to buy from the current stock. The online store deals with dollars and sterling, and all the items are illustrated and come with small background histories.

— Crafts

For all woodworkers
www.woodprojects.com

Browse through Wood Projects' hundreds of plans for inspiration. Once you have selected a plan, you will discover that some are free courtesy of the suppliers, while others can be bought straight off the page. References to practical books are sprinkled throughout, and the site's owner guarantees that the projects are linked to shops with the lowest prices.

Furniture and object design
www.house-of-design.nl

Find inspiration to design your own furniture and other bits and pieces for the house by viewing the work of other designers and using the links to categorized sites specializing in textiles, jewellery, and architecture. You can also view a catalogue of previous and current exhibitions.

Home Sewing Association
www.sewing.org

Containing free sewing projects, tips, and a comprehensive collection of online lessons, this site is absolutely ideal for all those that are wanting to design their

Wool Works **Patterns**

[Home | Patterns | Resources | Discussion | Stores | Gallery | Search | Craft | About this site]

These are patterns that are out of copyright or that the authors have given permission to have appear here. Before you write and ask, no, **I don't have any pictures of the finished projects unless the page explicitly says so**; if you make one of them and are willing to send me a picture, either printed or electronic, I'd love to add it.

Please consider using these patterns to make projects for any of the charities listed in the charities directory.

If you're looking for a specific pattern and can't find it here, please don't send me mail. I recommend a few other places to ask:

- The Usenet newsgroup rec.crafts.textiles.yarn
- The knitlist
- Wool Works's "Discuss knitting patterns" Web board

I've knit only two of these patterns (both of them facecloths), so I can't answer any technical questions about the rest of them. If you have questions, please ask the original author or consult one of the sources listed above.

- Sweaters
- Socks and slippers
- Cold-weather wear (scarves, mittens, etc.)
- Knitting for babies and children
- Afghans and throws
- Facecloths and dishcloths

Hand knitters can get all the information they need at www.woolworks.org

own clothes or just hoping to take up a pair of trousers. A page dedicated to younger readers contains fun tasks such as bean bags, dolls, and pet cushions.

Knitting compendium

www.woolworks.org

Providing information for those who like to knit, Wool Works has an archive of patterns including sweaters for adults, clothing for toddlers, and even dolls with accompanying accessories. There are photos of garments other readers have made as well as advanced hints and tips on subjects such as sock heal options.

The Lace Guild

www.laceguild.demon.co.uk

The Lace Guild's site will help you find out when the next UK lace exhibitions are happening; locate suppliers of relevant books, courses, and, of course, lace, and browse through a limited number of articles from the newsletter. There is also a small introduction to the craft and a mail order service to buy some books containing patterns direct from them.

Make your own candles

www.candlecauldron.com

Don't spend a fortune buying candles, when you can make your own for pennies. The Candle Cauldron gives advice on how to mix scents to make smelly candles,

www.ancestry.com allows genealogists to trace their, and other, families

as well as providing a dictionary of candle-making terms and a troubleshooting guide. The measurement conversion guide and colour-mixing chart make this a handy reference site.

Electronic parts and kits

Electronic Rainbow
www.rainbowkits.com
This US site supplies various electronics kits for all manner of weird and wonderful projects you may be interested in trying out for yourself. These include gadgets to attach to your CB radio, digital thermometers, and even a box that can control your home's heating and lighting when you call it on the phone. Purchase your next gimmick from this site and you'll be so involved putting it all together that your friends won't see you for days...

Electronics for the advanced
www.chipcenter.com
You can use ChipCenter to locate electronics components and find exactly the right websites to help you with your own electronics projects. It's all pretty techie on this particular site, so don't expect to pick up the basics here. However, if you

are already an electrical engineer and want to know more details about spectral analysis or IC design then this is a great starting place for you.

Rocketry online
www.rocketryonline.com

This site is all about the kind of homemade rockets that hobbyists can invest thousands of pounds in. The "INFOcentral" area provides a detailed introduction to the scene and there are links to the companies that sell mini altimeters, onboard computers, and engines. There are chat forums to discuss your experiences and news and reviews of events and products. A "Launch Calendar" gives you a month-by-month view of forthcoming rocketry events that are taking place around the world.

Genealogy

Cemetery records on the Internet
www.interment.net

This collection of largely US burial records has been made available on the Internet to aid genealogists research family histories. There are links to genealogy websites, including **www.distantcousin.com**, plus sites offering cemetery tours.

h

Online genealogy
www.ancestry.com

Ancestry.com is a professional-looking site offering daily news, software reviews, and searchable databases all aimed at the busy genealogist. Message boards are provided, too, care of **www.familyhistory.com**, which is owned by Ancestry.com. Another related site, **www.myfamily.com**, offers a free website service to help "connect family members".

Motoring

American Automobile Association
www.aaa.com

Enter your US zip code to find out what the road conditions in your area are like, pick up a few holiday ideas (using AAA membership benefits to cut the cost), and read the monthly reports on the average prices of airfares, lodgings, and rental cars. Get a quote online for the company's auto insurance or apply for a car.

Automobile Association
www.theaa.co.uk

Apply for membership of this popular UK breakdown service, receive motor insurance quotes online, and access the Internet version of the company's restaurant, pub, and hotel guides. You can also plan your routes, and find out where the cheapest fuel can be had. There is also a chat forum for those interested in transport issues.

Automobile buyer's guide
www.edmunds.com

Get the latest automobile prices (yes, it's a US site) and read reviews of all manner of gas guzzlers. There is plenty of useful consumer advice for those buying new and used cars, and valuable know-how on eyeing up the past history of your intended purchase.

Autotrader
www.autotrader.co.uk

The online equivalent of the popular car magazine is the site to visit if you want to find a vehicle in the western world. Search for new or used cars by location, model, year, and, of course, price. Its six-step plan will give you advice on what to look for and what to watch out for.

British Motorcyclists Federation
www.bmf.co.uk

UK Bikers can find out when rallies and other interesting events are taking place; read news stories tailored for road warriors; and take advantage of the library – which contains tips, law updates, and the low-down on other biker-issues. The advantages of membership to the federation are all listed, in order to entice you to sign up straight away.

Cars in the UK
www.carsource.co.uk

Don't be put off by the rather drab design – this is a brilliant place to visit if you're renewing your car insurance, want to price a second-hand car, or just browse the car photo library. The site will even try to locate the car of your dreams for you, should you leave details of your desires.

Institute of Advanced Motorists
www.iam.org.uk

If you'd like to improve your driving skills, whether you drive a car, an LGV, tow a caravan, or ride a motorcycle, then check out the official site of the Advanced

If you want an Aston Martin or an Austin Metro, new or used, then www.autotrader.co.uk is for you

Driving Test. You can also read about member benefits, cheaper car insurance, special services from the AA, and discounts from various companies.

Lorryspotting
www.lorryspotting.com

Do you find yourself checking out the liveries of lorries, hoping to spot a new Eddie Stobart vehicle? Lorry spotting must be a serious business because the incredibly in-depth search engine with over 15,000 lorries is only available to members, and membership costs around £17 per year. A gallery of images is available to non-members, who can join in the chat with fellow lorry lovers...

RAC Motoring Services
www.rac.co.uk

Receive live traffic news; read advice on buying, maintaining, and driving your car; and buy travel insurance, accessories, and maps online. The route planner covers the whole of Europe, and a "Hotel Finder" provides details of accommodation throughout the UK and Ireland. For a fee the site will even run a check on any registration number you provide, to ensure you aren't about to buy stolen goods.

Top Gear
www.topgear.beeb.com
The top-rated TV show has its own site here, with all the advice you could need. Choose your make and model and find out the lowdown from those in the know. There are tips on how to get the best deal and of course the staple of the show — the expert opinion on the test drives. There is even a car doctor for when things go wrong.

What Car? Online
www.whatcar.co.uk
Locate new or used cars in Britain, sell your old one, and find out how much you've been ripped off doing both on this site. There are a large number of articles here that detail the road tests this magazine has put all new models through, including a child seat test, so that you can get an idea of what to look for when taking a test drive yourself.

— Pot luck

Juggling Information Services
www.juggling.org
This excellent resource for jugglers has web versions of *Juggler's World*, instructions on how to juggle, and even details of juggling software that can help teach the techniques. There are movies of famous, old-time performers, and a list of organizations to join.

Online kite magazine
www.kitelife.com
Kite Flyers should come here to find out about international events, information on indoor kite flying, and photo galleries documenting kite expos. A "Feedback area" prints readers' comments along with responses. There are also links to places where you can buy kites to order.

Patenting advice
www.patentcafe.com
If your hobby has led you to create a fantastic invention, then this is the site for you. Aimed at inventors who want to create new devices and then protect them from unethical companies, the advice here will take you through from the stage of "having an idea" right up to when you can apply for a patent and start earning profits from it.

Puppetry
www.sagecraft.com/puppetry

Whether you are interested in traditional shadow puppets, Pinocchio-style marionettes, or computer animated figures there will be something here for you. Features include indices of worldwide puppet theatres, information on festivals and practical advice – including the use of smoke and how to write scripts.

— Space

Alien-locating program
setiathome.ssl.berkeley.edu

Download the screensaver software from this site and help search for other life forms in our universe. The SETI@home project provides individual pieces of data from the Arecibo Radio Telescope to you, the supporter. Your software then analyzes it and sends back the results. If your computer is involved in a discovery, you can be credited as a co-discoverer.

All things astronomical
www.stsci.edu/astroweb/astronomy.html

This one-stop-shop for astronomers doesn't look flash, and the front page frankly looks intimidating, but underneath the harsh exterior lies extensive information on large telescopes, data centres, and scary-looking governmental sites that thankfully feature some very pretty pictures. Professional scientists and child prodigies will get the most from this site, and the sites linked to it.

h

High-energy astronomy
imagine.gsfc.nasa.gov/docs/ask_astro

You might not want to know much about quasars right now, but there may be a time when you do, so remember that this site exists and return when you want to ask a question about high-energy astronomy. You can also browse through previously answered questions.

International Meteor Organization
www.imo.net

Start here if you are looking for information on meteors and meteorites. Showers are recorded, and "The Visual Meteor Database" contains over 1,500,000 records of sightings, although its name belies the fact that it lacks graphics of any kind. You'll just have to take your own photos, with the aid of the information on how to snap meteors that is available at this site.

—see also...

There are a huge array of sites offering advice and help on all sorts of activities. Model airplane enthusiasts can find out about Airfix Models (**www.airfix.com**) and buy plane kits, modelling tools, and spare parts from Hobby Hangar (**www.hobbyhangar.com**). If you'd actually like your model to take off, follow the advice at the many sites listed by the Large Radio Controlled Model Webring (**www.lmauk.8m.com/lmring.htm**). Killer model robot fans will enjoy the online presence of the TV show *Robot Wars* (**www.robotwars.co.uk**).

Entertainers are catered for with such excellent sites as All Magic Guide (**www.allmagicguide.com**), providing links to conjuring sites, while the Center For Puppetry Arts (**www.puppet.org**) features a museum, links, and a promotional video. Lovers of ballroom dancing should try The Ballroom Dance Resource (**www.ballroomdancers.com**) to brush up on their steps.

Healthcare for your furry companions may be found at Pet Education (**www.peteducation.com**). Water-bound friends are catered for at such sites as Aquarium Central (**www.aquariacentral.com**), which describes how to stock and build a good tank. Look after your own birds with advice from Bird On! (**birdcare.com/birdon**), which contains an encyclopedia of bird care articles. The House Rabbit Society (**www.rabbit.org**) is aimed at those who want a tame rabbit to roam around the house, while the Royal Society for the Prevention of Cruelty to Animals (**www.rspca.org.uk**) makes sure that people look after their pets properly, and provides helpful advice. If you can't have a real dog, why not adopt a computerized web version at Virtual Dog (**www.virtualdog.com**). You'll compete with other players to see who's the best overall owner. But if one pet is not enough, then you should visit Zig Zag Zoo (**www.zigzagzoo.com**) where you can buy and sell virtual animals and get involved in leagues; just be warned – it's a jungle out there…

Collectors and arts and crafts fans should find Aunt Annie's Crafts (**www.auntannie.com**) an extremely useful resource of advice on making all sorts of things, from paper airplanes to cuddly animals. The Craft Market (**www.craftmarket.co.uk**) will help you to locate craft fairs, while Potters.org (**www.potters.org**) has discussion forums based around potting, glazing, and other ceramic technologies. If you prefer your plates readymade, try the Franklin Mint (**www.franklinmint.com**), purveyor of ceramic collectables. It's possible you already have treasure stashed in your attic – check with Antique Talk (**www.antiquetalk.com**) to find out. Locate long-lost relatives and friends using the people search engine at WhoWhere? (**www.whowhere.lycos.com**). The Internet Address Finder (**www.iaf.net**) might also be able to find their email address for you…

h

There a large number of amateur photography sites at The Amateur Photography Ring (**www.gtdesigns.com/photoring**) while motorbike clothing, parts, services, and links can be found at MotoDirectory.com (**www.moto-directory.com**). Trainspotters should try The Historical Model Railway Society (**www.hmrs.org.uk**) for a history of the railway and the National Model Railroad Association (**www.ribbonrail.com/nmra**) for links to rail sites.

If your particular hobby hasn't been listed here, try one of the thousands of mailing lists that are categorized at Liszt (**www.liszt.com**).

h

HOME AND LIFESTYLE

If your personal computer sits in drab surroundings in a half-empty room, then these are all sites that will help you decorate, furnish and improve your surroundings and lifestyle. Whether you need plumbing advice, a comfy bed, want some antiques, or wonder whether a little feng-shui will improve your well-being then this list of sites should be able to help you. There are plenty of shops prepared to sell you the paint, nails, and other potential makings of a lovely abode, many with online calculators and guides to help you choose the colours of your walls, or work out how much wallpaper or wood you'll need for your latest project. Here you can also discover the luxury of buying clothes from the comfort of your own home.

— Clothes and jewellery —

Accessorize
www.accessorize.co.uk
This UK high street store has created a fun presence online, with a fresh approach to female accessories. A style guide will tell you what's "in", a gift guide will give you advice and, rather cheekily, a wish list of items that will then be emailed to your friends and family near your birthday. All in all, this is a successful creation of an online presence.

Freemans
www.freemans.co.uk
Do all your clothes shopping online this season. The site is broken down into four simple categories – women, men, kids, and sports. It offers a full searching facility,

The distinctive style of this clothes' retailer continues online at www.gap.com

saving you valuable page-turning time. You can fill in an online order form, or fill up your virtual trolley as you browse through the goodies on offer.

Gap
www.gap.com

This online presence follows the same style as the stylish offline branding. Choose men's or women's clothing on the home page, and browse the store at your convenience. The site also runs a great gift service. It has a store locator too, should you not know where you can get their clothes and accessories locally.

Links of London
www.linksoflondon.com

This online jewellery store delivers to the US, Canada, UK, and the rest of Europe. The distinctive products include photo frames, hip flasks, and clocks, rings, cuff links, and other jewellery. Get them giftwrapped, or get a gift recommendation by explaining who the present is for and your price range.

Online shopping mall
www.safestreet.co.uk

This online shopping centre offers shop space to anyone who wants to rent it, so if you need to set up a secure shopping site yourself, you can do so with the

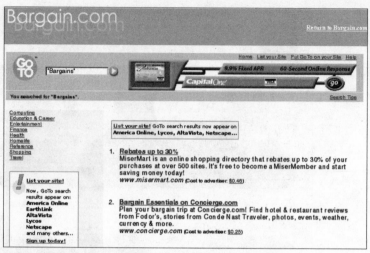

Bargains galore to be had for all types of home goods at www.bargain.com

minimum of technical skill. The rest of us can use it to do a spot of online shopping from the variety of shops that sell audio systems, jewellery, clothing, arts and crafts, and interiors and furniture.

h) — Discounts, ads, and auctions –

Bargains
www.bargain.com
A US site where you can get virtually anything you want by browsing through the many categories, from computers to gardening equipment. It also has its own auction house. Rather than list the actual items, the categories list various retailers who then justify why their site is so cheap. There are also links to sites with rebates or coupons. The light blue text sometimes makes it hard to read, but you can find some real bargains here.

Electronic Yellow Pages
uk.yell.com
Search for contact details of over 1.6 million companies without wearing your fingers out. This online version of the *Yellow Pages* also includes a dedicated travel section, a website for home buyers (HomeSight can be found at **www.homesight.co.uk**), and a shopping centre that lists sites conforming to its secure transaction specifications. It also has a useful business section for both UK

and international companies. You can see who has won this year's Yell Awards, which has become one of the most prestigious web design awards.

Exchange and Mart
www.ixm.co.uk
Find used cars, furniture, holidays, and business services in the online version of this classified ads paper. The site is also the home of other magazines like *Daltons Weekly*, *Auto Exchange*, and *Great Cars*. Garden tools and even properties for sale can also be found. You can place ads too, take part in online auctions, and browse through all the weird and wonderful items that always crop up in these sorts of places, like spy cameras and phone taps.

Group discounts
www.mercata.com
This is an interesting site that offers people the opportunity to club together and buy things in bulk. In theory they should get a discount and save money. Whether or not you can find someone in your area interested in buying garden gnomes or new baths only time will tell.

Internet auction
www.ebay.com
Take part in an Internet auction, buying and selling just about anything with people all over the world. There are localized versions of this site (**www.ebay.co.uk** for the UK), and the company offers to investigate should deals go wrong. You can view the track record of a seller's past, which may help you avoid the crooks that may be lurking around.

LOOT
www.loot.com
The famous classified ads paper has been online for a long time, and provides an easy way to place your own ads and to search for the things you want or need. It also has an auction site or chat with fellow buyers and sellers for advice at LootCafe. Particularly handy is the property section, where you can specify areas and prices – essential for finding student accommodation. (For other property sites see "Property and mortgages" in Money, pages 187–189.)

Online auctions
www.qxl.co.uk
You can easily buy and sell things over the Internet using this online auction house. QXL will handle all the bidding for you to keep things simple. You just receive an email when the auction has concluded, with the highest bidder's email

address – assuming that your reserve price has been reached of course. You should also check out the special offers, where auctions often begin from only £1.

Wanted
www.ewanted.com

Too lazy to search the auction sites for that particular hard-to-find item? Just post what you want on this site in its various categories and someone will eventually come along and offer you the item. Lots of fun to browse, even if you do not particularly want anything.

— Furnishings —

Advice on buying a bed
www.sleepcouncil.org.uk

Lumpy bed cramping your sleeping style? You need the online bed-buying advice that is only available online at The Sleep Council. This site also has tips on how to improve the quality of what little sleep you may get (why not do the Bed MOT – yes, really!). It also provides some fascinating statistics on which nationalities buy the biggest beds (the Brits like to snuggle up close, apparently).

Crate and Barrel
www.crateandbarrel.com

This online version of the US store is packed full of classic products for virtually every room in your home. Order the items of your choice online or simply view the catalogue. The site will even send you birthday reminders if you give them important dates for loved ones. If you live in the US you can also find out where your nearest store is so that you can see the furnishings for real.

Goods for your home
www.cucinadirect.co.uk

You could almost completely stock your home with the goods on offer here. There is cooking equipment, electrical appliances, food, barbecues, and linen. If you need any inspiration, there are some clever recipes designed to get your mouthwatering and your purse opening.

Habitat
www.habitat.co.uk

Europeans looking to spruce their homes up in a thoroughly modern fashion should pay Habitat's online showroom a visit. You can browse through a catalogue

Tempt yourself with the array of household goods on offer at www.habitat.co.uk

of sofas, beds, and office furniture, although you'll have to contact your local store directly to actually buy anything. Its rival company, the slightly more expensive Heals (**www.heals.co.uk**) does go one better by having online buying facilities.

House of Chesterfields
www.jf-upholstery.co.uk

You can choose specific wood and leather colours, and then order your classic leather furniture online. The short list of leather-care instructions may prove invaluable and a currency converter is supplied for those shopping from outside the UK. Unusually for an online store, you can also buy on credit!

Indigo Square
www.indigoSquare.com

Whether you want to buy a fridge, stereo system, or some flowers to brighten up a room, the stores in the IndigoSquare online mall have something to offer. The categories are clearly displayed on the home page with attendant icons (a plane denotes the travel category – simple eh?) that actually work. Special offers are flagged up on the home page if you want to get some real bargains.

The Internet Antique Shop
www.tias.com

This online shopping centre concentrates solely on antiques, and mainly the selling of them to you and, as such, is a good site for collectors (see "Collections"

Home · Shops · Showcase · Sell · Discover · News
Feedback · Help

TIAS.com
Antiques and Collectibles

What do you want to find from yesteryear?

Welcome to the Internet's largest catalog of antiques & collectibles

Search | Advanced Search | Curioscape Web Search

Over 1,300 categories with over 300,000 items.

Browse items by category ▾ | Go!

Click here to learn...
How To Sell With Us

Antique Malls
The place to bid for Antique Mall Treasures

Sell Antiques & Collectibles On-Line
Click Here

Antique Arts
THE source for fine art & antiques

Curioscape
websites about **COLLECTING**

Today's featured items on TIAS.com

Roseville Freesia Vase | CAST IRON STANDING YARD ROOSTER | Spangle Glass, Art Glass Pitcher and ... | Figural Candleholders, U S Zone | BLITHE MORNING HN2021

What's New
@TIAS.com

Monday, January 08, 2001
Down Home at Bushnell Creek Antiques Attention Globe Collectors!!! Just added three antique globes to our store, two are early Replogles. Check us out. Also, offering a 10% discount for all purchases made by personal check.
Grandma's Closet Grandma's Closet added a 1920's French hand beaded flapper dress, a 1950's darling pink sequined hat, and a 1920's white rose

New Shops
@TIAS.com

Monday, January 08, 2001
Honeypickle Collecting should be fun. I carry glass, porcelain and other collectibles from the 30s to the 70s. I often update my inventory of old china patterns to help you complete your set. Step into my little corner of Brooklyn!
Friday, January 05, 2001
Bear's Collectibles If you like interesting 'stuff,' this is the place for you! We are presenting the lifetime accumulations of a family of periods. There is no telling what you will find

Selling antiques is just one of the features at www.tias.com

in Hobbies on pages 152–4 for further collectible sites). However, if you are interested in flogging your heirlooms TIAS can help there too, with online auctions and classified advertising. You can search for the items for sale using an online database, by browsing through categories of objects, or simply looking at the antique showcase.

Richer Sounds
www.richersounds.com
The garish website of the hi-fi store allows you to order most of its catalogue items. Not content with selling you products, Richer Sounds spends considerable effort explaining hi-fi basics to all beginners, providing invaluable information such as how and where to mount your speakers. A "Tips" section provides a more in-depth look at ways to improve your aural experiences. Unfortunately, while you can see everything from the catalogue online, some items can only be bought in the store itself.

Shoppers Universe
www.shoppersuniverse.co.uk
Based in the UK, but shipping to anywhere in the world, this online shopping centre features a very wide range of items, including home audio/visual equipment, clothing, and toys. You'll need to visit to appreciate the range, and the good news for those in the UK is that delivery is free, regardless of the order size.

— Home improvement —

Achieving the look you want in your home
www.designviews.com

Do you choose the colour of your walls before or after decorating the rest of a room? How do you achieve an authentic country/industrial look? If similar questions keep you awake at night take note of the advice supplied by DesignViews. Simple to navigate, features include design projects, tips, useful books, and a guide to vintage style.

Better Homes and Gardens online
www.bhg.com

Whether you want to re-plan your garden or view an interactive tour of the house of the future, this site does it all in style. It also covers cookery, crafts, and health and fitness, with a special kids' section that provides, among other things, tooth-rotting recipes. It has a number of useful tools including Plan-a-Party and painting and kitchen guides.

Decor suppliers
www.homesbydesign.co.uk

Aimed at the house proud, though not necessarily those who prefer to do-it-themselves, Home By Design has a few hints and tips but concentrates mainly on its online database. This contains details of your nearest purveyors of wallpaper, paint, or soft furnishings, while the book section lists reviews on books on colour schemes and other home-related subjects that you can buy through a link to the online book store, Amazon.

Discussion site on home improvements
www.homeforums.com

This is largely a discussion forum for subjects related to home improvement. However, Home Forums also maintains a list of tips and articles including an informative note on Radon gas and information about drain and sink care.

DIY Limited
www.diy.ltd.uk

Pick up special offers on DIY equipment and read the "Howie's How To" articles which cover such categories as "Kitchen Projects", "Bathroom Projects", and "Garden Projects". So if you want to know how to construct a wooden posted fence, clear a gutter or wallpaper around corners, now you know where to go.

Dulux

www.dulux.co.uk

This manufacturer of paint has a "Colour Schemer" on its excellent site, which lets you paint a virtual room in different colours so you can get an idea of suitably pleasant schemes – do remember though that the web can only display 216 colours, so you will not be getting the whole picture. There are also expert decorating tips, a database of decorators on call, and a selection of articles from popular magazines.

Feng Shui

www.feng-shui-shop.co.uk

Not the prettiest of sites, but if you want to know where to put your plant pots, and what direction your sofa should point in, then this is the site for you. You can buy anything feng shui based, from candles to the eight-sided Pa Kua mirror to rid your home of its malignant "chi".

Greenfingers

www.Greenfingers.com

Anyone who who loves the great outdoors, or at least their own back garden, will be absolutely rivetted to this site. There is an online superstore for you to purchase all your gardening goods, a magazine section full of tips and ideas, and you can also receive expert advice from the Professional Gardener's Guild. Another advice section, "Ask George", will tell you where there are beautiful gardens to visit, where to hunt for specialist plant growers near you, and will also demystify gardening jargon for you.

Home and garden design programs

www.fasttrak.co.uk

Home to programs such as "Visual Home Professional", "3D Landscape Professional", and "3D Kitchen", this site can sell you software that may help you design your garden or rearrange rooms – on the computer if not in reality. You can order online or see a large list of local stockists if you'd rather pop in to buy it over the counter.

Homebase

www.homebase.co.uk

Seek inspiration for home makeovers from the people who can supply absolutely all the necessary accoutrements for change in both your home and garden. A sprinkling of tips, complete with a list of the necessary ingredients, and a "store locator", makes this DIY/interior decor site one to watch as it is bound to develop even further.

Choose the perfect paint colours for your style of room at the interactive www.dulux.co.uk

Home improvement ideas and advice
www.homeideas.com

Upgrade your home with the help of the articles here. For example, not only can you find out how to wallpaper your abode, but the online calculator will help you to work out exactly how much paper you'll need. There is even advice on how to reduce the static electricity-generating effect your home can produce.

Ideas for your home and garden
www.housenet.com

Home Improvement aims to educate you in the ways of colour balance, how to set up your first home, and will generally organize your life for you! There are sections on decorating, sewing, gardening, saving money, and buying a house and, with step-by-step projects on subjects like maintaining a garage door, you just can't go wrong.

Martha Stewart home improvements
www.marthastewart.com

One of the most popular US home improvements purveyors comes online here. Not only can you buy a range of products for every room in the house and every corner of the garden, but if you need inspiration or advice, this site will put your mind at rest. "Meeting Place" is a great archive of information where you can exchange creative ideas and techniques with other visitors and a group of experts will answer any queries you may have.

— Lifestyle

Direct Marketing Association
www.dma.org.uk

Find out what rights you have to prevent companies from selling your personal details to each other, and also learn what benefits can be had from actually allowing it to happen. Half of this (slightly bland) site is only open to members, but there is still plenty of useful stuff for non-members to be found here, especially if you run a business yourself. There are also events listings for direct marketing professionals.

Fraud protection
www.iescrow.com

Are you worried about buying and selling online or have you been stung when a cheque has bounced? This site will relieve all your worries about online payments as it ensures that buyers get what they pay for and also protects sellers against fraud. It is extremely useful if you are doing international transactions. Paypal (www.paypal.com) offers a very similar service.

How the media works
www.adbusters.org

A sometimes hard-hitting site that relies heavily on graphics to illustrate how the media works, often not to the good of the consumer. There are witty spoof adverts, and articles on how advertising has, to some extent, become an important defining elements to our lives.

Safety hints and tips
www.safewithin.com

Covering all aspects of personal and domestic safety, Safe Within offers short snippets on things like how to avoid hurting your back, prevent skidding a car on water, crime protection for the elderly, and how to shun hypothermia when out rambling. The information glosses the surface, and much will seem obvious to many, but it's nevertheless sound advice and, you never know, could even answer a question you didn't dare ask.

Shopping online with security
www.clicksure.com

Not sure which of those online shops are safe to use? This site gives trustworthy ones a certificate to prove that they are reliable and so will put your mind at rest. It's run by an advisory council, members of which include politicians, managing

ADBUSTERS

CAMPAIGNS MAGAZINE SPOOF ADS UNCOMMERCIALS ORDERS ? INFO

CULTURE JAM
THE UNCOOLING OF AMERICA
**NOW AVAILABLE
IN PAPERBACK**

SEARCH THE SITE
[   ] [Go!]

JAMMERS NETWORK
News releases and
strategic updates!
More information...
[your email] [Join]

/ CAMPAIGNS / HARPERS /
Jamming Harper's. Finally, the battle
against Big Tobacco is being fought on even
ground: advertisement to advertisement.
Look for this subvertisement in the
December issue of Harper's magazine.

/ CAMPAIGNS / BND /
**Buy Nothing Day 2000 was a great
success!** Check out the BND 2000 Report to
find selected personal accounts, photos,
posters and media coverage.

/ MAGAZINE /
Jan-Feb 2001. The latest issue of the
magazine features "Is the American Dream
Negotiable?", a blueprint for waking America
from its consumer trance, and the most
recent activist and media news from around
the globe. Check out the latest issue...

/ CREATIVERESISTANCE / JAMGALLERY /

WHY ARE
YOU BUYING
YOUR FOOD
FROM A
TOBACCO
COMPANY?

www.adbusters.org will give you the truth about all those adverts you watch every day

directors of Internet regulation companies, and business people. A similar scheme
is run by the Consumers' Association (**www.which.net/webtrader**), whose logo
you will often see on sites as a recommendation of safety.

Which? online
www.which.net
This site holds the Internet magazine of the Consumers' Association. It provides
unrivalled consumer legal advice, plus objective reviews of hundreds of products.
The site includes over 60,000 pages of content, and it is available for a free 30-
day trial – after that, aside from the little tasters there are, the content is strictly
for subscribers only.

Women's online magazine
www.femail.co.uk
Femail is a site aimed squarely at women and contains a mixture of advice,
magazine-style articles, and message boards. There are articles on shopping, sex
and relationships, and how to look and feel great. You can ask expert advice on
subjects as diverse as nutrition through to analyzing dreams. Sign up for the
newsletter to be kept up-to-date on what is happening on the site.

— Upkeep

All about chimneys
www.chimneys.com

Whether you want to learn how to set a successful fireplace, check a chimney, or find out how it all works then you are likely to find your answers at Chimneys.com. The sheer number of words, undiluted by diagrams, can be off-putting but true disciples of the chimney stack will find what they seek here.

Improve your home
www.improvenet.com

This is a home improvement site for those who find the thought of DIY just a little too much, or have the money to spend to do without the aggro! Search here for a designer, contractor, or architect to make your dream home. You can get help getting started and how to plan your project or go to the Pro advice library to get advice from the experts. You can also get help from the site in matching remodelling professionals to your particular job.

Maintaining an old home
www.oldhouseweb.com

If you own, or want to own, an old house and intend to learn how to fix and maintain it, the Old House Web is a good starting place. There is a glossary of construction and housing terms, an energy checklist (old houses can be real heat wasters), an introduction to new products, and gardening tips. The "Ask the Old-House Doctor" section will answer all your questions about bouncy floors and fixing cracks in plaster walls, and there is also a bulletin board.

Tackling carpet stains
www.a2zcarpet.com

When little Harry sloshes blackcurrant juice all over your brand new, authentic yak's wool rug a2zcarpet is the place to turn to. An interactive stain removal page offers both general and very specific information to help shift tricky marks. The terrifying phenomenon known as "Rug Ripple" is also tackled, and all manner of other carpet conundrums are cracked.

The Tide Clothesline
www.clothesline.com

Take care of your clothes and follow the laundry-oriented advice available from the manufacturers of Tide washing powder. The interactive "Stain Detective" works out how to attack your own stains (predictably with a large dose of Tide, in most cases) and those funny little symbols on clothes labels are finally explained.

Utilities

AT&T
www.att.com

Find out all about the services you did and didn't know AT&T provided, including its Cable TV services and Internet access. A handy Customer Service section can give you an online statement, and you can also learn about wireless fraud and how to safeguard yourself against it. If your phone system at home is completely satisfactory then there is also plenty of information on AT&T's services for your business.

British Telecommunications
www.bt.com

Visit this site to read in-depth information on BT's latest telephone services or just to check what the going call charges to various parts of the world are. There are also handy snippets on how to handle malicious calls, help for elderly or disabled customers, and details of the latest annoying phone number changes. Its magazine, *Innovations*, keeps you updated with the latest news from BT, and its extensive Internet subsidiary service provider can be found at its own site **www.btinternet.com.**

Cost-reducing power suppliers
www.powercheck.demon.co.uk

Not the prettiest of sites but utterly functional, PowerCheck's aim is to save you money by suggesting alternative suppliers of electricity, telephone services, and gas. A quick and easy savings calculator for gas is supplied, just to prove you'd be better off using PowerCheck's brokering services. There are also potential savings to be made with water suppliers.

Toilet repairs by the virtual plumber
members.home.com/doug.graham/toilet.htm

Don't be put off by the amateur web address, or the site's title. This classic website has been around for ages and offers advice on everything bowl-based. If your toilet takes too long to refill, moans after it's flushed, or simply just doesn't work then the advice in these hallowed pages will help. You may not need it today, but one day...

— see also... —

Get handy around the home, fixing it up and buying new accessories, by using the plethora of home-related websites that there are available. 411 Home Repair (**www.411homerepair.com**) provides help on maintaining your abode and choosing contractors to carry out important work. For large projects make use of the building techniques detailed at Andy's "How To" Home Building (**www.andyshowto.com**). RoofHelp (**www.roofhelp.com**) has instructions on fixing roofs, although those with less ambition should maybe stick to designing bathrooms and kitchens – try Kitchen-Bath.com (**www.kitchen-bath.com**). Damp basement? You need MisterFixit (**www.misterfixit.com**), who will also help sort out problems with household appliances. The Natural Handyman (**www.naturalhandyman.com**) is a good, general home repair site, if slow to load, while The Plumber (**www.theplumber.com**) discusses plumbing problems and documents the history of plumbing since ancient times. For those emergency repairs, This to That (**www.thistothat.com**) will inform you which type of glue you'll need to fix any two materials together. Other mundane household items are available to buy online at Homefree (**www.homefree.co.uk**).

High-tech homemakers might find the advice on computerized home automation (à la Jetsons) and X-10 Ideas (**www.x10ideas.com**) to their liking, while Try Tipz Time (**www.tipztime.com**) is handy for general household tips. New Homemaker (**www.newhomemaker.com**) is aimed at those who have just purchased a home, and has all sorts of information on parenting, decorating, managing money, and connecting with your community, but, for the less-than-perfect, the friendly and diverse discussion forums at That Home Site (**www.thathomesite.com**) will be of comfort. If you want to get rid of the woodchip, then get some new wallpaper at **www.wallpaperstore.com**. More home improvement, gardening, and sewing help is available at HouseNet (**www.housenet.com**). For a good variety of home and lifestyle offerings, The Housewife Pages (**www.hausfrauenseite.de/index_eng.html**) provides a weird mixture of homely recipes, wedding gift ideas, and some possibly offensive jokes, while almost as surreally, This is Wood Heat (**www.woodheat.org**) promotes the responsible use of wood as a home heating fuel. Details of exhibitions should check out the home and lifestyle section lists at **www.exhibitions.co.uk**.

Keen gardeners are amply provided for with such sites as The Backyard Gardener (**www.backyardgardener.com**), Burpee (**www.burpee.com**), and GardenWeb (**www.gardenweb.com**), which all offer an abundance of tips, seeds, and nutritional guides. If you'd rather see the fruits of someone else's horticultural labours, you could do worse than the Royal Botanical Gardens at Kew (**www.rbgkew.org.uk**), which contains details of festivals as well as an online tour of the gardens. There are good gardening articles at Home and Garden Television (**www.hgtv.com**), which also includes items on food, lifestyle and crafts, decor, building, and "remodelling".

Shopping on the web can be therapeutic, especially with sites that can provide you with real bargains. QVCUK.com (**www.qvcuk.com**) is an enormous online store stocked with health and beauty goods, jewellery, electrical items, fashion, and almost everything else. The Marks and Spencer site (**www.marks-and-spencer.co.uk**) is pleasant and replicates the store online excellently. US shoppers should try the Fashion Mall (**www.fashionmall.com**) where you can shop by "floor" or by brandname (Estée Lauder has a large presence here). Those with a big bonus to spend can visit the Conran Shop at **www.conran.co.uk**. Radio Rentals (**radiorentals.co.uk**) can provide a whole range of items for renting. To own your own TV, video, or other home entertainment equipment, browse Tempo's site (**www.tempo.co.uk**) as well as Web Electricals (**www.webelectricals.co.uk**) to find the best bargains.

h

MONEY

Banks, property, taxes, and other money matters; here wannabe stocks and shares dealers, homeowners, and other investors have access to the sort of free resources that they could only have dreamed of five or more years ago. There are guides for the uninitiated, online dealing services at competitive prices, and information that could save you or your business serious money. Online banking services are also available – offering control of your accounts directly from your computer – and you can peruse financial newspapers and share prices. You can also save days from your house-hunting schedule by viewing lists online. Job hunting through the web is also big business.

— Internet banks —

Abbey National
www.cahoot.com

The Abbey National online bank that caused a storm when it launched with its low customer rates is, like most of the online banks, very pleasant to look at (it is designed in Flash), but what of the content? It's not bad, giving you all the regular banking features, and it allows you to do your banking through your mobile phone. If the thought of checking your balance sends shivers down your spine, then go to Cahoot Capers and play some of their fun online games.

Barclays Bank
www.barclays.com

Barclays Bank was the first in the UK to provide its customers with the option of Internet banking, but it has not rested on its laurels. You can sign up for its Internet banking facility, apply for a bank account, subscribe to the free Internet access package, or trade stocks and shares using the Barclays Stockbrokers service – all online.

cahoot

log in · apply · home · mobile banking · cahoot products · demo · questions · cahoot capers · contact us

fast forward to...

{ in control }

about cahoot · behind cahoot · cahoot team · press centre · join us

about cahoot

five good reasons
to choose cahoot

- 5% off two credit card bills[†]

  Transfer the balances of your credit and store cards to cahoot and we'll reduce the amount you transfer on two balances by 5%[†]. For example, if you transfer two cards with a total balance of £1,000, that's a saving of £50.

Find out more

7.1%

Up to 7.1% gross p.a. AER on credit balances*

terms and conditions · legal notices · security and privacy · rates and fees

Abbey National has finally branched onto the web at www.cahoot.com with its own saving site

Egg
www.egg.com

There is a selection of financial articles available to download from this online-only bank's website. You can learn about making a will, saving and managing money, and even have your say about virtually anything in the "Egg-free Zone". It has recently expanded into partnerships with retailers to give its customers special offers on some goods. Oh, and people in the UK can apply for loans, a credit card, travel insurance, make a will, and use its other financial services.

First-e
www.first-e.com

Claiming to be the first bank to work solely from the Internet, First-e offers high rates of interest to savers in the UK, France, Germany, and Spain. There is a demo of the service online and a full list of all the different accounts and services, including current and investment accounts. It also has its own area to shop at your "favourite high street stores".

MasterCard
www.mastercard.com

Remind yourself of the services your credit card company offers you, and discover the latest technologies, such as the MasterCard (Electronic) Wallet, that should enable you to shop with ultra-safety and convenience on the Internet. Cardholders can subscribe to a special mailing list and receive exclusive offers that might include cheap CDs, travel tickets, or beauty products.

m

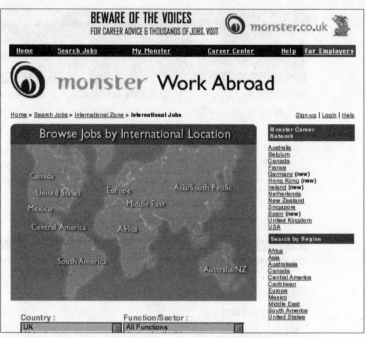

www.monster.co.uk is one of the most comprehensive job-finding websites around

National Westminster
www.natwest.com

This site has a good, simple design and is full of services, including links for mobile banking and online share dealing. Lots of advice is given on travelling abroad (including, of course, the chance to use their currency converter and bureau de change), and small businesses have their own section. You can also access your bank account through Yahoo.

Smile: The Co-operative Bank
www.smile.co.uk

Sign up at the UK's first fully Internet-run bank to get a current, savings, or credit card account. Because the bank runs completely online, you'll see your statements here as well as receiving them by email. There is also a competitive rate of interest, because a bank without high street branches has less overheads.

US online banks list
www.moneypage.com

Websites that consist almost entirely of links to other sites are generally bad news but The Money Page's comprehensive selection is unusually good. There is a large list of American online banks and investment-related links. The discussion forum doesn't see much discussion, but it's easier to use than many others around.

Visa International
www.visa.com

Find out what discounts and offers cardholders are entitled to. You can also find your nearest cash machine anywhere in the world, pick up tips for safe online shopping, and discover new ways to use your card, such as in public phones.

— Jobs

Career Magazine
www.careermag.com

The online presence of the job-hunting bible is full of features to help you get a better career. Upload your resume for employees to look over. See if you really are worth it in the Jobhunt IQ test or you can Ask Mr CEO some questions to help you through the nerveracking episode that is a job interview.

Headhunters
www.headhunter.net

Search by job type or industry for your perfect job – though it may not feel like it – there are over 250,000 to choose from internationally. There is also an extensive resources section with interview assistance, information on new cities that you might want to work in, and links to the best training resources on the web. You can also make money through their affiliate programme.

Internet job search
www.monster.co.uk

If you've just had an argument with the boss and want to find a new job, use this site and do your research on company time. It includes special advice for graduates, as well as specialized job markets such as healthcare. You can have help on your CV, advice on interview techniques, and search through almost half a million jobs worldwide.

Reed Online
www.reed.co.uk

Navigate the different categories of sites or search for one requiring your expertize, in your preferred location, for a specified salary. The "Job Sleuth" records your personal details and will send you an email or mobile phone text message when a suitable job becomes available. The site also features handy tips for writing your own killer CV and performing your best at all those interviews.

Search for jobs or potential employees
www.jobsearch.co.uk

Search for jobs at this recruitment site, and find contact details, job descriptions, and salary details online. You can also submit your CV to the site so that it can be accessed by employers. So, if you are an employer, this is a great place to vet potential employees. For a similar site on jobs in the US visit **www.hotjobs.com**.

— Money management —

The Bank of England
www.bankofengland.co.uk

The central bank of the UK has historical and political interest, but its website also provides useful background information on issues like the Euro and the bank's role in setting interest rates. A full archive of press releases is available, as is a mind-boggling statistics section.

BankSITE
www.banksite.com

A no-frills site containing a selection of interactive work sheets, BankSITE takes the pain out of making financial decisions. There is a "One Minute Loan Test" to assess how easy it will be for you to borrow money, and students will do well to follow the advice on financing an education and how to manage money after graduating from a degree course.

Blays financial services
www.blays.co.uk

The established financial information services has opened some of its doors to the public via the web. Get impartial advice on mortgages, savings, utilities, and business and personal banking. There is also an area to help students in particular. The information on savings and mortgages is updated daily taking into account the fluctuating nature of these two areas.

Family Money
www.familymoney.com

It is possible to plan your family's savings and investments without having to learn how to be a city trader. This site has extensive sections on investing and how to manage family finances, online calculators to work out the true value of mortgages, loans, and pensions, and gives sound budgeting advice. The approach is a similar style to lifestyle magazines. Some will find it friendly, others patronizing (one section is called "Women and Money"…).

Financial Information Net Directory
www.find.co.uk

Locate financial services with this directory, which includes listings of investments, insurance, advice, mortgages, and other services. There are online calculators to work out what sort of mortgage, loan, or investments you can afford, or not.

Financial Strategy Center
www.money.com

With advice and articles on almost all aspects of money management this site is hard to fault. It even has features on how to spot an Internet fraud, investing using the Internet, and the mistakes you'll make – with tips on how to avoid them. Complete newcomers should check out the "Money101" section for a lowdown on the essentials.

The Financial Times
www.ft.com

The *Financial Times*' offering is an utterly essential website for anyone with an interest in making money or the people who make it. The latest financial news and

The *Financial Times* website (www.ft.com) has all the financial advice that you will need

analysis are provided along with a truly gargantuan archive of articles that contains many free pieces, as well as some from other publications costing money. It is also a useful source of information on the international financial markets.

HM Treasury
www.hm-treasury.gov.uk
Catch up on the latest government budget details, press releases, and the Chancellor of the Exchequer's recent speeches at the unexciting but thorough official Treasury site. There is also in-depth information on ISAs and CATs, as well as ministerial biographies (for those long, rainy days) and all you have ever wanted to know about the UK's economic policy, including info on the budgets since 1994.

Money Extra
www.moneyextra.co.uk
If you are wanting to make your money go further this excellent site, with lots of calculators and comparison tools, will more than adequately satisfy your financial curiosities. Compare Stocks and ISAs, mortgages, deposits, and travel insurance.

The Motley Fool UK
www.fool.co.uk
Despite a frivolous-sounding name, "the Fool" is one of the web's most respected financial sites and aims to offer sound financial advice, albeit served in a potentially humorous manner. Help can be found on investment strategies, personal finance, and other areas. Novices can learn about finance at the Fool School. This site is UK-based, so American investors should try **www.fool.com**.

Society of Financial Advisers
www.sofa.org
Whether you are an adviser yourself, or want to receive online financial advice, you'll find interesting material here. Consumers can find online guides, and an easy way to locate their nearest adviser – independent or otherwise. The advice even gives information on how to evaluate your adviser once you've found one.

Virgin Money
www.virginmoney.com
One of Richard Branson's many web fingers can be found on this money site (indeed the bearded one's smile beams out at you from the home page). You can receive lots of advice here, of course all leading towards telling you that the best company for your savings, ISAs etc is… Virgin. There is a fun Flash-run section on shares should you want to browse around the site.

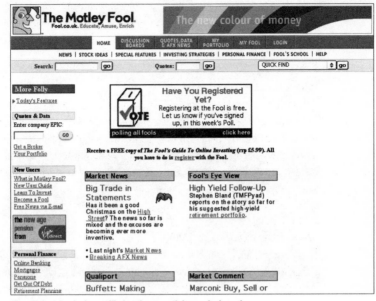

The Motley Fool.
Fool.co.uk, Educate, Amuse, Enrich

The new colour of money

| HOME | DISCUSSION BOARDS | QUOTES, DATA & AFX NEWS | MY PORTFOLIO | MY FOOL | LOGIN |

NEWS | STOCK IDEAS | SPECIAL FEATURES | INVESTING STRATEGIES | PERSONAL FINANCE | FOOL'S SCHOOL | HELP

Search: [   ] go   Quotes: [   ] go   QUICK FIND [÷] go

More Folly
▸ Today's Features

Quotes & Data
Enter company EPIC:
[   ] GO

Get a Broker
Your Portfolio

New Users
What is Motley Fool?
New User Guide
Learn To Invest
Become a Fool
Free News via E-mail

the new age pension from [direct]

Personal Finance
Online Banking
Mortgages
Pensions
Get Out Of Debt
Retirement Planning

Have You Registered Yet?
Registering at the Fool is free.
Let us know if you've signed up, in this week's Poll.
polling all fools   click here

Receive a FREE copy of *The Fool's Guide To Online Investing* (rrp £5.99). All you have to do is register with the Fool.

Market News

Big Trade in Statements
Has it been a good Christmas on the High Street? The news so far is mixed and the excuses are becoming ever more inventive.

• Last night's Market News
• Breaking AFX News

Qualiport

Buffett: Making

Fool's Eye View

High Yield Follow-Up
Stephen Bland (TMFPyad) reports on the story so far for his suggested high-yield retirement portfolio.

Market Comment

Marconi: Buy, Sell or

Financial advice is demystified at the essential www.fool.co.uk

Worth
www.worth.com

Access the online version of *Worth* magazine, and learn about investing, pensions, and just about everything else related to money. The latest quotes on the Nasdaq, Dow Jones, and other indexes are shown across the top of the site and refreshed frequently during trading hours. But most interesting, and unlike most financial sites, is its section on philanthropy and the best ways to give away your wealth — very refreshing.

— Property and mortgages —

Car loans
www.wheels.eloan.com

If you live in the US then you can get leases and loans on new and used vehicles from this site. It will allow you to apply for them in two minutes without the normal hassle that you can get from car dealerships. On the site you can also find out exactly what you should be paying for your new old banger. For further, more extensive loan information you should, however, log into the parent site, **www.eloan.com**.

UpMyStreet

The real-life guide to your neighbourhood
Discover local services and stores, examine property prices, nearby schools and your council's record, search classified ads and entertainment listings and much more

Enter your postcode or town

[   ] **Go!**

eg: N5 2PL or York
Don't know the postcode? Try Royal Mail's postcode finder

What's new **Place a FREE classified ad**
For a limited period, you can place a FREE ad for a property, used car, job or other items on our classifieds pages.

Latest property prices
What are properties worth in your area? Take a look at our updated Land Registry data for the low-down.

'Tenth best site of all time'
theNet Magazine rates UpMyStreet at number 10 in its '50 best sites of all time'. Find out more

School league tables
Check out the latest rankings on secondary schools and sixth forms in your area.

Link to us | About UpMyStreet | Feedback

Use www.upmystreet.com to find out all about your neighbourhood

Find a Property
www.findaproperty.com

Find a house or flat to rent or buy at this listings site. You can select local editions to restrict your searches to the most relevant areas and, although the main areas are London, Surrey, and a few other places in the South East of England, there are versions for the whole of the rest of the UK, and for Europe. You have to be quick though, as the best properties are often snapped up quickly.

Guide to buying, selling, and renting
www.houseweb.co.uk

HouseWeb is an all-inclusive property site, containing a good set of guides on how to buy, sell, and move house; an updated list of average UK house prices based on different regions; and a formidable set of handy links. There are good sections on mortgages and insurance. The chat forum is unusually well populated and stocked with sensible advice.

How to sell your home
www.homegain.com

HomeGain.com offers an introduction service for house sellers and estate agents. It also provides thousands of articles and guides on diverse topics – from choosing an estate agent to readying your house before a sale. A home valuation tool may help you decide on your asking price. It also includes a list of its greatest success stories for all those doubting Thomases that there are among you.

International Real Estate Digest
www.ired.com
Covering 50 US states and 115 countries worldwide, this is the mother of all real estate directories. Not just a host of extensive links, IRED also publishes articles and news stories regularly. Although the site claims most of its visitors are real estate professionals, there are some great articles for consumers too.

Research your chosen area
www.upmystreet.com
This original site will let you chart UK national statistics such as the average flat price, A-level results, council tax and truancy figures against those of the area you are considering moving to. Smug home owners just curious about their current area's status are advised to prepare themselves for a shock.

UK property database
www.homepages.co.uk
Homepages contains a large, searchable database of UK properties. Details of properties include photographs, a map, and local details including schools, crime statistics, removal firms, and train timetables. Leave your details and receive email alerts when a property fitting your requirements comes on the market. Once you find the correct property, you can get advice on moving.

Virtual Relocation
www.monstermoving.com
Find out what other US cities are like before you up sticks and move there. This website will automatically link you up with sites based on the area you plan to relocate to, and can also find resources such as schools, businesses, and other services for you.

— Stocks and shares —————

American Association of Individual Investors
www.aaii.org
Whether you want to know how to track your portfolio's performance, or need advice on spending during retirement, this site has everything that you need. Many of the articles are for members only, but don't let that put you off visiting

the site. There is still plenty to read and the membership isn't expensive anyway. You can always take a free two-week trial first, just to make sure that the site's got what you want.

Charles Schwab Worldwide
www.schwab-worldwide.com

Claiming to be one of the world's largest online brokers, the Charles Schwab Corporation's website will deal in global funds and securities, and is suitable for traders, amateur, or otherwise in Asia, Canada, the Caribbean, Europe, Latin America, and the United States. A joint Schwab-Reuters service publishes 20-minute-old stock price quotes. The day's Dow Jones graph is always published on the home page too.

DLJ Direct
www.dljdirect.co.uk

If you would like to take part in the current online stock trading frenzy, DLJ Direct is a good place to start. See the latest company quotes, and settle down and browse through the introductory investment guide. For the uninitiated, view the demo of a trade taking place on the site.

E*Trade UK
www.etrade.co.uk

If you fancy making your fortune on the stock exchange from your desk, this is the place to visit. Account holders can participate in real-time trading in UK equities, with each transaction costing less than £15. A further £5 per month will authorize access to the share price information service, complete with quote and portfolio tools. US moneymakers will probably find that the sister site **www.etrade.com** is more useful.

Financial journals online
www.financial-freebies.com

Investing is a daunting prospect for many, made more so by the sheer numbers of specialist publications available. Try many of them for free, using this site. It will take requests for sample copies of some of the world's most popular and respected journals, including the *Wall Street Journal*, the *Investors Chronicle*, and the *Penny Share Guide*.

Interactive Investor International
www.iii.co.uk

This powerful investment site is suitable for absolutely anyone, from complete beginners with a desire to learn through to professionals who know everything

Make (or lose) a fortune from your desktop at www.etrade.co.uk

but the latest pension fund performance figures. The free, online portfolio makes tracking shares, whether they are real or imaginary, almost too easy. If you only visit one site in this whole section, then make sure that it this one. Thoroughly recommended.

Internet trading
www.datek.com

Why not trade shares online at the site of one of the pioneers of Internet trading. This particular site prides itself on its real-time services – your portfolio will be updated while you are online. You can get free quotes on Nasdaq as well as other quotes, and also do your trading in extended hours (until 8pm Eastern Standard Time).

An introduction to bonds
www.bondsonline.com

Learn all about the many different types of bonds there are, starting with the basics and progressing through the intricacies, courtesy of the "Bond Professor". A glossary of terms, lists of frequently asked questions (FAQs), and a "Question of the Week" make this site an instantly accessible resource. The latest headlines will keep experienced investors coming time and time again to the Bonds Online website too.

If stocks and shares are your thing, then watch yours go up (and down) live at www.thestreet.com

ISP Shares

www.totalise.net

Totalise is one of many sites that offer you shares in the business in return for using their services. Positioning themselves as a service provider, you get shares for using their email and dial-up networking services. If you buy from one of their affiliates, then you will also get cashback and the chance for more shares. Blue Carrots (**www.bluecarrots.com**) run a similar scheme, though theirs is a more fun approach to the whole subject. It is worth registering here, though, as there is little to lose.

Latest investment news

www.thestreet.com

Boasting an impressive up-to-the-second news feed and market analysis, TheStreet.com is an attractive option for both new and advanced investors alike. The site also features an interesting range of articles, which comment on a whole range of current financial affairs. Some areas of the website, such as the "Basics" pages, are freely available, but you'll need to pay for a proper subscription before you will be able to access more than half of the pages that can be found on this site. Why don't you give the free trial a whirl first before committing yourself, to find out if the site is what you are after.

Learn about the world of Internet stockbroking
www.kiplinger.com

Learn the truth about Internet stock brokers, read how to pick stocks, and play with the large gallery of calculators to work out how much investment risk you can afford, what your current dividend yield is, and compute an appropriate amount of life insurance.

Loyalty points
www.ipoints.co.uk

This is a loyalty website where you are rewarded for shopping at affiliates of this company. Shop online at various partners and you will be rewarded with ipoints, which in turn you can exchange for high street or online vouchers to spend at various shops. Like most loyalty sites though, you need to spend a lot first to gain any of the benefits.

NASD Regulation
www.nasdr.com

The guardian angel of investors, the National Association of Securities Dealers has a website containing help for those with complaints to make against brokers. It can also aid new investors in choosing a broker, and advise what to do when telemarketing salesmen call.

Online investment guide
www.wisebuy.co.uk

Home of the excellent *AAA Investment Guide*, this site offers you the opportunity to read large chunks of this online book. Some of it is only available to subscribers, who pay around £30 for two years of unlimited access. The guide, which is aimed at UK investors, is also available on CD-ROM.

— Your money —

Accounting for everyone
www.accountingweb.co.uk

Once you've registered with the site (for free) you will have access to a dedicated resource for accountants containing bluffers' guides, workshops, and industry news. The website is also relevant to non-accounting professionals as it has a useful facility enabling you to locate an accountant, by location and speciality, from nearly 16,000 firms. It even has a humour section, which goes to show that accountants should really not be typecast.

Financial advice
www.ftyourmoney.com

The *Financial Times* newspaper has branched out and decided to offer impartial advice on your finances. As well as giving the latest financial news, get help on topics such as buying your first home or planning your retirement. There is an extensive section on ISAs and other ways to save your money. If you want advice from true professionals, then this site is worth bookmarking.

HM Customs & Excise
www.hmce.gov.uk

If you're not sure where you stand with VAT (Value Added Tax) payments when importing goods, perhaps paid for using the Internet, HM Customs & Excise will be able to put you straight. The site also advises on buying cars in the EU and explains how to calculate VAT when bringing items into the UK from abroad.

Inland Revenue
www.inlandrevenue.gov.uk

Providing the official source of information on UK income tax and self assessment, the government's Internet home of the tax man benefits from a simple design — for most articles you can choose a text or graphics version. Aimed at individuals, businesses, and tax professionals, the site has a list of frequently asked questions alongside electronic versions of Inland Revenue leaflets and other publications.

Internet taxation
e-tax.org.uk

As people start to purchase items using the Internet, sometimes from abroad, the government has realized it may be missing a tax opportunity. This site discusses the issues and provides international links. The news is provided by an external service and is not strictly relevant to Internet taxation.

The UK Insurance Centre
www.theinsurancecentre.co.uk

Save time, energy, and hair when shopping around for cheap insurance by using the services of this site. Fill in your details in a simple online questionnaire and it will provide quotes from a number of companies on motor, pet, house, travel, and healthcare cover. It's as easy as that — no frills, no nonsense.

US Customs Service
www.customs.ustreas.gov

More exciting than its UK counterpart, this site not only has information about import, export, and enforcement, but has pictures of smugglers caught in the act.

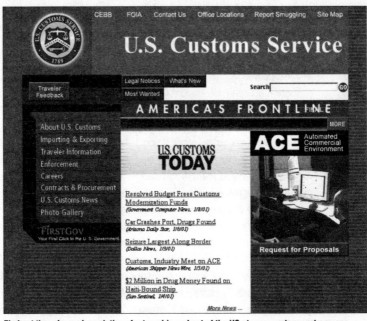

Find out the rules and regulations for travel in and out of the US at www.customs.ustreas.gov

The rules and regulations are outlined, and there is traveller information regarding mailing goods to the US. It also provides all you need to know about taking your pets and medications, for example, in and out of the country.

— see also...

Before you do anything in life, and especially buying anything on the web, you will need a bank account – and there are many to oblige you, so here are just a few of them: **www.firstdirect.co.uk**, **www.lloydstsb.co.uk**, **www.nationwide.co.uk**, and **www.wellsfargo.com**. Break out of that rut and get a new job using an online recruitment agency like Manpower (**www.manpower.com**), Brook Street (**www.brookstreet.co.uk**), or Top Jobs on the Net (**www.topjobs.co.uk**). Once the income is flowing you can investigate other ways to save. Cheapskate Monthly Online (**www.cheapskatemonthly.com**) offers advice about living on a budget, while the Financecenter (**www.financenter.com**) and FinPlanDotCom (**www.finplan.com**) provide online calculators to help you plan your finances. The Financial Pipeline (**www.finpipe.com**) has general financial advice and My Money (**www.mymoney.com.au**) aims to help you take control of your finances, as does Smart Money (**www.smartmoney.com**). If you need one-on-one advice then find an independent financial advisor at **www.find-an-ifa.co.uk** – very helpful when buying property. Property prices are pretty high in south-east England, so it would be sensible to check out the prices at **www.hot-property.com**.

There is an immense amount of help for potential and experienced investors on the Internet. Investing Basics (**www.aaii.com/invbas**) is a good place to start, while more specialist advice, including taxation, is available at Vanguard Group's website (**www.vanguard.com**). If you'd like to know more about the stock market before throwing away your money try Edustock (**library.thinkquest.org/3088**). As ever Yahoo has a magnificent section on finance (**finance.yahoo.com**). Find out about the place where US money is physically created at the Bureau of Engraving and Printing (**www.bep.treas.gov**).

More investment and general money-handling advice is available from iVillage MoneyLife (**www.ivillagemoneylife.com**) and FinancialWeb University (**www.financialweb.com**), while glossaries of technical terms can be found at the Glossary of Trading Terms (**centrex.com/terms.html**) and MoneyWords (**www.moneywords.com**). UK Share Net (**www.uksharenet.co.uk**) is a good general source of investment resources. If you're really getting your teeth into wheeling and dealing, try Turtle Trader (**www.turtletrader.com**), The Hedgehog (**www.hedge-hog.com**), and Sensible-Investor (**www.sensible-investor.com**) for some top tips. You can also get the low-down on the movers and shakers at The Syndicate (**moneypages.com/syndicate**).

Once you've put together a nest egg you'll want to protect it. Try Investor Protection Trust (**www.investorprotection.org**) and the Federal Deposit Insurance Corporation (**www.fdic.gov/deposit/investments/investments**) for essential investment advice. And don't forget to keep your pension healthy – try Pension Information (**www.dss.gov.uk**) to find out what you need to do.

It makes sense to write a will, and Crash Course In Wills & Trusts (**www.mtpalermo.com**) will help. And if it all goes wrong? Bankruptcy Lawfinder (**www.agin.com/lawfind**) might prove invaluable. Let's hope not.

m

MUSIC

Music is one area of the Internet that is growing at an exponential rate. The advent of MP3 has meant that never has so much music, in all its different forms, been available to so many across the world. Music of all forms is catered for – want to form a garage band? Or do you want to learn how to read music? You may just be desperate to find out where and when your favourite band is playing its next concert and want to buy a ticket, or even their latest CD as well. The Internet will do all this for you. Many companies that began by just selling CDs branched out into selling videos, games etc so these sites are listed within "Entertainment" on pages 96-99. However, the section below also includes special Internet radio stations, as well as all your favourite music magazines that are now online.

Concert information ⓜ

Gigs USA: previews, news, and tickets
www.gigmania.com
Not just a static listing of live music performances, this site also provides video and audio clips, concert reviews, previews of the latest CDs, and the ability to buy concert tickets online. Chat to other users to find out their opinions, or report on the gigs you've most recently attended. Check out the featured scenes in selected American cities.

Pollstar: the concert hotwire
www.pollstar.com
Find out where your favourite musicians are playing, all over the world, and check out the band gossip. There are a few online concerts listed, too, if you don't mind connecting to the Internet for a couple of hours to listen to low-quality sounds.

www.aandronline.com gives budding musicians the chance to get their music noticed

What's on in the UK
uk.ents24.com

Find out what's on where, with this event listings. It covers live music, clubs, theatre, and comedy, and you can even have updates beamed straight to your mobile phone. The latest tour dates are always listed here. There is a good mixture of famous, tribute, and unsigned bands here, and each entry is accompanied by a small map to help you find the venue.

For musicians

A&R Online
www.aandronline.com

The place to get yourself noticed by the professionals who will (you hope) get you noticed. Submit your music to be showcased, and learn how to copyright your songs online. Artists are showcased each month, with long promotional sheets and the chance to listen to their work in MP3, real Audio. Pass your comments on these artists onto others in the discussion forums.

Get Signed
www.getsigned.com

If you're hoping to make it big in the world of music, then here is a plethora of insider information to get you started. Find out about all the record labels and what they look for in an artist, how to book your own tour, and reasons why your demo could be rejected. Sister site **www.garageband.com** gives you the chance to listen to what other bands are doing too.

Hints and tips for budding stars
www.lyricalline.com

If your idea of a good time is to write angst-ridden songs about your teenage years, or you feel you are a budding rock and roller, then Lyrical Line Songwriting Resource has plenty of advice to offer, even including a rhyming dictionary! There are articles on objectively judging your own material and opportunities to post your lyrics on the site for constructive criticism. Unfortunately, most of those who do the latter haven't read the former, I'll wager.

Locate sheet music
www.sheet-music.com

If you have trouble locating sheet music for the pieces you need, try this excellent, searchable site. You'll have to order and pay for the manuscripts, of course, but the size of the stock and the search engine makes this much more convenient than using your local library or music shop. If you join the SMC as a member, you'll receive cashback benefits. Modern pop music is available, as well as classical works.

Music industry database
www.1212.com

The site states that it is the largest database of music industry related web information in over 50 countries. Find out information about session musicians, legal services, buy and sell used equipment, and even locate security bodyguards at this huge site.

Resource centre for music makers
www.harmony-central.com

If you want to make music using computers, guitars, basses, or synthesizers then this is a great resource. There are articles on buying equipment, touring, and building and maintaining your instruments. Product news sits alongside the articles and, although the stories are largely copies of press releases, they'll appeal to music shop addicts.

Shareware for musicians
www.hitsquad.com

This is the top place to find shareware for musicians, and it also acts as a gateway to a range of other musical sites, including ones with books, sheet music, advice on getting your band signed, and guitar tablature. There are music-making tutorials and discussion forums so that you can benefit from other people's expertize, opinions, and criticism.

Teach yourself to compose
www.musicarrangers.com

This site sets itself a serious target: to teach you how to orchestrate, write, compose, create film scores, and so on. The course for beginners is ideal for GCSE-level studies, although it does get more advanced. The "Instruments" section is strong, too, providing a guide to all of the standard instruments in an orchestra.

— Magazines

Mix Magazine Online
www.mixonline.com

Mix Magazine Online is a recording magazine aimed at pro and semi-pro DJs and producers. Unusually, this online version of a paper magazine actually provides exclusive material, rather than using the archives of previously published articles.

Music 365
www.music365.co.uk

This online music magazine features a guide to the best albums of the millennium, news stories about today's acts, and a shop that offers CDs, tickets to gigs, and the opportunity to create your own compilation CD online. There are also competitions, artist profiles, UK charts, festival information, and a database containing album listings and band discographies.

New Musical Express
www.nme.com

Recently redesigned, the online version of this opinionated music mag is an improvement on the physical thing. Check out the news, gig and album reviews from recent years, and find out who's on tour, where and when. There are charts of all different types of music and you can buy gig tickets online. The video index allows you to watch video promos and interviews of your favourite stars.

Q Magazine
www.q4music.com

The online version of this popular music magazine contains huge numbers of music reviews, over 18,000 in fact, and a virtual mixing studio where you can

www.mp3.com is just one site where you can download your favourite music from the web

arrange your own music. If you like what you read here then you can always follow their advice and buy the recommended CDs through its shopping facility.

Rolling Stone
www.rollingstone.com

This music magazine has created a quite brilliant website that not only has all the usual news, reviews, and competitions, but also contains a massive artist archive. Each band, or performer, has a dedicated page with an introduction, other articles, biographies, discographies, discussion forums, and links to places where you can read more and buy the music. Watch your favourite promos on the "Videos on Demand" section.

— MP3

Download music
www.mp3.com

Download sound files in a digital format (MP3) containing the tunes of thousands of artists worldwide. You won't find anything by the likes of Britney Spears but you will be able to access some really different, and sometimes good, music from largely unsigned bands. You can also order CDs that contain both normal and MP3 format songs.

www.bbcmusicmagazine.beeb.com has all the latest classical music news and concert information

Info on MP3s
www.mp3yes.com

Find out everything you need to know about MP3s and also download them. You can discover what software exists to play the songs that are available on the Internet, and learn how to transfer your MP3s onto CDs. Most of the material is linked from other sites.

Lycos MP3 search
music.lycos.com/downloads

Quite simply this is the world's biggest MP3 directory with over half a million files online. You can search files by genre, or by the biggest artists. It has its own features with official downloads, and the chance to see web chats with the biggest stars. It also offers you videos to view. The site has its own good, but rather garish, media player available for download too.

MP3board
www.mp3board.com

Certainly not pretty but very effective, you can search not just over the Internet, but through ftp sites (see the Glossary on pages 307–9 for an explanation of these) for your favourite tracks. The gnutella search system (similar to Napster, see next entry) is also good for finding tracks. If you cannot be bothered to do a specific search for something, then why not just browse through the various categories that are available here?

Napster
www.napster.com

The site that probably gained the most column inches in the year 2000, with some artists and music companies up in arms over its open attitude of sharing music. The basic premise is that you download the special software and share all the music on your hard drive with hundreds of thousands of people around the world. A simple concept that means that you never need browse second-hand record or CD shops for that hard-to-find song ever again.

— Musicals and classical music -

BBC Music Magazine
www.bbcmusicmagazine.beeb.com

Highly respected, mostly classical, music magazine in its online form and, being under the Beeb banner, it gives you the chance to purchase recommended items. Find out about local concert listings by region or search the large review database.

Classical composers archive
voyager.physics.unlv.edu/webpages2/archive_pop.html

Find out the names, nationalities, and periods of classical composers, using this basic but comprehensive database. You can also search by birthday to find out which geniuses share your own birthday, and discover important dates in their lives, as well as when they died.

m

Directory of classical music sites
www.classicalmusic.co.uk

This site contains a directory of other classical music sites, with categories including bassoonists, CD-ROMs, early music, and live webcasts. If you "Join the Upper Circle" the site will email you with the latest concerts in your area. The online shop provides classical music CDs, videos, and books, while a set of mailing lists aims to keep musicians in touch.

Everything you need to know about musicals
www.musicals101.com

This outstanding effort is a one-man project documenting musical theatre and film. There are mini-histories of different eras, low-downs on the composers and directors, and even some modern reviews. The author clearly loves his subject and much of the site is his own subjective opinion. It is a very well written site and worth visiting if you are interested in musicals at all.

Global Music Network
www.gmn.com

A site to suit lovers of classical and/or jazz music. Watch webcasts or read reviews of the latest classical or jazz CDs. The two areas are separated completely, so no annoying scrolling. And there are the obligatory Real Audio clips too.

Musical Theatre in Europe
www.eur.com

Musical Theatre in Europe is a great way to find out where your nearest opera house is, although the inconsistent spelling of theatres is rather irritating. Each entry is accompanied by an exterior photo and includes details of the theatre's repertoire. You can also use the site to find out where and when your favourite "artistes" are appearing.

The world of classical music
www.classical.net

This site includes handy advice on how to pursue your interest in listening to classical music, reviews of a mind-numbingly large number of CDs organized by composer, and a fantastic selection of links to help you find concerts as well as information on composers and orchestras.

— Popular music ——————

The Beatles
www.thebeatles.com

This official Flash-based website for the Fab Four was launched at the same time as the record-breaking Greatest Hits album in 2000. A long time coming, it is still impressive, mainly because it gives web access to video and audio clips seldom available due to Apple's strict vetting of all Beatles material. The site currently focuses on the 27 singles, but each is meticulously accompanied by biographical and recording information, chart positions, audio and video. So if you want to see the Beatles performing *Get Back* on the roof of Apple Studios, then come here. More content is promised, so it is worth revisiting.

CD database
www.gracenote.com

Previously known as **www.cddb.com**, this database holds the titles and track names for every CD you can think of and hundreds of thousands more. If you play CDs using your computer you can use this database to update your software so

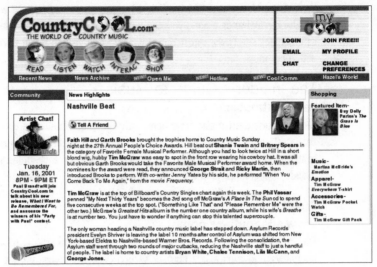

Listen to all your favourite top country stars at www.countrycool.com

that when you insert a CD it displays the artist's name, which album it is, and what tracks are playing. It also has a list of charts, featured CD players/samplers, and advice on how to build your own computer media player. Indispensable.

Chart lists worldwide
www.lanet.lv/misc/charts
If your interest in chart music isn't limited to the buying habits of those in the US or UK, check out this comprehensive list of links to music charts all over the world. Okay, so the site's design is basic to say the least, but you won't find a link to Latvia's Rietumu Radio Top 13 on the same page as Malta's Top 10 Albums anywhere else!

Country Music
www.countrycool.com
Garth and Emmylou are waiting for you here at this extensive site. Its unique features include the "Open Mic" section where fans can voice their opinions to others. You can listen to MP3s of top country stars, or watch webcasts.

Gossip and news from the music world
www.ubl.com
A great resource for those who need news about the world of pop and rock, this site condenses stories from diverse sources into one easy list. You'll find links to BBC Radio One, CNN, NME, and MTV, and a search engine for every band site in

the web world. If you're into the industry gossip you'll find yourself well catered for. The Lester Bangs among you can post your own reviews. The related iMusic communities site (www.imusic.com) is also worth visiting if you want to natter with other music fans.

The Insider's Guide to Music
www.dotmusic.com

Get the latest chart music news here, with full-length interviews with the stars, the latest charts, a number of band microsites, a special dance music section, some audio clips of latest hits, and in-depth articles on highlighted bands that include discographies and discussion forums.

Jazz
www.allaboutjazz.com

Everything you want to know about jazz is here. There are articles, news, reviews, interviews, and even a jazz humour section (yes, jazz lovers are not all serious musos). With such a diverse musical genre, you can choose your favourite style of jazz and search the site in that manner – find news and reviews on contemporary or ambient space jazz, whichever takes your fancy.

MTV Online
www.mtv.com

Packed with up-to-the-minute information and special music features, the popular music channel's website is a formidable construction. There are profiles of cult shows on the channel, and "The Vault", where you can find old news stories, video clips, and reviews stored by band name. You can even remix your favourite tracks online.

Rare records and CDs
www.netsounds.com

It ain't pretty but it sure is thorough… Record shops from all over the UK send a database of their stock to this site to create a huge central database, from which you can search for virtually every record or CD released, however rare. The search engine can be a little inconsistent, but it is a must site for any music buyer.

Sonic Net
www.sonicnet.com

Every form of music is catered for here from rock to jazz, and classical to country. You can even add your favourite artists to the home page for quick access and find discographies, biographies, reviews, news, audio, videos, and concert listings. The site also has its own radio station.

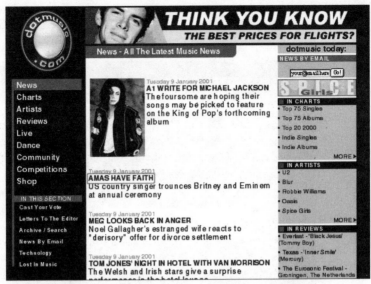

The latest official UK singles and albums charts can be found at www.dotmusic.com

Up-to-the-minute singles reviews
www.ukmix.net

UK Mix is a handy little site, giving honest-sounding reviews of the week's singles. It will also find websites dedicated to your favourite artist and provide a weekly news feed, as well as links to lyrics and multimedia. The features on the bands du jour are a little lightweight, and the whole set-up is based around the charts, but unless you're into a truly alternative scene it'll do the job admirably.

World Pop
www.worldpop.com

This site really does cater for all – some of the biggest UK names in the music and DJ world are associated with this site and it shows. You can buy tickets, read reviews, find out the latest gossip about the boy bands, and enter competitions.

Radio

Connecting yourself to Internet radio
www.radiospy.com

RadioSpy is the home of a top piece of free PC software that you can use to find and connect to thousands of Internet radio stations. It can help you locate small,

Listen to Internet radio stations from all over the world at www.netradio.com

fast channels suitable for Internet users with modems or even help you host your own webcast. The program will scan radio stations' play lists for your favourite bands so you shouldn't be disappointed.

Online radio stations
www.netradio.com

Locate and listen to various Internet radio stations from all over the world, and find out about all the different musical genres – there are 120 programmed music channels to choose from. When you find an area that you are interested in you can tune in to a station or buy CDs in that particular style from an online store. The news stories, however, are not this site's strong point, as it just focuses on mainstream AOR.

Radio broadcasting resource
www.radioearth.com

This resource for professional radio broadcasters has advice on preparing a show as well as a host of wacky, potentially amusing (or irritating) links that could provide show material. Think more Howard Stern than David Dimbleby and you won't be far off. There is a jobs page too, which might be what you need if you follow all of Radioearth's advice...

— see also...

Learn about the calming influence of music at the American Music Therapy Association (**www.musictherapy.org**), and possibly less relaxing music at A Brief History of Banned Music in the United States (**ericnuzum.com/banned**).

Guitar players wishing to learn music by their favourite artist should visit **www.olga.net**. Professional guitar information is available at Sound on Sound (**www.sospubs.co.uk**). Buying your gear should be done at **www.digibid.com**. If you fancy trying out a bit of music making using your computer, try Cakewalk's site (**www.cakewalk.com**) for details of its popular software. Synthesizer lovers should head to **www.synthzone.com**, and all music makers should love **www.makingmusic.co.uk** and **www.pcmusic.org**. Evolution Electronics (**www.evolution-uk.com**) will sell you both software and synth-style keyboards while those at a level approaching professional should try Sonic Foundry (**www.sonicfoundry.com**) for its ACID music and Sound Forge range of programs. Try The Sonic Spot (**www.sonicspot.com**) for music software reviews, news, and discussion forums.

Saturday night performers should read gloriously tacky Karaoke Scene Magazine Online (**www.karaokescene.com**) for details of equipment, events, and club listings, while the Karaoke Yellow Pages (**www.karaoke.com**) has a searchable catalogue of tapes you can order. The more cultured music lover will find themselves tempted to buy CDs of 42nd Street and other theatre hits at **www.dresscircle.co.uk**.

Visit Creative Music (**www.creativemusic.com/features/dictionary.html**) for an online dictionary of musical terms and The Library of Congress Recorded Sound Reference Center (**lcweb.loc.gov/rr/record**) for its collections of recorded sound from American history. View images of CD album covers at Mega Search (**mega-search.net**), though if you are deliberately obscure with your search then you'll hit a brick wall. You can buy film and TV music from links provided by Soundtrack (**www.soundtrack.net**).

Fans of country music will enjoy the fan club directory at the International Fan Club Organization (**ifco.countrycool.com**), while those into fishnet stockings and other paraphernalia will be satisfied with The Official UK Rocky Horror Fan Club (**www.timewarp.org.uk**). More genteel listeners, and players, will appreciate a visit to the National Association of Youth Orchestras (**www.nayo.org.uk**) for a list of concerts, details of exchange visits, and music festivals. Try the austere Royal College of Music site (**www.rcm.ac.uk**) for access to the college's library catalogue, and information on The Early Printed and Manuscript Music Project.

Impress your friends after taking notes at Operas and Composers: A Pronunciation Guide (**gray.music.rhodes.edu/operahtmls/works.html**). It contains audio instructions on how to say names like "Aïda". Many sites dedicated to deceased composers exist – try **www.jsbach.org** for starters. For a hobby where talking, let alone pronunciation, is irrelevant, visit The Ringing World Online (**www.luna.co.uk/~ringingw**), the weekly journal for church bell ringers.

Begin your search for a good Internet radio station at Radio Moi (**www.radiomoi.com**), which provides streaming sounds from a customizable site. Spinner (**www.spinner.com**) also provide Internet broadcasts. Tune into Asian music, plus news and other channels, at Radio of India (**www.radioofindia.com**). News of what's happening on the radio station belonging to the famous ginger bloke is found at **www.virginradio.com**.

There are thousands of sites for popular groups so here, sigh, are just a few of them – Abba (**www.abbasite.com**), Garth Brooks (**www.simplygarth.com**), Radiohead (**www.radiohead.com**), REM (**www.remhq.co.uk**), and S Club 7 (**www.sclub7.co.uk**). The url is often pretty obvious. Many good quality music portals also abound, such as the *Top of the Pops* site (**www.totp.beeb.com**), Click Music (**www.clickmusic.com**), and All Music (**www.allmusic.com**). If you are nostalgic for a particular decade, the 1960s (**www.sixtiespop.com**), the 1970s (**www.doremi.co.uk/glam**), and 1980s (**www.inthe80s.com**) are well catered for. Get all the lyrics you could care for at **www.lyricsworld.com**. Of the hundreds of MP3 sites that are available, **www.audiofind.com**, **www.mp3yes.com**, and **www.emp3finder.com** are all worth a look, while Icrunch (**www.crunch.co.uk**) will suit the more left field music lover.

m

THE NATURAL WORLD

We often forget that before we began surfing through cyberspace there was already a huge world around us with plenty to recommend it. And sure enough, online there is a huge plethora of information about zoos, ecology centres, and a host of museums and organizations to prove it. While there are some highly academic sites, there are more than enough sites willing to enlighten children and most adults. The Internet also makes it easier than ever to do your part to protect wildlife or the planet itself, and you will find some of the most important conservation organizations listed within this section.

Conservation groups

British Mycological Society
www.ulst.ac.uk/faculty/science/bms
Interested in fungi? Come to this site to gather information on how to pick wild mushrooms, and view the society's schedule of events. Cost-priced publications are available from the contacts provided. Best of all, there is a very large list of specialized fungi sites. It's just a shame that the design is so rudimentary.

British Trust for Conservation Volunteers
www.btcv.org
Why not give Ibiza a miss this year and break your fingernails building stone walls in the Pennines? You can choose from a wide variety of international working holidays on this site and book them online. There is also a discussion forum available where you can contact the organization and pose questions.

Countryside management & nature conservation
www.naturenet.net
Those interested in conservation, particularly in the UK, can use this site to find out where the country's protected areas are, what the countryside law entails, and

how on earth to work out if you're allowed to cross a farmer's field while you are out on a Sunday afternoon walk. For your more specific questions, you can "Ask the Ranger".

Ecology and biodiversity
conbio.rice.edu/vl
Find out all about various animals and their habitats. This virtual library has links to a broad range of related sites – so it is a good starting place to find detailed information. There is also an endangered species list, including an extinct category, and a section on pollution.

English Nature
www.english-nature.org.uk
Responsible for looking after England's wild plants and animals, this official government-funded organization has a website containing its press releases, a database of walks and other events, and lists of the publications and maps available to buy online. You can download files with information on areas of special interest, although you'll need a GIS (Geographic Information System) to read them.

Friends of the Earth
www.foe.co.uk
Read about the local, national, and international campaigns run and supported by this organization. There are press releases available online as well as articles on GM foods, the World Trade Organization, and other contentious issues. There is even help on buying "green" energy for your home.

National Trust
www.nationaltrust.org.uk

Working to save the most important sites in Britain, manmade or otherwise, this informative site has a list of events, education pages, and much, much more. The list of places to visit includes various National Trust buildings as well as places of incredible natural beauty.

Royal Society for the Protection of Birds
www.rspb.org.uk
Learn all about the issues surrounding nature reserves and wildlife protection, and find out what you can do to help the cause. The latest news stories are published online, as are details of special events and holidays for young bird enthusiasts out there. You can also watch the fascinating live webcams that have been placed in special places throughout Britain.

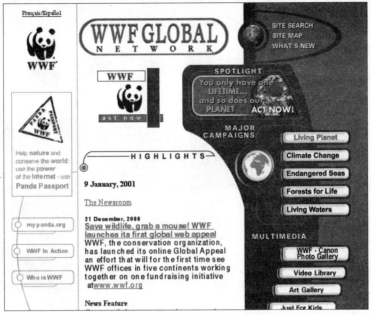

Find out what the World Wildlife Fund is doing at the moment at www.panda.org

US Fish and Wildlife Service
www.fws.gov
Catch up on conservation issues, read about endangered species, and learn how to become a volunteer. If you need a permit for importing or exporting plants and animals, or for hunting and fishing, you can fill in online application forms.

World Society for the Protection of Animals
www.wspa.org.uk
This organization's website highlights its endeavours to make life better for animals. There are details of its campaigns against the fur trade, civet farming (for perfume), cruel sports, and other ways in which animals are abused. There are also news stories on actions and successes, as well as some background information on WSPA. You can join the organization here or just simply make a donation.

World Wildlife Fund
www.panda.org
Read the weekly news reports about the state of our environment and the animals that live in it, discover what the WWF is doing about it all, and find out how you can help. A catalogue of publications is available online, as are competitions, quizzes, and free resources for teachers. The UK version is at **www.wwf-uk.org**.

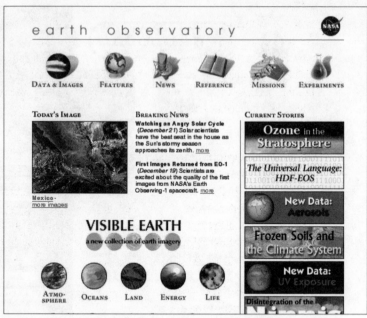

Follow the Terra satellite from your desktop at earthobservatory.nasa.gov

— Geography and environment —

Debunking eco-scare stories
www.ecotrop.org

Get an alternative view of the state of our ecology. The author of this site, who is a professor of biogeography, has some controversial views on topics such as global warming and GM crops. There's a scary world population clock that increases in front of you and essays about why the media is purposefully misleading about green issues.

Earth Observatory
earthobservatory.nasa.gov

Follow the progress of the Terra satellite, which is watching over our planet, taking measurements of our land, ocean, and atmosphere, from this site. You can customize and generate animations of ozone depletion over a number of years, and choose other sets of data to create visuals for an idea of what is happening on a global scale. You can also access the library of reference material on all things environmental that is available here.

Eco-news
www.e-guana.com
For the latest in high-tech eco-news, e-guana's site is hard to beat. The site provides access to a plethora of web resources for those wanting to get active about the environment, and also insights for the armchair eco-warrior. The EnviroEngine search tool is handy, but it does have a bias toward mainly US-oriented environmental resources.

Environment Agency of England and Wales
www.environment-agency.gov.uk
Learn more about this public body, which is responsible for regulating the environment in England and Wales. There is some very specialized news, and articles on important issues. If you want to know what's going on in your backyard, a special section is devoted to informing you. There are also articles about how your household affects the environment, and suggestions on how you can reduce the negative effects.

Farmers' Almanac
www.farmersalmanac.com
Not just for farmers, this almanac claims to know which are the best days of the month to bake, make jam and jellies, and mow the grass in order to increase growth. It also offers US weather forecasts for up to two months ahead and boasts a special astronomy section, with a date of full moons and other information. Many of the site's other subjects, such as astronomy, are catered for by external links to US naval and other reliable sites.

Farming news
www.farmgate.co.uk
You'll need to register (for free) to enter this convergence of a number of agricultural magazines. On the site there are news stories, categorized into different farming areas, as well as general topics that affect farming countrywide. There is also a "Farming Forum" that enables readers to discuss issues, and an agricultural archive.

Greenpeace
www.greenpeace.org
Keep in touch with what this environmentally interested group is up to, and read news stories about the issues that will affect all of us and the events that Greenpeace have organized. Typical subjects covered include toxic waste, nuclear fuel, whaling, genetic modification of crops, and deforestation. There is also information on how to join.

Hubble Space Telescope
www.hubble.stsci.edu
Your chance to see what the Hubble is looking at in outer space, this site also allows you to look at far away galaxies in awe-inspiring details. All pictures are clickable to look at in further detail and come with detailed yet concise, and relatively simple, explanations.

The Hurricane Hunters
www.hurricanehunters.com
Fancy seeing what the inside of a hurricane looks like? Well, now you can with the images recorded by the scientists who fly into some very serious storms and take snaps. You can take a virtual "Cyberflight", which involves seeing the planning that goes into each flight, taking a peek inside the plane, and reading an account of flying into particular storms.

National Geographic
www.nationalgeographic.com
Read featured articles, view eye-catching photographs, and see what your part of the world looks like using the satellite-imaged maps available on this site. Its interactive features are marvellous, including the chance to see how truly deep the wreck of the USS Yorktown, which sank at the Battle of Midway, is, and you can also read the survivors' stories in the forum. There is also a calendar of National Geographic events in the US with information on how to apply for tickets. Younger researchers are catered for very well here, as there are interactive stories, the opportunity to create a cartoon, an online quiz, and fun ideas of experiments and recipes for you to try at home.

Oceanography database
www.mth.uea.ac.uk/ocean/vl
Students of the sea should find all sorts of useful and sometimes interesting sites listed at this directory. The links are organized by geographical location and by subject, so if you want to find out about wave vectors or the depth of the ocean, this is the place to come.

The Old Farmer's Almanac
www.almanac.com
Get the latest gen on tidal times, learn how to predict the weather using a pig's spleen (yes, really), and, oddly enough, scan a selection of recipes. There are also tips for beginners in the garden to be had here and even advice on how to choose a hammer. An active discussion forum completes this mixture of slightly off-the-wall articles.

www.nationalgeographic.com is an impressive website to match the revered magazine

Planet Ark
www.planetark.org

Get all the environmental news you can handle here, thanks to a partnership with Reuters. Read today's news and view the latest pictures of environment stories. There are also details on how to recycle, an Internet radio broadcast ("Pulse of the Planet"), and a searchable archive of news stories. You can sign up to receive the environmental news headlines via email each weekday for free, and there is even downloadable environmental software in both Mac and PC formats.

Rainforest Action
www.ran.org

If you feel strongly about the destruction of the rainforests and the indigenous tribes that live in them, then visit this site. A "Kids' Action" team exists here to enlist youngsters before things get worse.

Resource Renewal Institute
www.rri.org

Find out how you can employ green strategies that will help to ensure a better life for future generations. Don't expect to find home projects here, though, because the emphasis is on pressurizing governments and public opinion. There are also articles about countries where green plans are already successfully in place.

Sierra Club
www.sierraclub.com

This group acts as an environmental conscience and aims to protect and preserve the environment for future generations. Based in the US, it considers the problem of pollution on a global scale and suggests ways to live in sympathy with nature. Articles and letters from the *Sierra* magazine are there for you to read.

Tsunami
www.geophys.washington.edu/tsunami

This site features advice on how to recognize the non-visual signs of an incoming wave and what to do about it. There is a link to the Alaska Tsunami Warning Center (**wcatwc.gov**), and facts about how the waves are formed and behave.

Volcano World
volcano.und.edu

Find out all about volcanoes, and check the Top 101 questions and answers. There are news of recent eruptions and images of the fiery mountains all over the world. There is also a kids' section, with pictures painted by children and stories explaining the origins of volcanoes.

Windows to the Universe
www.windows.ucar.edu

Find out about our planet, the way it works, and how it relates to other planets in our solar system. You can view images of asteroids "in the wild", and compare the Earth's surface with Mars'. There are also always very recent images of the sun, using different wavelengths, and other "space weather" pictures.

— Learn about nature —

Alligators and crocodiles
crocodilian.com

Anything you'll ever want to know about the history and conservation of alligators and crocodiles can be found at this site, along with some excellent pictures too. Should you feel the need to seek out further information, then there are links provided, along with some extra on site articles, including a serious care guide to keeping crocs!

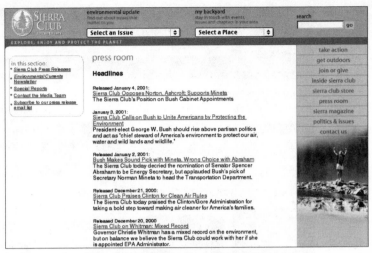

See how www.sierraclub.com aims to protect and preserve the environment

Amphibian Embryology Tutorial
worms.zoology.wisc.edu/frogs/index.html

University students of amphibian life can use this tutorial to find out more about our slippery little friends. There are embedded movie files and a thorough glossary is provided. If the words "gastrulation" or "neurulation" mean anything to you then this is the site for you.

Artificial life
alifegarden.com

Alife, or Artificial Life, is the computer synthesis of life systems. At this site you can download software to create your own tanks full of pretend creatures that will eat, breed, die, and evolve. The creatures have DNA and the breeding process takes genetics into account. Fascinating stuff, and certainly more interesting than many school biology textbooks. Show this site to your kids and let them be enthralled by their newly found friends.

Centre for Alternative Technology
www.cat.org.uk

View some sample publications from this educational charity, whose aim it is to balance out the relationship between people, nature, and technology. If you are interested in the possibilities of alternative technology then look no further. For example, you can buy instructions on how to erect a windmill in your garden and, at the same time, cock a snoot at the nuclear power everyone else in your street is benefiting from.

Discovery.com Discover Something New Every Day · Ecards · Weather · Stocks · Maps

Order Robo-dog now at the Discovery Store

very best pet
Discovery.com

Provide Your **PET** With The **VERY BEST**
S W E E P S T A K E S
CLICK HERE

Tools For Everyday Adventures   Discovery Store   SEARCH [ ] GO

Discovery.com

My Discovery

Explore by Subject
Dinosaurs
History
Human Behavior
Planet Earth
Space
Tech
Weather

Favorites
Games
Live Cams
Discovery Store
Christopher Lowell
Home Matters
Puzzlemakers
Crocodile Hunter
Expeditions

January 9, 2001
Current News
Mir's Death Warrant Signed

Probe To Crash Into Asteroid

Falling to Earth Soon

· Local Weather · Stocks

Explore Amazing Space
It's 2001. What better time to blast off on your own space odyssey? And check the schedule on the direct flight from Jupiter to Saturn, too!

More From Space

Network Homepages
Discovery TLC
Discovery Health
travel Animal Planet

· All our TV Channels and Schedules
· On TV? Find it Fast!

Discovery STORE

All you want to know about the natural world can be found at the excellent www.discovery.com

Children's Butterfly Site
www.mesc.usgs.gov/butterfly
Browse through the photo gallery containing colour images of common butterflies from all over the world. The author has gone for a wide choice, rather than a fully comprehensive selection of species. There are black and white illustrations describing the life cycles of butterflies and moths, which can be printed out and then coloured in.

Cyberpet
www.cyberpet.com
Everything that you might want to know about cats and dogs is available here. Get past the jokey home page and revel in the feline and canine information at hand. Chat with others about your pet, smirk at the breeders' showcase, and browse the list of pet rescue groups.

Discovery Channel Online
www.discovery.com
This is one of the most fun and entertaining sites on the web. All you might need to know about animals is available at this vast site; not to mention information on dinosaurs, space, and the weather – basically anything that can be discovered is looked at in detail here. Much of the content is child-friendly, and the young

ones can learn through videos, pictures, and other forms of interactive teaching. There is just too much to go into detail about, but a good example is the Yucky Worm area – choose the Flash-based version for an extra yucky experience.

The Froggy Page
www.frogsonice.com

This simple but excellent frog-based page is a mixture of fun stuff and links to more serious, science-based pages and sites. The Froggy Page provides sounds, pictures, and stories of frogs. There are songs (including Kermit's *Bein' Green*); famous stories such as those from Brothers Grimm; and linked sites, which have dissection tutorials, pictures of deformed frogs, and advice on keeping pet frogs.

Hummingbirds
www.hummingbirds.net

Whether you want to watch, feed, or study these little birds, this site hopes to provide you with enough handy information to help. There is a page identifying different species, a list of ways to attract hummers to your garden, and migration maps. A photo gallery is useful for those of us without a garden packed with exotic wildlife, and a quick Q&A section on the home page should help to answer your immediate questions.

The Life of Birds
www.pbs.org/lifeofbirds

Sir David Attenborough's TV programme of the same name is documented here, along with a background to how it was made and a lot of information from the actual broadcasts. Bird behaviour, evolution, record-breaking species, and even audio clips of bird songs are all covered, and, as if that wasn't enough, there is a healthy library of links to other bird-related sites.

Orchid cultivation
www.orchidcloset.com/orchids/psf.html

Pick up some useful hints and tips on cultivating orchids, and have a look at some pretty pictures, too (especially if you choose the Flash version of the site). There is a series of instructions on how to successfully care for the plants and a glossary of terms. You can also buy special equipment here, although bear in mind the location is the United States and the orchid flasks are very fragile...

Virtual expeditions
www.terraquest.com

Travel to exciting parts of the world using the resources on Terraquest. Join others on a trip to the Galapagos Islands, visit the Antarctic, or go rock climbing in

Yosemite National Park – all from the comfort of your armchair. Panoramic photography adds to the overall stunning effect. You can also surf the site to learn more about your choice of "destination". Read up on the latest ecology issues, explore the local wildlife, or relive its past history.

Virtual game reserve
www.africam.com

Claiming to be the world's first virtual game reserve, AfriCam offers nearly live photos from different parts of real reserves. The game drive cameras are mounted on Land Rovers, which are driven around the bush looking for interesting photo subjects, such as an elephant or lion, which are posted here. You can also get the latest Eco news, and the article on "Making Sense of Scents" is just one of the ways in which you get to discover the wonders of African wildlife.

Wildlife preservation for children
www.thewildones.org

This multi-national site is aimed at teaching children about wildlife preservation and there are articles about individual species of animals at risk. Many entries include a sound file, so you can hear what a jaguar or aye-aye lemur sounds like. Some schools have published the findings of their projects on the site, and children can contribute their own artwork of animals and habitat too.

— Museums, zoos, and parks —

American Museum of Natural History
www.amnh.org

Experience an online tour of the butterfly exhibition, see a massive giant squid, and learn about extinction and biodiversity. Likely to appeal largely to the younger visitor, this New York museum's site is a must for up-and-coming naturalists everywhere. Grown-ups who still crave education will be interested in the lectures and talks available.

Birmingham Zoo
www.birminghamzoo.com

Go straight to the "Visit the Animals" section to see photos and read about some of this zoo's residents. There are also movies you can download to see some of the animals being fed or just wandering around. Best of all, the "Animal Omnibus" will find other pages on the Internet to help further your education. There are also pages for children to print and colour in.

Find out about the exhibitions at the National History Museum by visiting www.nhm.ac.uk

The Museum of Palaeontology
www.ucmp.berkeley.edu
Find information about dinosaurs, fossils, and evolution, as well as links to other related sites. Teachers could make use of the description on how to learn from fossil records, and online exhibits explain how animals and plants have developed. The "Explorations Through Time" tours are fun and interesting.

The Natural History Museum (UK)
www.nhm.ac.uk
Go straight to the "Galleries" to see a guide to the museum, stunning 360-degree panoramic photos, and details of the temporary exhibitions. There is also a live video of a leafcutter ant colony. The excellent "Interactive" section will bring explorations and scientific events to life. A "virtual reality fossil experiment" is just one of the other fascinating things available.

Natural History online magazine
www.naturalhistory.com
This promising effort from the American Museum of Natural History provides a selection of articles from the print version of its own magazine. The "Questions and Answers" section, where visitors can consult experts on science and nature, should sort out those natural history disputes.

New England Aquarium
www.neaq.org

This US aquarium has a well designed virtual tour that allows you to visit the exhibits almost as if you were actually there. With the online tour you are guaranteed to see the sneaky octopuses, sea otters, and other shy undersea dwellers. When you've exhausted this, you can also browse through the monthly electronic newsletters.

San Diego Zoo
www.sandiegozoo.org

This well designed site will take you on a cyber-safari around the world famous San Diego Zoo. You can learn about the pandas and other endangered wildlife, read about the zoo's part in animal conservation and download video clips of the keepers in action.

SeaWorld
www.seaworld.org

Another San Diego attraction, the SeaWorld park's website has an online database with answers to frequently asked questions about animals and articles on aquarium keeping, endangered species, and career advice. Send your questions in by email. There are a range of teachers' guides and a "Penguin Cam", showing live coverage of the park's flightless residents.

The Smithsonian Institution
www.si.edu

From folklife to film, postal history to palaeontology (dinosaurs), the Smithsonian Institution has it all. View photos of the animals at the National Zoo, bones and butterflies at the National Museum of Natural History, and discover the truth about giant squid. The breadth of quality information here is astonishing.

n

— see also... —

Read about conservation schemes, discover the burning issues surrounding our planet, and help if you possibly can using the information from such sites as the African Wildlife Foundation (**www.awf.org**) and the Born Free Foundation (**www.bornfree.org.uk**), which are concerned with saving elephants, wolves, and other endangered species. The world's rarest mammals are documented at **www.animalinfo.org**. The International Wildlife Coalition (**iwc.org**) protects general wildlife and highlights problems on its news pages. The National Botanical

Institute – South Africa (**www.nbi.ac.za**) is concerned with South African conservation, and the South African White Shark Research Institute (**www.whiteshark.co.za**) is, as you'd expect, interested in saving big, scary fish.

The threat to the world's gorilla population is highlighted at Gorillas Online (**www.selu.com/bio/gorilla**), while the World Conservation Monitoring Centre (**www.wcmc.org.uk**) takes an interest in the whole business of saving the world. Closer to home, if you live in the UK that is, is The Game Conservancy Trust (**www.game-conservancy.org.uk**), while the National Biodiversity Network (**www.nbn.org.uk**) is concerned with conserving our general natural heritage. Many miles away The British Antarctic Survey (**www.antarctica.ac.uk**) is keeping an eye on the state of the Earth and penguins (apparently there is a rumour they fall over when watching low-flying aircraft).

You can learn about unknown species, including the Loch Ness Monster, at Cryptozoology (**www.ncf.carleton.ca/~bz050/HomePage.cryptoz.html**), as well as more feasible mysteries like the beast of Bodmin moor. Enquiring minds can get easy explanations of germs and what they do at Microbe Zoo (**commtechlab.msu.edu/sites/dlc-me/zoo**). Back in the land of the furry, the Mammal Society (**www.abdn.ac.uk/mammal**) provides free fact sheets on British mammals, as well as the regrettable road kill surveys. Read about animals from Antarctica, as well as accessing geological information from Glacier (**www.glacier.rice.edu**), and get news and information about wildlife in the Shetland Isles at Shetland Wildlife (**www.wildlife.shetland.co.uk**). Those with an interest in birds from far off places should try the Oriental Bird Club (**www.orientalbirdclub.org**), which covers birds from an area spanning India, Mongolia, and Japan.

Find out about government help for farmers, GM foods and beef issues at the National Farmers' Union (**www.nfu.org.uk**). Details of the next Royal Horticultural Society London Flower Show can be found at the Royal Horticultural Society's website (**www.rhs.org.uk**). ParkNet: Gateway to the National Park Service (**www.nps.gov**) is home to information on US parks, and also contains links to cultural history pages. And after all that, relax to the sounds of nature at Naturesongs.com (**www.naturesongs.com**), where you can listen to free recordings of, among other things, birdsong. Horse and pony lovers will find **www.equiworld.net** and **www.haynet.net** both invaluable resources.

n

NEWS

The immediacy of the Internet makes it an ideal way to broadcast and receive news, which can be downloaded to your desktop in a matter of seconds. What is more, most of this information is free and many sites allow you to customize the news to suit your particular interests, be it the latest political news or the gossip on your favourite soap. But the beauty of the web is the scope of news that is available – interested in what Chinese or Russians read? You can find that out too. Whatever slant you want on the news, there are TV networks, tabloid newspapers, and revolutionary parties all waiting out there to give it to you.

— Financial and business news —

American City Business Journals
www.amcity.com

Keep up with all that's happening in the American City market with distilled headlines from ACBJ's large list of newspapers. Expert business tips will be interesting to anyone starting or running a small business, news can be filtered through each particular area of industry, and there's even a weather report for travelling businessmen.

Bloomberg News
www.bloomberg.com

This leading financial news site has investment advice, market and industry analysis, and insights from top Wall Street experts. Including a regularly updated market snapshot, this is a useful site for those managing a financial portfolio.

Citywire: news to make investors money
www.citywire.co.uk

The huge amount of daily financial news that is available on this site is accompanied by research reports and news on funds such as investment trusts,

One of the world's leading business authorities goes online at www.forbes.com

unit trusts, ISAs, and PEPs. An insider section will also help you to keep tabs on what all the big boys are up to out there, investment-wise that is.

Dow Jones
www.dowjones.com

This is an excellent resource for news on business and markets. Categories are organized by industry area. There is an excellent area on how to set up your business – the various tools include how to organize your office, a list of company profiles, and how to manage a payroll.

Forbes magazine
www.forbes.com

The online presence of the business magazine is a flashy affair where you can find out about the world's richest people. The normal business categories are also there, and you can track your own portfolio.

New Statesman
www.newstatesman.co.uk

Excellent site, different in style to other news companies, it follows its offline sister. Read the articles of its various columnists, who each have their own page. Interestingly, you can download the complete magazine, with exactly the same format, in Adobe Acrobat, though it will set you back £2.

Financial news is up to the minute at The Wall Street Journal – www.wsj.com

Reuters Group Plc

www.reuters.com

Financial news, stock quotes, and all the top news stories are available from this focussed and well established site. You can choose your main area of interest, be it European, American, or African, or go straight to the different story categories.

The Wall Street Journal

www.wsj.com

This site is not free so be prepared to take a quick tour and perhaps sign up for the free two-week trial. Or you can try the "Daily Edition", which will keep you up-to-date with business news, but you'll have to live without the full content of the site.

See also "The Financial Times" in Money, page 185.

— Have we got news for you —

Expat World

www.expatworld.net

Moved away from your country of origin? You'll need Expat World, the news source that aims to break through bureaucracy and make your life easier. The site claims that frequent travellers will benefit, too. There are a few free issues available to download (in Adobe Acrobat format), but you'll have to shell out if you want to subscribe properly.

Home and Away: news for British expats
www.homeandaway.com

No, this site has nothing to do with the Aussie soap of the same name. Rather, it is aimed at British expatriates that are desperately wanting to catch up with goings-on in the UK. The site provides links to major newspapers, TV, and radio sites, as well as having more light-hearted nostalgia and gossip pages too. This is truly a celebration of English, Irish, Scottish, and Welshness on the Internet so you don't need to be an expat to enjoy it.

The Onion: spoof news
www.theonion.com

Hilarious or utterly offensive, this website takes a sideways view of the media, presenting spoof stories that are sometimes uncomfortably too close to the real thing. Language isn't so much of a problem, but the site is intended for over 18s, and so it should be.

Private Eye
www.private-eye.co.uk

The website of the satirical rag of the same name carries articles from otherwise unavailable back issues, as well as the latest front cover, an animation of the Yobs, and other favourites. You can submit your own small ad online (if you have a credit/debit card) and also follow links to a strange mixture of useful and very silly websites. Worth a look.

Reviews of UK media
www.anorak.co.uk

Read daily reviews of the performances of UK newspapers and other media. The results are caustic, often funny, and sometimes in poor taste. At its best when it's slagging off newspapers rather than soap opera actresses. There is a pretty respectable set of links to press websites, while the "Daily Toon" is always worth a quick view.

Virtual newsroom
www.assignmenteditor.com

Assignment Editor provides lots of links – and that's all. But they are such a well chosen selection that this website is an essential for any self-respecting researcher, journalist, or student. The main emphasis is on newspapers, with journals from all over the world, local US papers, and a few Internet ones, but you can also find maps, telephone and fax listings, and a list of government directories.

News on demand

Directory of news sites
www.thepaperboy.com

If you have a very specific idea of the sort of news you want then try this advanced web directory. "The Paperboy" will find newspapers and non-newspaper news from sources all over the world for you. The main international headlines are detailed and there are links to online radio stations. A special UK section (**www.thepaperboy.co.uk**) lets you overload on current events.

Personalized news to your desktop
www.infogate.com

Get news headlines, weather reports, and sports results up on your computer's desktop without even bothering to visit a website. This site provides a ticker program that sits on your screen feeding you the sort of information that you want to see (Yahoo Messenger from **www.yahoo.com** does the same sort of thing). If stock quotes are your thing, so be it. Other features help to organize your Internet passwords and fill in those annoying registration forms that are needed to access so many web pages these days.

Search engine for news sites
www.news365.com

This user-friendly Internet web directory organizes news-providing sites into easily accessible categories, in much the same way as the popular Yahoo! search engine does. Find a subject area that interests you and follow the links until you come to a set of appropriate sites. Some will be general links, while others will zoom you straight to a specific section – for example, the BBC's science section of its news site. This is a great site to remember.

Up-to-date information
www.ananova.com

A rather different news site, where the latest info is disseminated through an animated character by the name of Ana Nova (hence the site's name). You can have stories fed straight to your email address every day for no charge. This site can also provide up-to-the-minute news straight to your website, if you have one; and again, it's completely free.

The Big Issue was set up in 1991 to give homeless people the chance to make an income. It campaigns on behalf of homeless people and highlights the major social issues of the day. It allows homeless people to voice their views and opinions.

THE BILDERBERG PAPERS
World exclusive: Leaked minutes from confidential meetings of the world's

Help the homeless online by paying to read the articles at www.bigissue.com

Papers and magazines

The Big Issue
www.bigissue.com
Campaigning for the rights and welfare of homeless people, the paper is distributed on the streets by the people it aims to help, and it is now global. Don't expect to read the contents of these papers for free here – that's against the point of the project – but there are features that should help you part with your cash.

Electronic Telegraph
www.telegraph.co.uk
The original, and arguably the best, online newspaper in the UK presents all the day's main stories, while a complete archive of previous issues can be searched. There are dozens of subsections, a bit like the Sunday version, to delve into.

Evening Standard
www.thisislondon.co.uk
The online branch of the London *Evening Standard* is an excellent news service. As an evening paper offline, it means that the articles are very up-to-date – it is a good source for finding out what is going on in London as well...

Gay Times
www.gaytimes.co.uk

You will find extracts from this gay news and features magazine, and a shop selling books, videos, and CDs. There are also chat forums and links to other sites. At the time of writing there had been a merger of two big gay companies, so expect some changes on the site...

The Guardian/The Observer
www.guardian.co.uk

The content of both *The Guardian* and its Sunday equivalent can be found live at this excellent site. There are headlines, breaking news stories, and special reports to be read here. The site also includes columns and short links to useful items, such as weather reports, TV listings, and information on events in the UK (unsurprisingly, each one of them is sponsored by the paper). There are many sister sites too, equally as good, among them **www.booksunlimited.co.uk** and **www.footballunlimited.co.uk**.

The Independent
www.independent.co.uk

This newspaper's website was originally one of the online pioneers, but was desperately in need of a re-design, which it has recently had. The site not only offers news but also provides a Top 50 listing of, well, anything it seems. If you want to know what to buy people for Christmas, which beaches are worth a visit, or how to be more ecologically friendly you'll find help here. The site also has online shopping for books, wine, videos, music, and travel, as well as the normal newspaper sections.

International Herald Tribune
www.iht.com

"The World's Daily Newspaper" brings stories from all over together into one, handy location. Features and special reports often seem a long time in coming, but news is published daily – you'll just have to subscribe to the real thing if you want instant access to it all.

The Irish Times
www.ireland.com

Read the special features, find out what entertainment events are going on in Dublin, and get all the sports news. Obviously, politics is high on the agenda too, but so are festivals. International news generally makes the headlines here. Get the main headlines from here emailed straight to your inbox if the size of the site worries you.

Janes
janes.com

Jane's provides news on defence, transport, and law enforcement. In the defence section, you can find out about who's attacking whom, what's "in" this season, and which planes have crashed during manoeuvres. You'll get more detail here about military stories than any national newspaper can provide. Its "Regional News" section allows you to look at the latest happenings in areas across the globe.

The Mirror
www.mirror.co.uk

Catch the latest headlines, receive advice from Miriam Stoppard, and find out what Victor Lewis-Smith doesn't like about TV today. You won't find a full set of stories online, so you'll only be really happy with this site if you're interested in the sport section, which is the single largest area covered. Their other site is found at **www.sundaymirror.co.uk**.

The Moscow Times
www.moscowtimes.ru

This English language newspaper publishes news based around Moscow and Russia in general. You can (try to) get to grips with the Russian stock market, discover what films and other entertainments are available, and browse the usually empty classified ads section. The majority of the international news relates to Russia in one way or another.

The Muslim News
www.muslimnews.co.uk

Providing news for Muslims in the UK, this site claims to be objective and independent of country or political party. There is a large archive of past issues, and a mailing list for those who want to receive the site's press releases.

n

National Enquirer
www.nationalenquirer.com

Don't expect deep analysis of the Irish peace process here. You're more likely to find details of Hollywood stars going into analysis or getting out of marriages, as well as stories you almost cannot believe are true. You can trace specific gossip back over a large period of time by entering a star's name into the search engine.

New Scientist
www.newscientist.com

You can read a fair chunk of features and news stories from the paper version of this technology and science-based magazine. There are also sections exclusively

The Sun may not be high-brow, but there is still high entertainment value at www.the-sun.co.uk

available on the web so even current subscribers will find something new. In fact, some printed stories actually refer the reader to this site for further information.

New York Times
www.nytimes.com

Find full reports from this US paper, neatly sorted into arts, business, international, and so on. You can find out what happened "On This Day" in various years, and even view a copy of the paper's front page from a featured year. A useful "Learning Network" section is aimed at teachers, parents, and students.

The Scotsman
www.scotsman.com

The stories that can be found here include Scottish issues and events, as well as the usual general UK and international coverage. A property section will prove handy to those who fancy buying or renting north of the border. There's a web camera, providing 20-minute views of Edinburgh's top attractions, and a weather report for different regions.

South China Morning Post
www.scmp.com

The Internet edition of Hong Kong's English language paper features news from all over the world, but concentrates on local and mainland China news. A searchable archive of stories is available, but you'll have to pay for the privilege of reading the results. There are links to other *SCMP* sites, including dedicated technology and horse racing papers.

The Sun
www.the-sun.co.uk

The newspaper scorned but read by millions now has its own up-to-date website, featuring the day's headlines as well as a gossip, cartoons, and today's weather. The most comprehensive part of the site contains a database of page three girl images, of course. Its Sunday equivalent, the *News of the World* is found at **www.newsoftheworld.co.uk**.

Time magazine
www.time.com

Probably the world's most famous magazine has a remarkable online presence, with excellent resources and up-to-date information. Special features include Person of the Year and the Time 100 most important people of the century, and you can also look at their magazine photos. There are different versions for each continent making this a truly global site.

The Times
www.thetimes.co.uk

Find news stories from one of the UK's most respected newspapers online. The site can actually be temperamental at times, but if you persevere you'll find daily news, obituaries, and all the usual business, weather, and highly opinionated stories that you'd expect from this paper.

T2 Online
www.t2online.com

The Electronic Telegraph (see page 231) has produced this online magazine, which is aimed at teenage readers. It features fashion, sport, and reviews of music, computer games, and films. There are puzzles, cartoons, and an opportunity to write in with your views. There are always plenty of competitions to keep you interested, too.

USA Today
www.usatoday.com

Get a summary of the stories available in the print edition, or view stories that have been listed in simple groups. There is the much parodied "USA Snapshot" – a look at the statistics that shape our lives – as well as in-depth political and financial articles.

The Washington Post

www.washingtonpost.com

You can find a full range of US news stories here, including a section devoted to coverage in the morning paper. There is also work from a large staff of columnists and a searchable archive of stories, which could be a helpful homework resource.

The Week

www.theweek.co.uk

Why read all of the newspapers every day when you can find the week's news condensed into one, easily digestible magazine? Not only do you get the stories explained in plain English, but you can also see how different newspapers view the same events. Essential reading for anyone with an interest in the media.

— Radio

BBC Radio 4

www.bbc.co.uk/radio4

Browse the programming schedule, vote for your own "Pick of the Week" broadcast, and listen to the radio station online. Special features and favourites, such as "Letter from America", make this a site worthy of your attention. Many of the site's apparent offerings are served from the BBC's main site.

Virtual Tuner

www.radio-on-the-internet.com

Search for Internet radio broadcasts using this dedicated website. You won't find any news, just links to news providers. You can choose the nationality and type of stories you are interested in here, which is very useful.

Voice of America

www.voa.gov

International, regional, and US news is broadcast from this radio station in 52 languages. You can find which frequency you should use to tune in to, and just one click will call up an Internet broadcast in English. Written news stories are updated on the site every five minutes.

World Radio Network

www.wrn.org

Listen to a variety of audio news reports in different languages from various countries on this site. There are live broadcasts from WRN's own service as well as

All the technological news that you could possibly need can be found at www.wired.com

many different links to other sources. The site also includes programmes for those that are interested in the arts, sports, music, and science rather than news.

— Technology news —

New Media Age
www.nma.co.uk
Probably the leading UK Internet magazine caters for those interested in online advertising, marketing, and publishing. Find out about the Top 100 media agencies. An editorial feature called "Today's Comment" is updated daily, while articles from the magazine are reproduced online. There is also a large job section.

News on everything technological
www.wired.com
Aimed at people who use technology in their work, or has it as a serious hobby. Wired runs news stories on anything from mobile phones to the Hubble telescope.

The Standard
www.thestandard.com
Business news for Internet-based companies is available here. You can register to get access to its informative daily newsletter for all the latest industry information.

There are excellent in-depth articles to browse through as well. American web workers should have a look at the Business 2.0 site (**www.business2.com**) though in this integrated world, many stories overlap.

The world of high technology
www.ntk.net

Weird, retro design aside, this site provides a weekly view on high-tech news, complete with snide comments and sceptical outlook. There are links to some very rude but occasionally funny sites, so keep an eye on the kids – who probably won't get most of the "jokes" anyway.

— TV

ABC News
www.abcnews.go.com

Displaying almost 100 per cent US news, the straightforward layout makes this an easy news site to get to grips with – there are lots of live newsfeeds and audio and visual media to satiate your news demands. Other non-news features are also built into this site, including a shopping guide and a homework helper.

BBC News
news.bbc.co.uk

This top site from a news source respected the world over provides an excellent service. Watch video footage, listen to reports, and follow links to build up an overview of world situations. The world service is available in many languages at **www.bbc.co.uk/worldservice**.

CBS
www.cbs.com

This well designed site lets you know what's coming up on CBS in the coming week. Showfinder takes you to the pages dedicated to TV shows like *David Letterman* or *Chicago Hope*. For those who like to be "in the know", there's also some gossip from behind the scenes of the top shows and exclusive interviews with top CBS stars.

CNN
www.cnn.com

There's something for everyone at this news site cum Internet portal. There is more US than "World" news, as you might expect, but other handy areas include

"Technology", "Health", "Entertainment", and "Politics" (US). UK readers may find that they get a better Internet performance by visiting the European site that can be found at **europe.cnn.com**.

Fox News
www.foxnews.com

You can access a good mixture of current affairs news stories from this TV network's site. Special reports are included and there are weather maps covering the whole world that are updated at least twice a day too. You can also create your own newscast by compiling separate reports into a single video stream. This is a very clever site...

ITN
www.itn.co.uk

This independent news site offers some useful features. There are live video news broadcasts, audio bulletins, and a news ticker that sits on your desktop, piping in the latest headlines as you work or play. An archive of stories going back one year can be searched.

Microsoft and NBC
www.msnbc.com

This website is a combination of Microsoft and the NBC news network. It covers international and US-specific news, with lots of audio and video, or you can type in your ZIP code for local sports and weather. The site also provides links to the US regional news affiliates, so that you can see what's going on in your own back yard too.

News Now
www.newsnow.co.uk

Updated every five minutes, this site condenses news stories from multiple sources, including the BBC, CNN, and MTV, categorizing them into appropriate sections. US and UK news stories are denoted by little flags, so you can easily restrict your view to a national one. The most popular stories are listed so you can hone your search even further.

Sky News
www.sky.com/news

There is plenty of UK news here, as well as coverage of what is going on in the rest of the world. You may not care so much about the presenters, but if you do then their profiles are available, too. Stories are categorized into sections, making the site easier to navigate than a paper journal.

Teletext
www.teletext.co.uk

Carrying the same concise news stories as its TV service, Teletext's site is faster and less frustrating to use. You won't find detailed analysis here, just pithy headlines and the odd quote – ideal for those with limited time or small attention spans.

See also "TV, Radio, and ADs" in Entertainment pages 102–104.

— Weather

The Met Office
www.meto.gov.uk

Receive weather reports from the UK's official Meteorological Office, and learn about the automatic weather stations – you can even get forecasts delivered to your mobile phone. A-Level Geography students might find the section on taking measurements in urban areas interesting. The tropical cyclone forecasting section is particularly good, since it includes links to advisories all over the world.

Weather reports for the active
www.intellicast.com

If you are planning a trip in the great outdoors, you'd be wise to check the weather reports. Intellicast is aimed at just such adventurers, providing information on where the best places to play golf are, specialized forecasts for sailors, and regionalized entries for US national parks and other recreation areas. The current weather chart for the US is regularly updated on the home page.

n

— see also...

Almost all newspapers, broadsheets, and tabloids are now online, whether you want to look at the *Irish Post* (**www.irishpost.co.uk**) or the *Daily Star* (**www.megastar.co.uk**). The UK radio station Independent Radio News (**www.irn.co.uk**) provides audio national and international news bulletins, while anyone looking for international news from internal sources should check out such sites as *The Times of India* (**www.timesofindia.com**), China Online (**www.chinaonline.com**), and the Canadian Sympatico (**www.ab.sympatico.ca**). For out-of-this-world news of events in space try Space Daily (**www.spacer.com**). There is more high-tech news at SciTech Daily Review (**www.scitechdaily.com**)

and Silicon (**www.silicon.com**), which also features web-based TV broadcasts. Use the customizable news ticker at News Index (**www.newsindex.com**) to have the latest headlines piped straight to your desktop. InfoBeat Inc (**www.infobeat.com**) will provide free news via email, while Genie Internet (**www.genie.cellnet.co.uk**) will go one better and beam stories directly to your mobile phone. See yourself as a hack? Join other journalists in the Fleet Street Forum (**www.fleetstreet.org.uk**).

If you only want the day's news summarized in one place, try Info Junkie (**www.infojunkie.com**), which provides links to the most important stories. The Omnivore (**way.net/omnivore**) brings in news from all over the world. Yahoo! News (**dailynews.yahoo.com**) keeps the headlines in an easily accessible place – should you use its search engine too. If you're fed up with the gloom and doom of most news reports, read Good News Network (**www.goodnewsnetwork.org**) for news with a positive spin.

The Children's Express (**www.childrens-express.org**) is a news agency and website run by under-18s, while the Drudge Report site (**www.drudgereport.com**) is a sometimes scurrilous gossip/news column frequently only suitable for older readers. Gossip from the underworld is available at Intelligence Online (**www.intelligenceonline.com**), where the security services pick up their specialist news. Media, business, and financial news can be found at PR Newswire (**www.prnewswire.com**), while the electronic version of *The Economist* (**www.economist.com**) provides world political and business coverage. Media UK (**www.mediauk.com**) carries a directory of UK TV, newspapers, and other media sites. It also includes a downloadable TV guide that stays up-to-date using the Internet.

n

REFERENCE

This section deals with the sort of subjects you might delve through your 40-book set of encyclopedias for. Luckily, it is much easier to discover referential information on the Internet, with museums, encyclopedias, and libraries happy to share their resources with the general public. Whether you want to see the relics of a distant museum or need advice on complex legal issues, there are thousands of sites out there to help you with your specific tasks.

— Any questions? ——

Ask an Expert
www.askanexpert.com
This site does exactly as it says, and you can challenge the experts with particularly difficult questions. There is an expert of the month to answer your questions. You can browse by categories to ask the correct expert too.

Find out how to do just about anything
www.ehow.com
The answers to all those awkward questions (which direction do you shave in, how can busy people eat breakfast, which PR firm is right for my business?) are all contained within this site. The terminally disorganized may wish to use the personal reminder service, which sends you an email on the appropriate date that you need to be reminded of something important, like a family birthday.

How Stuff Works
www.howstuffworks.com
This is possibly the coolest website in the world. If you have ever wondered how anything works, then this is the place to satisfy your curiosity or those infuriating family arguments. Just a handful of the "stuff" explained includes: telephones, engines, toilets, power grids, sun tans, the world, stocks, and razors. This site is absolutely indispensable.

Finding out how space suits work is one of the many fascinating facts at www.howstuffworks.com

Internet FAQ Consortium
www.faqs.org

If you use the Internet regularly you may have discovered a special type of free discussion forum called newsgroups, or "Usenet". Despite the rather basic look, you'll find it a useful information source. Each group has a set of rules and regulations, as well as lists of answers to particular questions that are asked so frequently that it's easier to document them than have to continually answer them. Try here first, before annoying other subscribers.

Scoot
www.scoot.co.uk

Search for businesses or services in any part of the UK and find the ones nearest to you. A "People Finder" lets you run a search to track down long-lost friends, while the cinema guide has phone numbers, addresses, and programmes, as well as the ability to send you emails with updates for your local cinema.

Teach yourself to...
www.learn2.com

Learn all manner of new skills using the advice offered by this handy site. The site is exceedingly varied; examples include how to: sink a putt in golf, toilet train a cat, and iron a shirt. These are all essential tasks that, should you not know how

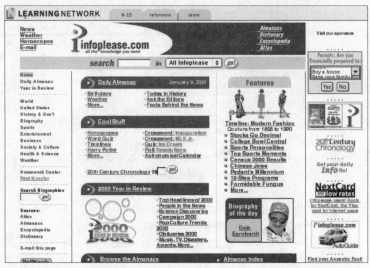

An online dictionary, encyclopedia, and almanac combined can be found at www.infoplease.com

to do them, you can't ask anyone and keep your pride now can you? Use **www.anonymizer.com** (see "Computers", page 53) to gain access to this site if you're really ashamed.

Bits and pieces

All About Jewels
www.allaboutjewels.com/jewel/glossary
This site won't tell you where to mine jewels, or how to steal them, but if you want to know the difference between abalone and zamak then this is the place to come. This is actually part of a set of sites hosted by **www.enchantedlearning.com**, which concentrates on children's educational sites.

The place for pictures
www.ditto.com
Whether you want pictures to print out, to adorn your computer's screen with, or to jazz up your website, ditto is a good starting place to find them. You can search for images of pop stars, animals, or even 1980s home computers. The pictures are provided by other websites, and a link is provided, so if you are searching for an image of a certain model of car, you will probably find a page devoted to it too that you can peruse at your leisure.

— Dictionaries/encyclopedias —

Acronym Finder
www.acronymfinder.com

As this site's name aptly suggests, the Acronym Finder contains meanings for thousands of abbreviations, many of which IMHO (In My Honest Opinion, for the less-knowledgeable among you), will have you ROTFL (Rolling On The Floor Laughing). Some descriptions, such as that for SNAFU (Simultaneous Navy Army Foul Up), have been sanitized to protect the sensitive. You can also discover what is allegedly the world's longest acronym.

All your questions answered
www.infoplease.com

This online dictionary, encyclopedia, and almanac provides a quick way to look up general facts and figures. "The Kids' Almanac" sounds a bit cozy but actually highlights places where human suffering has been caused by other people, nature or both, such as Auschwitz, The Black Hole of Calcutta, Belfast, and Mozambique. However, "Fun Facts" tells kids all they want to know about heroes from Greek mythology, fairies, and dragons, and even lists the top bestselling books ever. The content is biased towards US events though, so will appeal most to US browsers.

Dictionaries combined
www.onelook.com

If you just want to know the meaning of a word and can't be bothered trawling through all of the online dictionaries available (and we've listed just a few here) then try this site. It submits the word you are interested in to, at the time of writing, 650 different dictionaries.

A dictionary of visual art
www.artlex.com

Aimed at artists, students, and teachers, this encyclopedia for arty-types contains the meanings of a multitude of technical terms and abbreviations. If you don't know your earth colours from your passe-partout then give ArtLex a try. A respectable number of links to other sites adds to the site's usefulness.

Encarta online
encarta.msn.com

Microsoft's answer to an all-encompassing encyclopedia, the online version of Encarta has 16,000 cut-down articles and a world atlas. The Deluxe version is

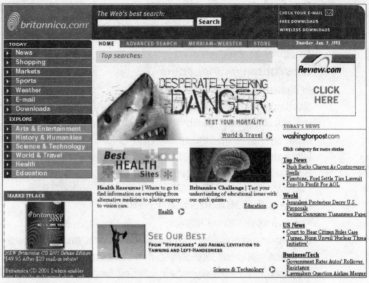

The ultimate encyclopedia is online at www.britannica.com – and it is completely free

also available for a seven-day free trial. The search engine allows you to ask a question and it will endeavour to take you to the answer. A reference and educational section will prove useful for those with sticky homework problems, while the "Schoolhouse" section provides resources for teachers.

Encyclopaedia Britannica
www.britannica.com
The ultimate encyclopedia is online and 100 per cent free. You can search more than 70,000 articles, a combination of articles and rated websites, or just the entire Internet. The latest news is also provided to keep things nice and current. There is a very handy Schools Tool area for youngsters.

Encyclopedia
www.encyclopedia.com
There is a ridiculously large amount of information about anything and everything in the site that calls itself "the Internet's premier free encyclopedia". You can browse the articles by clicking on the appropriate letter.

Encyclopedia, dictionary, and world news
www.funkandwagnalls.com
Funk and Wagnalls's offers a solution to undoable homework. The free resources include a 29-volume encyclopedia complete with animations, photos, and sounds.

There is also a dictionary, thesaurus, and even a world atlas. A dictionary is also available, with a pronunciation guide, and world news supplied direct from Reuters is on tap.

Encyclopedia of mythology
www.pantheon.org/mythica
This illustrated online dictionary of mythology covers all major world mythologies. It contains a massive database of characters and stories that can be browsed by genre or searched using keywords. The excellent hyperlink cross-referencing of information makes it the perfect tool for academic research.

Getty Thesaurus of Geographic Names
shiva.pub.getty.edu/tgn_browser
Research the names of different places in the world. You can find out what your home town was called in the "olden days" and discover how many other cities exist with the same name. You can then view the district, county, country, and continent that the place you have searched for exists in.

A glossary of literary terms
www.uky.edu/ArtsSciences/Classics/Harris/rhetform.html
This essential resource for English literature students is free, helping those on a grant to save their money for more righteous, liquid pursuits. Find out the difference between alliteration and assonance, parody and pulp fiction, and get an iron-clad definition of irony. The searchable database makes it easy to cross link terms and write killer essays.

Grappling with grammar
www.edunet.com/english/grammar/
Maybe you've forgotten what an adverb is, or perhaps you're unsure if the cat that belongs to Mr Jones is Mr Joneses, Jones's or Jones'. Whatever you need to know about English grammar, all of the usual terms and definitions we were supposed to learn at school are published here. Check it out before the kids ask you awkward homework questions.

Help with words
www.dictionary.com
Featuring its own dictionary and thesaurus, this site also has crosswords and other word games, and will even translate web pages written in foreign languages so you don't have to. If you have a question about words and grammar, then you can "Ask Doctor Dictionary". The links to writing style sites should be read by all students and, sadly, a fair number of journalists.

Search for the meanings of difficult words at www.yourdictionary.com

Online dictionary, word games, and bookstore
www.m-w.com

This is possibly one of the most popular online dictionaries – it is certainly one of the most linked-to. Merriam-Webster offers much more than just a boring word-search facility – there are "cool" words of the day, online word games, and a sort of online store where you can buy reference CD-ROMs and books via a real online store.

The Rap Dictionary
www.rapdict.org

If someone asks if you are "dissing" them, or wonders if your "homey" is a "Willy" and you're not sure whether to take offence, don't worry. Check what they mean using this site's explanation of terms and you might avoid a "cap" in "yo ass".

A web of online dictionaries
www.yourdictionary.com

Choose from a vast selection of foreign language dictionaries, thesauri, and specialized English dictionaries. The latter includes dedicated references to diverse subjects including astronomy, politics, and music. If you have trouble with pronunciation or grammar, there are sites to help. On a wackier note, you can also find out about pretend languages that are found in role-playing games.

World Book online
www.worldbookonline.com
Visit the online version of this respected print encyclopedia, which is fortified and kept up-to-date by information from newspapers and magazines. It has an annual subscription rate of around $50, but you can try it out free for 30 days first.

The World Factbook
www.odci.gov/cia/publications/factbook
Although run by the CIA you won't find the answers to any *X-Files*-style conspiracies here – just lots of information about different countries, their populations, and economies. An essential resource for students with homework projects and adults who ought to know where Cambodia is but have forgotten. Clear maps are available, along with details of border disputes.

— Legal issues

The Court Service
www.courtservice.gov.uk
If you are interested in what's happening in the UK courts then this is the place to come to get the information from the right honourable horse's mouth. Many cases we read about in the papers are presented here, and it is interesting, if you have the time, to see what the papers choose to report on, and ignore.

Desktop Lawyer
www.desktoplawyer.net
Buy pre-prepared legal documents from this site for a great deal less than you'd pay in a solicitor's office. You can get legal support over the phone and online legal advice for beginners. The latest legal developments are published as mini news stories. A bestsellers list gives you a quick link to the most popular documents, which, unsurprisingly, are dominated by wills and divorces.

Divorce advice
www.divorcenet.com
If you are in the unfortunate situation where you are about to go through a divorce, then get advice here at this American site. Search by State for

professional resources, while the "On The Couch" section has a question and answer session with a professional. Share your comments and thoughts with others in the divorce chatroom.

Dumb Laws
www.dumblaws.com

This site is great fun to browse and find out what silly laws have been made in various countries, such as the right to marry your horse etc. Search by the engine or by categories and find out that it is legal to drive down a one-way street the wrong way in Alabama if you have a lantern attached to the front of your car. Or why in Texas you cannot shoot a buffalo from the second storey of a hotel.

Law advice
www.findlaw.com

An easy way to search the web for law advice. Advice for legal professionals, students, and businesses on virtually everything that you can think of. You can find a local lawyer and get the latest legal news too.

Law for All
www.nolo.com

The site for self help on law matters with advice on all issues from wills and retirement to debt and bankruptcy. You can also buy all the legal advice you want from its online bookstore. Its tools include a legal encyclopedia and a house affordability calculator.

National Fraud Information Center
www.fraud.org

The National Consumers League in the US has been advising consumers on the dangers of Internet fraud since 1992. There is also information on telemarketing fraud and fraud against the elderly. Although much of the consumer legal information is US-specific, the Fraud Site is still an informative place to gen up on the technology issues behind Internet fraud.

Museums

The British Museum
www.thebritishmuseum.ac.uk

Recently redesigned, you can read about the exhibits in the museum through its world map and make the most of your visit by planning your expedition. The

www.nolo.com is the site to visit if you want advice on legal matters

Ancient Egypt section is especially good. You can view some of the highlights online, including the newly covered "Great Court", but you'll need to turn off the computer and actually go out to experience the museum properly.

Imperial War Museum
www.iwm.org.uk
Spanning the history of conflict from World War I to the present day, this museum occasionally puts selected exhibitions online, although you are guaranteed to always be able to get detailed information about each of the showcases. There is a notable espionage section, which young secret agents should be briefed on. Information is supplied on HMS Belfast, the Cabinet War Rooms, and Duxford – which is where the museum's aircraft are exhibited.

London Transport Museum
www.ltmuseum.co.uk
Get details of the famous London Transport Museum and plan your next visit there. Download an oral history of London transport in World War II, and watch nearly live shots of the Covent Garden Piazza from a video set outside the entrance. Interesting...

Museum of Science
www.mos.org
The online exhibitions from this museum have included Mount Everest, Leonardo Da Vinci, and the sea. Unlike some museums' efforts, here you can read full, non-

What's Happening!
Omni, Planetarium, Laser Show Info and more.

General Info
Hours, prices, directions, job opportunities, etc.

Buy It Online
From tickets to t-shirts and more.

Exhibits
Online and in the Exhibit Halls.

Learn More
Courses & Travel plus learning resources for all ages.

Support the Museum
Help us keep the Museum great!

Email Us | Find

© Copyright 1999, Boston Museum of Science

The Museum of Science will provide all the scientific material you need at www.mos.org

patronizing, and educational texts accompanied by clear diagrams. Relevant links to scientific sites, often government ones, make this a very useful place to visit.

Museum of Science and Industry
www.msichicago.org
Plan your visit to the museum and find out about the latest exhibitions, both permanent and temporary. You can also preview forthcoming shows at the Omnimax theatre, a five-storey domed screen featuring films of places such as Everest and the Amazon.

National Art Library, Victoria and Albert Museum
www.nal.vam.ac.uk
Access the library's online catalogue, which contains a large chunk of the two million items held in the V&A. Because this is the backbone of the library's online services, and because it is text based, don't expect to see lots of flashy graphics.

National Maritime Museum
www.nmm.ac.uk
This museum is concerned will all things nautical, and it houses many painting, chart, and book collections. You can find out about Lord Admiral Nelson, the Prime Meridian, and search the frequently asked questions and library catalogues

online. You can also get help in planning your physical visit to the museum, and there is a reasonable resource for maritime links on the web here too.

The Tech Museum of Innovation
www.thetech.org

Home of the "Robot Zoo", where robot versions of animals are used to explain how the real things work, and "The PC Webopedia", this site is aimed at young technicians. The "Webopedia" stores over 4000 computing terms, which will probably be easily understood by younger readers with built-in computer literacy.

UK museums and galleries
www.24hourmuseum.org.uk

Designed to make finding worthwhile UK museums, art galleries, and heritage attractions easier, this site only lists those it considers worthy. Follow the "Trails" to learn more about the sites in your local area. An excellent online magazine announces new exhibitions and contains features on such subjects as the River Thames and Manchester Museum's latest developments.

See also "Museums, zoos, and parks" in The Natural World, pages 222–224.

— Myths and conspiracies —

Conspiracy theories
www.cruzio.com/~blackops

Those wanting to find the stories behind the headlines may want to pop in on Black-Ops. This directory of conspiracy theories on the Internet makes for interesting reading. But make sure you don't fear going to bed at night as a result.

Greek mythology
www.thanasis.com/myth.htm

This website provides a humorous take on Greek myth and legend. Stories are presented by cartoon smoothie "Myth Man", and come complete with homework wizards. An archive of myths can be viewed. Packed with info – if you can separate the "fact" from the slightly odd editorial comment...

r

Independent Urban Dwellers
www.geocities.com/Heartland/Ranch/1216/index.html

Paranoia lies at the heart of city life for some Americans. Take this site, for instance. Some might call it wacko, but there's no doubting the sincerity of the

Plan your revolution with other anarchists at www.worldrevolution.org

Sanders family's commitment to surviving the catastrophe they expect around every neighbourhood corner. Self-sufficient power, provisions, home-schooling, and an essay or two on the encroaching power of the US government are the order of the day. Just see for yourself.

Urban Legends Archive
www.urbanlegends.com

Myth-making didn't stop in the Middle Ages. Some types are still at it. Take the story about the family that didn't know they'd got burgled until they developed their camera film, for instance. In any case, this site provides the most comprehensive collection of shaggy dog stories on the Internet. They're true – every one of 'em.

The World Revolution
www.worldrevolution.org

With instant access to millions of minds, the web is a perfect home for anarchists and activists. This site's title gives you no small clue as to what it's all about. Conspiracy theories abound here – and there's plenty of optimistic talk about bringing the established order down. All this is accompanied by some pretty fancy design too. This site is guerrilla warfare with a touch of glamour. And if you want to get involved, then there are plenty of email contacts you can try out. Make sure you know what you are letting yourself in for first though...

— see also...

English scholars, especially poverty-stricken students, will be delighted to discover the wealth of reference works free on the web. The Quotation Center (**cyber-nation.com/victory/quotations**) will help you look up those elusive famous quotes while Thesaurus (**www.thesaurus.com**) provides a handy online thesaurus dictionary. If you're more interested in graphic symbols than words, try the encyclopedia of symbols at **www.symbols.com**.

There are many online libraries and museums including the impressive Internet Public Library (**www.ipl.org**), and the Online Computer Library Center (**www.oclc.org**), which explains all about the Dewey Decimal System. There is a directory of library and reference sites at Library Spot (**www.libraryspot.com**), and other good reference resources can be found at Refdesk (**www.refdesk.com**) and Research-It! (**www.itools.com/research-it**). The Internet Law Library (**www.priweb.com/internetlawlib**) provides easy access to details of US law, while free legal tips on the same subject can be found at Free Advice (**www.freeadvice.com**).

Macabre past disasters may be found documented at The Living Almanac of Disasters (**www.disasterium.com**), and try Global Metric Time Service (**www.globalmetric.com**) to discover the time in any country. Look up The Nobel Foundation (**www.nobel.se**) for a history of the famous awards scheme while potential winners of the science award should acquaint themselves with the Periodic Table of the Elements (**pearl1.lanl.gov/periodic**).

r

SOCIETY, POLITICS, AND RELIGION

As much as the Internet has to offer in entertainment, it also includes some informative sites on a huge variety of social issues. Charities, political parties, and religious groups all rely on the Internet to spread their messages and, as a result, have a wealth of information that they want you to have access to. So if your religious beliefs don't correspond with what's going on in your local church, you should be able to find like-minded people on the Internet to share your views and discuss the meaning of life. Similarly, if you have an axe to grind on social issues, or just want to know more about the machinations of government, then check out the varied sites listed in this section.

— Charities

Amnesty International UK
www.amnesty.org.uk
Amnesty's award-winning website is easy to navigate, and is packed with research and campaign information on the charity's work promoting human rights worldwide. Internet users can join AI online, as well as take a peek at its monthly magazine. Serial letters from political prisoners make heart-rending reading.

Help the Aged
www.helptheaged.org.uk
UK charity Help the Aged provides resources for Internet-savvy senior citizens and their carers. There are also links to information on Help the Aged's 24-hour SeniorLink helpline. "Infopoint" is full of useful advice, including how to keep out the cold in winter. And if the text is too small, there is a tool to make it bigger.

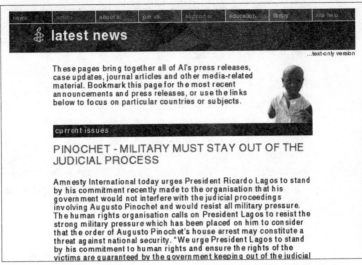

news | action | about al | join us | support al | education | library | site help

⚜ latest news

...text-only version

These pages bring together all of Al's press releases, case updates, journal articles and other media-related material. Bookmark this page for the most recent announcements and press releases, or use the links below to focus on particular countries or subjects.

current issues

PINOCHET - MILITARY MUST STAY OUT OF THE JUDICIAL PROCESS

Amnesty International today urges President Ricardo Lagos to stand by his commitment recently made to the organisation that his government would not interfere with the judicial proceedings involving Augusto Pinochet and would resist all military pressure. The human rights organisation calls on President Lagos to resist the strong military pressure which has been placed on him to consider that the order of Augusto Pinochet's house arrest may constitute a threat against national security. "We urge President Lagos to stand by his commitment to human rights and ensure the rights of the victims are guaranteed by the government keeping out of the judicial

Read the latest info on those wrongly imprisoned around the world at www.amnesty.org.uk

International Committee of the Red Cross
www.icrc.org

Find out about this organization that "aims to protect the lives of victims of war and internal violence", discover the issues it is most concerned about, and get clued up on international humanitarian law. There is a history of the Red Cross, a photo library showing scenes from conflicts around the world, and links to related sites – including the United Nations and non-governmental organizations.

The Samaritans
www.samaritans.org.uk

Everyone's heard of the crisis-counselling Samaritans service, but did you know the organization provides help on the web, too? You won't get one-to-one help via IRC or email, but the site includes a great many downloadable help sheets on specific problem areas, which might just provide the support you're looking for.

— National culture

s

British Council
www.britcoun.org

This is the web organ of the cultural organization aimed at spreading the gospel according to Britannia. This site provides links and information on learning English plus courses that are available both in the UK and abroad, as well as giving an online showcase to UK business, science, and arts interests throughout the country. This site is a worthwhile stop-off for those in need of a dose of unquestioning patriotism.

Royal Families of the World
www.royalfamily.com
A trip to the Royal Families of the World website can be an enlightening experience. It's a directory of official royal sites on the Internet, and covers monarchy the world over. Many of the sites provide pictures of past and present incumbents of the various world thrones. It rapidly becomes unsurprising to discover that these people have been breeding among themselves for centuries...

The Royal Family
www.royal.gov.uk
The British Royal Family was hardly the first to get itself on the web, but its burgeoning website is certainly one of the most impressive out there. It's packed with family trees, royal history, and details of the current line-up's engagements. It also features a fairly schmaltzy tribute to Diana, Princess of Wales.

— Political parties and issues —

Conservative Party
www.conservatives.com
The official site of the British Conservative Party is an all-singing, all-dancing site featuring the new, if half-baked, Action Man look of leader William Hague. It provides complete listings of MPs, MEPs, and shadow cabinet, together with topical news and views. It also allows users to join the party while online.

Conspiracy Theory
www.conspire.com
There have always been conspiracy theories, and this site covers some – naturally, the most famous ones, like the death of JFK, get their own category. From UFOs to terrorist activities, there is very little the site does not cover.

Current affairs
www.modpol.com
For a light-hearted approach to current affairs, check out this site. Billed as "the backseat where modern politics and popular culture make out weekly", this

Read current affairs from a humanitarian perspective at www.oneworld.org

regular online digest is home to some off-the-wall musings on life. An archive gives you a peep at the previous fruits of these slightly addled brains.

Current affairs: aiming for a better world
www.oneworld.org

The superb One World site takes a look at current affairs from a humanitarian perspective. At the site you'll find detailed coverage of many stories that get little or no mention in the UK media. The site also hosts a passionate debate daily. This is truly a set of pages that demonstrates the Internet at its caring best. The site is available in most European languages.

Democratic Party
www.democrats.org

Updated daily, the official US Democratic Party website has the latest party political news, including the usual spin-doctored press releases, and campaign news. There is a voter outreach section to try and enlist more supporters. The party history is given and there are links to local branches of the Democratic tree.

European parliament
www.europarl.eu.int

The multi-lingual European Parliament site gives the official line on life in the European Parliament. With the heavy text content here it's not quite riveting

Curious about New Labour's open government? All the info you need is at www.open.gov.uk

reading, but is still a useful insight into those goings-on in Strasbourg and the Hague. Europarl provides detailed information on European legislation, and outlines procedures by which ordinary citizens can access European resources.

House of Commons
www.parliament.uk
The Houses of Parliament website is the authoritative site on the political institutions of the UK. Its massive archive from the parliamentary record Hansard is unbeatable. Plenty of information can also be gained here about the people and procedures of the Houses. You will also be able to read details of current and timetabled legislation.

Labour Party
www.labour.org.uk
This is the British Labour Party's official home site. It includes up-to-date governmental news from the party's perspective (such as the budget or the Queen's speech), together with facilities for joining the Party, but it doesn't have a list of MPs. You can find out about all their policies here though.

Liberal Democrats
www.libdems.org.uk
This is the most thoughtful of the three major British parties' sites. It provides a detailed history of the party and outlines some of the personalities. News stories are updated regularly, and an archive of speeches contains all the major oratory from the party's conference.

Local Government Association
www.lga.gov.uk

This umbrella body for local government bodies in the UK provides up-to-date news from Westminster and elsewhere, but it is mostly of interest to politicos. What is useful, though, is its database of local authority sites on the web – just the thing for tracking down the elusive URL of your council's site.

No. 10 Downing Street
www.number-10.gov.uk

This official site of the Prime Minister's residence is both stylish and informative. A "History" section outlines the development of both office and house, and lists previous incumbents (with potted biographies of the most recent). There is the opportunity to have your say in the forums and the chance to view broadcasts of the incumbent PM. News available in the "UK Today" section of the site takes on a decidedly partisan slant.

Open Government
www.open.gov.uk

New Labour's professed desire for open government gets an outing on the web in the form of this directory of government services. This database tells you who does what, and how to complain if they're not doing it to your liking.

Party Finances
www.opensecrets.org

Ever wondered how those US political campaigns became so glitzy? Well this site will tell you where the money for these campaigns comes from. Find out which companies contributed the most funds to the Bush vs Gore presidential race. Find out about the congressional races, and read political profiles too.

Red Pepper
www.redpepper.org.uk

Trendy journal *Red Pepper's* website is the place to go for up-to-the-minute political analysis with a left-wing slant. While its web presence doesn't reproduce the entire contents of current printed editions, a formidable archive of news and features can be trawled for something of interest. The site also curiously includes a "Recipes" section – mostly using peppers...

s

Republican Party
www.rnc.org

Popularly known as "The Grand Old Party" the US Republican Party's site includes political stories with a predictably large portion of bias. This is the party's official site and so it includes campaign updates, candidate news, and also has a section for the "online activist", if you wish to make a donation or register to vote.

Slate
slate.msn.com

Slate magazine, the political pundits' corner of Microsoft's MSN network, has some worthy but interesting views on global affairs. Much of the content scratches the underbelly of US politics, and may not make much sense to readers in the UK. That said, the invitation to "Join the Fray" in frenzied email discussions of, among other topics, McDonalds vs the Environment, may prove all too tempting.

United Nations
www.un.org

This is the official home page of the world's leading political organization. The site provides information about current UN policy and activities across the globe, from peace and security to human rights and humanitarian affairs, together with text and audio excerpts from debates in the Assembly and Security Council. This site is vast, so make the "Site index" your first point of call to pinpoint the information you're after. The CyberSchool Bus section is a good reference point for teachers.

The White House
www.whitehouse.gov

This official site is dedicated to the best-known residence on Pennsylvania Avenue, Washington DC. There's little in the way of current politics here, but the site has plenty of content about the seat of US government. The "Virtual Library" has an archive of White House documents, but sadly only those that have been publicly released. A beautiful line drawing illustrates the development of the House, and a presidential history shows the motley collection of the White House's previous tenants. The Kid's section contains pictures of the infamous White House cat, Socks.

Religious sites

Buddhism
www.geocities.com/Tokyo/5215

The graphics on this site, Dharma & Nirvana, may be over-the-top, but overall it's an excellent primer on Buddhist theory and practice. All sections are laid out in simple, numbered points, and they are very easy to understand. This bizarre site even includes some slightly quirky Buddhist-inspired comics...

Catholic Online
www.catholic.org
This Catholic Internet provider's website is a must for Catholics who want to keep in touch. News is provided courtesy of the "Catholic News Service", and a collaboration with Amazon brings you a massive range of books and videos. The "Saint Search" engine is particularly fine, pinpointing information about holy types on the Internet. Recent additions include Catholic job searching and even a shopping section where you can buy your rosary beads and other goodies.

The Church of England
www.cofe.anglican.org
This is the official website of the UK's established faith. Information sections provide write-ups on the history of the church, together with its articles of faith, and a manifesto of the church's views on a range of social issues – its social campaigning stance can make interesting reading. It also tells you how to become more involved with the church. If you want to find out where anglicanism is at in the 21st century, check this site out.

Church of Scientology
www.scientology.org.uk
Back in the 1970s, thousands followed in the wake of disco star John Travolta's *Saturday Night Fever* moves. Oddly, fewer seem as keen to ape the actor's conversion to Scientology. However, if you want to hear the official line on the religion founded by sci-fi writer L Ron Hubbard, then here it is from the horse's mouth. A handy "Global Locator" tells you where you can find your local organization in the UK.

Pagan Federation Online
www.paganfed.demon.co.uk
The British Pagan Federation provides contact between like-minded seekers of the "Old Ways". This online home gives would-be nature-worshippers information on how to contact their nearest branch in Britain and Europe, and provides links to pages offering more specific information on practices, with links to shamanism, seasonal festivals, and the mysteriously named "Wheel of the Year".

Religious tolerance
www.religioustolerance.org

If you are more interested in finding out more about new religions around the world, then this is the place to look. The site covers new religious movements, including most cults, and describes their ethical systems. Examining every viewpoint, this site definitely promotes religious tolerance.

Sikhism
www.sikhs.org

This user-friendly site is a worthwhile introduction to the Sikh religion, providing both information for believers and an introduction for general readers. The site is stylishly illustrated and easy to navigate. Coverage is a little academic, but still comprehensive – the section on Sikh history is particularly worth taking a look at.

Society for Promoting Christian Knowledge
www.spck.org.uk

The Society for Promoting Christian Knowledge (SPCK) has been doing just that since 1698 – in fact, it's the oldest anglican missionary organization there is. Here they are, in 21st-century mode, evangelizing on the web. This site provides information about the society's aims and its history, plus a directory of the UK bookshops through which SPCK's Christian message is channelled. It also has a new site with assembly material for primary schools at **www.assemblies.org.uk**.

Statistics on religions
www.adherents.com

This religious resource provides statistical information for researchers on the distribution and demographic breakdown of followers for over 4000 world religions, churches, faith groups, and tribes. Results come complete with links to original sources, and can be viewed via alphabetical or geographical indices. The site also features a basic keyword search facility.

Virtual Jerusalem
www.virtualjerusalem.com

Bringing Jewish life right up-to-date, the living pages of Virtual Jerusalem handle, among others, such quirky topics as body piercings and tattoos versus Jewish theology. Well worth a look, this site takes a wry and progressive look at Judaism.

— Social issues —

Be more racially aware
www.britkid.org

This good-looking site for kids and young adults is aimed at tackling racism. It's headed up by an interactive game that highlights issues to make children more aware of racism – even if they don't actually live in an ethnically mixed environment. The site also carries information in a much weightier vein, with topics linked to parent and teacher resources: an invaluable teaching aid.

www.britkid.org is for British children, telling them about race, racism and other social issues

Britain's Security Services
www.five.org.uk

Secret dossier styling gives these web pages a very hush-hush feel, but in fact the information that is contained within them is far from explosive – shame. This site provides the low-down primarily on MI5 and MI6, together with some links to quite helpful articles in the British press – although they are all written from a slightly paranoid slant.

CIA
www.cia.gov

Like it or loathe it, there's every chance the Central Intelligence Agency is watching you. This website gives its users just a glimpse at the operations of one of the world's most pervasive organizations, together with providing a good dollop of jingoistic propaganda from them too. There are links to the CIA's website for kids, too. No, really.

Citizens Advice Bureau Advice Guide
www.adviceguide.org.uk/nacab/plsql/nacab.homepage

While this is no substitute for popping into a CAB advice centre on your high street, the Citizens Advice Bureau's Advice Guide site does provide basic advice on a range of issues, and may save a few pounds down at the solicitor's. A subject, keyword, or alphabetical search can be used to turn up the information you require. Articles are cross-referenced, and checked regularly for accuracy. There is a separate section for Scotland.

Disability information and news services
www.disabilitynet.co.uk
Sporadically updated, but nevertheless comprehensive, DisabilityNet gives disabled users access to information and services in the UK. There are lots of forums to chat with others, an impressive jobs section, and a big shopping area that includes links to books, vehicles, and holidays.

The Metropolitan Police
www.met.police.uk
In the wake of the Stephen Lawrence inquiry, the Met has been trying to get up to speed. The news section of its Internet presence is marked by the same desire to brush up on PR, while the "Crimestoppers" section gives details on how to help your local community in its fight against crime. There's also a rogues' gallery of wanted offenders, and the chance to sign up for the life in blue online.

— see also... —

Religion was an early starter, and few faiths are as primordial as the Druids. They're still alive and kicking today of course. Visit their woodland grove in cyberspace at **www.druidorder.demon.co.uk**. More bearded shenanigans are available at **www.shamanism.co.uk**. Alternatively, make a quick pilgrimage to visit the Pope at the Vatican (**www.vatican.va**). For a cooler religious experience, young Jews should visit the trendy Generation J site (**www.generationj.com**). Westerners wanting to know about Islam could do worse than visit Islamic City (**www.islamiccity.org**), which describes the fundamental tenants of Islam in layman (or heathen?) terms. Worldwide news with an Islamic spin can be found at Muslim News (**www.muslimnews.co.uk**).

Some like their religion exclusive. You'll find a run-down of some of the world's freakiest cults at **www.mayhem.net/Crime/cults1.html**. Those seeking to avoid the attentions of the Moonies and others should definitely check out **www.newsoncults.com**. The testimonies of ex-cult members at **www.ex-cult.org** makes harrowing reading.

Politics has its share of oddities, too. Those on the fringes of UK political life also have a presence on the web: where else could you find Communist daily *The Morning Star* (**www.poptel.org.uk/morning-star**) cheek-by-jowl with Class War (**www.geocities.com/CapitolHill/9482/**) and the Natural Law Party (**www.natural-law-party.org.uk**)? The last, amusingly, trumpets itself as "the only party with effective and proven solutions". The more rational left-wing intellectual Noam Chomsky has his own archive (**www.zmag.org/chomsky**)

mostly focusing on his scathing views of US foreign policy. Read FBI documents released as part of the Freedom of Information Act (**www.fbi.gov**) or get into the real machinations of US politics at the House of Representatives (**www.house.gov**) and the Senate (**www.senate.gov**). At the other extreme, we have an anarchist site (**www.spunk.org**) that ironically is rather easy to navigate.

For a more mainstream take of current affairs, the UK Politics site (**www.ukpol.co.uk**) provides over 2500 political links. Seek out the annals of the Hansard Society (**www.hansard-society.org.uk**) if you fancy getting involved for yourself. That sort of community spirit is exactly what **www.kidsthinklink.com** is trying to propagate in future generations across the globe. The Office for National Statistics (**www.statistics.gov.uk**) can tell you about the state of British society, while **www.citizen.org.uk** aims to make the Brits better members of society. Behave yourself, and you may avoid a visit from **www.police.uk**. Be bad, and there's no escaping **www.interpol.com**.

But caring and sharing's what it's all about, really. And that takes work. Those in need of a little extra support with their loved ones will find it at **relationshipweb.com/odat**, while disabled users can find love at Handidate (**www.btinternet.com/~handidate**), an Internet dating agency. Broken, at **www.geocities.com/HotSprings/Villa/3877/divorce.html**, tackles divorce from a child's perspective and may help with problems on the home front.

SPORT

If you have interests in something more physical than tapping away on a keyboard, then the Internet will more than satiate your demands for sporting activity. There are thousands of sports sites, both professional and personal, that will cater with your thirst for information, statistics, or buying sporting equipment. There are plenty of archives, and sites that will bring you live audio coverage or feed you the latest scores, as well as places where you can learn how to play better yourself. Extreme sporters will not be disappointed either, as there is every hair-raising form of madness imaginable on the web too.

— Athletics ——————————————————————

International Amateur Athletic Federation
www.iaaf.org

Essential reading for any serious athlete or athletics fan, this official site publishes all the latest news, results, any number of forums, and photos of awards and other events. There are training tips, too, that are aimed at newcomers and appraised by the site's editor.

Online resource for runners
kicksports.com

Refine your training, discover new ways to motivate yourself when you just cannot be bothered to leave the house, and know when those aches and pains mean "give it a rest". There are recipes to improve your performance and detailed information on the effectiveness of sports bars (the cereal versions, not the pubs).

Where athletes and fans interact
www.athletedirect.com

Visit a series of websites written by famous athletes and read their journal entries. There are also games to play, news to catch up on, and schedules to study. Most

Get grid-iron statistics galore at the informative American football site, www.nfltalk.com

of the celebrity athletes are American (although Anna Kournikova does appear), so this site will probably appeal more to US fans. There are links to all the other major American sports.

Ball sports

American football
www.nfltalk.com

Read the latest rumours, gossip, and analysis on all things to do with American football. You can hear what the experts say after going through the statistics with a fine-tooth comb, post your opinions (and argue with others) on the message boards, and discover what it takes to be a pro. For those interested in a professional career, there are columns written by NFL agents.

Baseball Links
www.baseball-links.com

Claiming to publish the web's most comprehensive collection of baseball links, this site will provide supporters with a route to the sites of their favourite teams and players. It will also provide a full set of results for their games. Official sites are highlighted, which is a good thing, because there are plenty of non-professional efforts listed too. Other areas include collectibles, software, and coaching sites, as well as the chance to have your say on the "Baseball Soapbox".

WG Grace would be proud of the information and statistics available at www.cricket365.co.uk

Basketball worldwide
www.telebasket.com

A database of over 34,000 players and coaches, plus daily basketball news postings are just two of the features of this globally encompassing basketball site. Sadly the involved way that the site has been designed means that it takes a while to get to where you want to. Die-hard basketballers will find perseverance worthwhile though.

Bowling
bowling.about.com

Visit the library at this bowling based resource and you can catch up on the rules according to the American Bowling Congress (ABC). There are also details of (US) events and an online shop selling the latest (very US) bowling fashions, of course. There is also the chance to play some online bowling games here too so why not give it a try?

Cricket Online
www.cricket365.co.uk

Part of the excellent 365 network, all the cricket information that you could ever want can be found here. Follow the live scorecards. There are player profiles, both home and abroad, and the latest information on county cricket. All the statistics you could ever want are a few clicks away too. Other sites on the network, with a similar look and feel, include www.football365.co.uk (see opposite) and www.rugby365.co.uk.

English Ice Hockey Association
www.eiha.co.uk

This is not the flashiest of websites but if you are one of the increasing number of ice hockey players, or are just a fan of the sport, it will allow you to catch up on the results of recent games and consult a glossary of terms. The EIHA site is also part of a web ring, which means it is linked up to many other, similar sites. Start here and you'll certainly find something you like.

ESPN: world sports news
www.espn.com

Packed with information about sport, this largely news-based website mainly covers the US, although oversees events are also included. However, the linked UK site **www.soccernet.com** will appeal more to British football fans. That site has a similar design but deals almost exclusively with European matches, transfers, and other European football issues. You can also check the latest fixtures and the player profiles.

International Australian Football Council
www.iafc.org.au

Listing the countries, teams, and rules of the game, this site charts the game's history and publishes updates from teams all over the world. News is provided by a link to The International Footballer (**www.websports.onthenet.com.au/tif**), the Council's official organ – but for really up-to-the-minute stuff you'll want to check out **www.oztips.com**.

International Federation of Netball Associations
www.netball.org

Read the rules, scan the headlines, and make sure that you know about future events. There are links to netball-related sites all over the world here, as well as an archive of World Netball Championship results for fans to mull over. And if you think that this is a girl's game, then try reading "Men's Netball" news, which will immediately set you straight.

Live soccer results
www.football365.com

Follow the latest results, live, from the comfort of your desk, and read walk-through descriptions of the matches. Newsflashes can be made to appear in a small box on your screen so that you can stay informed the whole time that you are working. This excellent site features all the results, a guide to radio and television coverage, and the league tables. You can also submit your views and questions to the site.

National Basketball Association
www.nba.com

This site has all that you might want from the world of basketball – players and game stats, the latest news, interviews, and when all the big games are taking place. It does also have a section on the global basketball world for those that live outside the US.

National Wheelchair Basketball Association
www.nwba.org

Find out all about how the National Wheelchair Basketball Association started, what the rules are, and where your nearest (US) team is. You can also subscribe to an email mailing list to keep completely up-to-date with the development of divisional information. There is also a good set of links to various other sites for disabled sports men and women.

Pool and billiards instructions
www.poolschool.com

The College of Cueing Arts and Sciences (really) offers tutorials to those living in Dallas, Texas. The rest of us can pick up tips for our pool game from their online video clips, or by simply reading the basic advice on techniques such as how to hold the cue and the thinking behind the Bridge. The links section directs you to more lessons and online rule books.

Rugby
www.planetrugby.com

Aimed at providing information to rugby union fans, this site has the latest news on all the international teams and their players, a fantasy rugby spread betting game, world rankings, and features on the players who have shaped the sport throughout the game's international history. Major professionals give their views on the state of the game. Upcoming international fixtures are given with time and place to ensure that you don't miss the kick-off. The content is similar to **www.sportonair.com**.

When Saturday Comes
www.wsc.co.uk

This is the online version of the independent football magazine, and all the same features are available here. For example, it is home to "The Half Decent Pub Guide", which is a database of drinking establishments that are suitable for soccer fans the world over. Each pub is rated and assigned an in-depth description, which includes whether or not there are "intrusive music/fights/entertainers" to spoil the game.

Big sporting events

British Olympic Association
www.olympics.org.uk

Find out about the history of the Olympics and read about the latest issues, including unsporting drug abuse, women's issues, and politics. You can read the occasional interview with a medallist but if you are looking for really in-depth information, you might well find that you would actually be better off with www98.pair.com/msmonaco/Almanac.

Commonwealth Games 2002
www.commonwealthgames2002.org.uk

The 2002 games will be held in Manchester in the UK and this site aims to fill us in with details of the latest developments, including the actual games venues, the programmes, and information on how to become involved as a volunteer. The site is very slow, so you'll have to be patient.

Olympic Almanac
www98.pair.com/msmonaco/Almanac

View the image library of a large number of the Olympic torches, find out what are counted as Olympic sports these days, and read the list of frequently asked questions to catch up on the trivia.

s

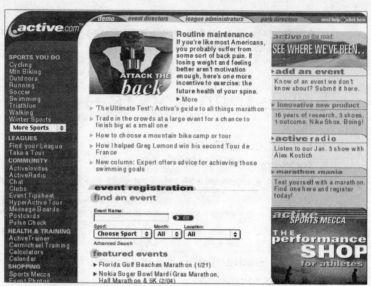

Active sport lovers can find out what is happening across the States at www.activeusa.com

— Contact sports —

Boxing
www.sky.com/sports/boxing
Look up the boxing ratings and see who's top of the pile. You can also find out when the next fight is due to be shown on Sky TV and remind yourself how to order Sky Box Office. There are boxing-related headlines, features on the day's important fights, and a round up of the winners and the losers.

Powerlifting and bodybuilding
staff.washington.edu/griffin/weights.html
The author of this bodybuilding endeavour provides handy, scientific know-how to help build muscle and avoid damage. There is advice on what equipment to get, a sample workout for beginners, mental tricks to improve your lifting, and training spreadsheets for you to download.

World Wrestling Federation
www.wwf.com
Find out when your favourite wrestler is pretending to give some damage – be it on TV or at a live event – and view his or her photos and particulars. Merchandize

is, unsurprisingly, top of the bill with the online shop featuring replica belts, clothes, and a Badd Ass Bear. You may prefer World Championship Wrestling, but its site, at **www.wcw.com**, has less to offer.

Equestrian sports

For all equestrians
www.equestriansonline.com
If you have ever suffered a horse balking at the ingate at one time or another then this well constructed horsy site is the place for you. There are training tips, online chat forums, and articles on many different aspects of the horsing world, including breeding and grooming. For all your horsing goods, there is a classified section.

Horse racing tips
www.racetips.com
Interviews with owners and trainers, tips on horses to follow in the long term, and articles on great races makes this an essential spot for the dedicated punter. There are jockey profiles, a message board for amateur tips and opinions, and a notebook that keeps track of promising and potential winners.

Extreme sports

Active USA
www.activeusa.com
Dedicated to active participants in sporting life, this US site will let you search for events, clubs, and news within each State. There are also features on, among other things, nutrition, skiing, and surfing. Also included are car reviews, a well organized and searchable set of external links, and even an online store offering sports gear.

Aviation Aspirations
www.avasp.com
This impressive site features information on how to find a flight school, what you should expect from training courses, and reveals those hidden expenses. If you want to get a private pilot's licence then this is a good place to visit. Incredibly, a lot of the sections are available in as many as eight languages, and UK and US-specific sections are highlighted for ease of use.

Boarding: surf...snow...skate...
www.boardpark.com
This "portal" is a springboard (inadvisable pun intended) to surfing, snowboarding, and skateboarding websites. Think of a specialist search engine and you won't be far wrong. There is also a list of webcams set up on beaches for surfers to check out the waves, and on mountains for the snow-minded to investigate the weather situation. The "SheWhoRides" section is a collection of links to boarding sites aimed at Boardy women.

British Hang Gliding and Paragliding Association
www.bhpa.co.uk
If your idea of fun is to find yourself high in the sky with nothing keeping you there except more air then visit this site and locate your nearest club. There are competitions to see who can fall most accurately, and links to equipment shops.

British Mountaineering Council
www.thebmc.co.uk
This is the place to seek out rock-climbing clubs, essential advice on fundamental safety techniques, and a directory of climbing walls in the UK. You can also find out how accessible the various places for climbing are at the moment. There is also a sub-site for young climbers, with information to calm concerned parents.

Bungee Jumping
www.bungeezone.com
Locate a bungee jump near you and take your life into your own hands. The database includes the UK, US, Hong Kong, and seemingly everywhere else in the world too. There is also a full background on the history of risking life and limb on the end of an elastic band, a category describing the different types of jumps, and a photo gallery if you still need convincing that it's perfectly "safe".

Cross country skiing
www.xcskiworld.com
For those who would rather eschew the safety of the regular runs, there is the gruelling cross country skiing experience. You can learn about different techniques, discover roller skiing, and read the hefty guide to the equipment you'll need to use. There are also adverts for suppliers close at hand...

Outdoor activity
www.explore.com
Hiking, snowboarding, and adventure holidays, can all be found here. To tempt you to the extremes of the earth, the site has features with breathtaking

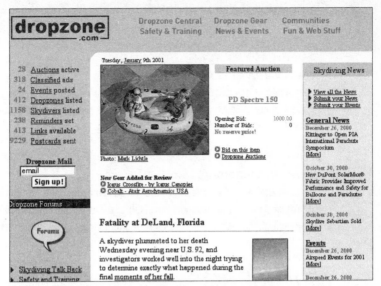

Not for the fainthearted – skydivers should drop in at www.dropzone.com

photography, from the temples of the Maya to twilight images across Antarctic waste. There are communities where other people living on the edge can meet up, as well as sections on less extreme sports like skiing, snowboarding, and sailing.

Power kiting
www.kites.org/jo
Taking kites out of the realm of children in the park and turning it into an extreme sport, power kiting involves using very efficient kites that can end up dragging the kiter around. This works particularly well if the said kiter is sitting on a go-kart, or buggy. Interested? The site also includes loads of links, some to UK kite shops.

Skydiving
www.dropzone.com
Read reviews of skydiving equipment, view information on safety and training, browse a database of global parachute centres, and find out where the most happening events will be going down. A chat forum for skydiving students, photo galleries, auctions, and, amazingly, skydiving software are all available.

Snowboarding
www.aboutsnowboarding.com
Part of the MountainZone.com web of sites, this sub-section offers news, photos, and interviews with sportspeople and coaches. There are also sections on skiing,

hiking, mountain biking, and photography, and weather reports and resort news are also available. Check out the auctions for bargain prices on snow sports gear.

Surfer Resources
www.surfstation.co.uk
Up-to-date surf report information for the UK. Find out about surfcams, clubs, schools, shops, and boards of all kinds. Message boards mean that you can find out who is going where and locate where the best waves are.

Triathletes
www.triathletemag.com
The website for what must be the most gruelling sport. It has the latest information on the race calendar, invaluable guides to nutrition, and the gear that is needed to be a success in this sport of endurance.

— Martial arts

Aikido
www.aikiweb.com
Find out about the aikido martial art: its philosophy, techniques, weapons, and language. There's a comprehensive dojo search, so you can find your local centre of learning. And don't think it won't cover your area – the database seems to span the entire world. There are at least three dojos in one small part of Cornwall!

Black Belt Magazine
www.blackbeltmag.com
Whether you want to consult the martial arts dictionary, search for a local dojo (in any martial art), or pick up a few tips then this is a good starting place. You will also find advice on how to choose a suitable art and then a school – there are tips for beginners that are easy to follow, though don't try them while online. The dojo search is more suitable for US residents, as the European entries are really a little spartan.

The Wing Chun Archives

www.wingchunkuen.com/archives
Read about the history and technical details of the martial art known as wing chun kuen. The lineage of this southern Chinese kung fu is tracked through different families, with detailed lists. The site includes a dictionary of martial arts terms in Cantonese (using the English alphabet) and further reading lists.

Motor sports

Autosport online
www.autosportmag.com
Everything you'll ever want to know about fast cars, who's driving them, and which team has been accused of cheating this month. Competitions including Formula One, Nascar, and World Rally are all covered with regular news stories, while the driver profiles should keep the statisticians happy.

Ford Racing
www.fordracing.net
If you are interested in rally driving, Formula One, or the British Touring Car Championship you should check out Ford's dedicated site. It includes the low-down on events, drivers, and cars, as well as photos, video footage, and race diaries. The latest results and standings are all here as well.

Formula One
www.formula1.com
This unofficial Formula One site offers a strong news section, analysis of popular stories, and graphical walkthroughs of the circuits – complete with statistics. Read the personal profiles of the drivers for a little excitement – especially as it's a no-holds-barred, speak-as-you-find affair. Live commentary is broadcast in season, with testing summaries out of season.

Formula One from ITV
www.itv-f1.com
The juicy gossip from the pits is flowing from this Formula One news site and you can have the daily news delivered by email direct to you. Alternatively, you can download pictures and movies complete with sound for free (apart from your phone bill). Just to set the tone, be aware that there is a "Pit Babes" section too...

Sports news and information

British Wheelchair Sports
www.lboro.ac.uk/research/paad/wheelpower
Promoting the British Wheelchair Sports Foundation, this site highlights the many sporting competitions that are available to people with physical disabilities –

which includes those with visual impairments right through to people in a wheelchair. Contacts are included with each of the numerous entries so you can learn where local events are and how to attend.

The science behind sport
www.exploratorium.edu/sports
Taking a scientific approach to sport, "Sport! Science @ the Exploratorium" analyzes a number of sports, discussing the chemical makeup of "fast ice" in ice hockey, the physics behind hitting the perfect baseball home run, and why climbing up a mountain can be more tiring than you'd think.

Sport globally
www.sports.com
A truly global sporting site with mirror sites based all over the world, but sharing all the sports in the world. You can therefore read the site in most European languages. The emphasis is mostly on football here, but other sports are also covered in depth.

Sporting Life
www.sporting-life.com
This exceptional sports news resource covers most of the popular sports including soccer, racing, ruby, golf, cricket, and tennis. There is a live soccer vidiprinter, which prints up results, goal events, and half and full times as they happen. "Betting Headlines" will give you the odds on sporting events to come. If you have a strong opinion, then you can get it published in the "Fanzine" section.

Sport on Air
www.sportonair.com
This news site contains stories spanning the most popular sports, many of which feature audio interviews. An hourly audio bulletin allows you to "hear all about it". You can also read a round-up of what the papers have said that day and take part in the polls, normally for who is the best footballer.

Sportszine UK
www.sportszine.co.uk

The news on this site is handily divided into sporting categories, so that you can easily view all the stories relating to you favourite type of competition or pastime. The rest of the site acts as a useful directory to other websites on a huge range of subjects on just about every sort of event going – including kayaking, skydiving, and snooker. You can also locate online sports gear stores to help get you fully equipped for your sport.

Target sports

British Association for Shooting & Conservation
www.basc.org.uk
If you are interested in taking part in shooting in the UK then you'll need to know about the recent changes of the law. It's all spelled out here, along with a set of links to other gun and conservation-type sites. You can also apply to join BASC while you are online.

Darts
www.shootersedge.com
Buy darts, flights, boards, and other accessories from this online shop, which also features an online darts game that you can play from your web browsing program. Orders from outside the USA are acceptable so get that nylon athletic jacket you've had your eye on…

News for archers and bowhunters
www.archerynetwork.com
Pick up some interesting introductory hints on shooting a bow and follow the large number of outdoors and hunting-based links. Watch and hear the arrows fly in the audiovisual section. The chat forum is surprisingly (if disturbingly) busy, with much talk about guns and hunting with your bare teeth (nearly). Hearing about the "ones that got away" is pretty cheering, though.

Water sports

British Canoe Union
www.bcu.org.uk
Find out where you can learn to canoe, the different sorts of boats available, and what other equipment you'll need. There are lists of general outdoor events and details of the benefits of joining the union. If you want to know where to paddle, for relaxation or competition, the information is here.

Sailing
www.yacht.co.uk
This sailing site contains details of UK sailing clubs, links to weather report sites, sailing charts, and equipment suppliers. The site doesn't actually include much

information itself, but, nevertheless it should prove to be a useful starting place for those sailors who are not yet familiar with navigating the web.

Swimming
www.swiminfo.com

Maybe you just want to swim to get fit, or perhaps you're a serious triathlete needing some help on tweaking your performance. Either way, the workout and techniques sections of this site should help. There is also an online shop and a new service that will keep you fully equipped with goggles and gossip.

— see also... —

For general sports information go to All In 1 Sports (**www.allin1sports.com**) and Sport Quest (**www.sportquest.com**) for information and links to the best sites. Sports on Line (**www.sportsonline.co.uk**) provides a search engine for British sports sites while a more general sports-related index is available at Sport Search (**www.sportsearch.com**). If you like playing fantasy sports games, see page 126 in Games, or give Fantasy League Net (**www.fantasyleaguenet.com**) a shot, as it provides info to help you pick winning teams. For football news, player, and team information, there are dozens of sites (well, it is the global game); Sportal (**www.sportal.com**) and Teamtalk (**www.teamtalk.com**) are among the most popular, the latter for its very speculative transfer gossip.

Visit the Ezbets (**www.ezbets.com**) online casino and sports betting emporium in all the sports you could dream of. Armchair athletes will discover decent coverage of future international sporting events at Sportcal International (**www.sportcal.co.uk**), while Sport Live (**www.sportlive.net**) provides sports news and analysis. Real nerds will find the results and statistics at Soccer STATS (**www.soccerstats.com**) irresistible. Darts fans should try Cyber Darts (**www.cyberdarts.com**), which has playing hints, tips, and a tournament calendar.

Tennis fans won't be able to tear themselves away from 1st Serve (**www.1stserve.com**), with its scores lists, fantasy tournaments, and player profiles, and The Tennis Directory (**www.tennisnetwork.com/directory**) lists courts (both public and private), rules, fitness routines, and many other tennis-related articles. If you need someone to play with, try Player Select (**www.playerselect.com**) and Sports Geek (**www.sportsgeek.com**). Both provide communities where you may be able to find a fitness partner. Badminton players can check out the latest on rules, technique, and equipment, as well as the world's best players at **www.badmintoncentral.com**. Otherwise, look up your local club in the directory and then go out there and play a game!

World TEAM Sports (**www.worldteamsports.org**) encourages sportspeople of all ages and abilities, publishing details of events it has organized on its site. Lone sportspeople may find the articles on Runner's Web (**www.runnersweb.com**) handy. They include a marathon calendar, editorial columns, news, and sports medicine links. Swim News (**www.swimnews.com**) publishes swimming news, results, biographies of participants, and an online magazine. For white knuckle stories and books try *Climbing* magazine (**www.climbing.com**).

Feel the wind in your hair at Adventure Cycling (**www.adv-cycling.org**), which has touring resources including maps and details of cycling clubs. Pete's Bikindex (**www.bikindex.com**) details popular dealers, features a travel partner finder, and offers expert opinions on all things two-wheeled. If you'd rather be behind a windscreen then you may find the performance motoring sites Auto 1000 (**www.auto1000.com**) and TNN Motorsports (**www.tnnracing.com**) are much more appealing.

Karate Net (**karatenet.com**) provides an "ask the experts" section, seminar ratings, and downloadable video files. Boxing lovers will be knocked against the ropes by visiting **www.boxing.com**. Baseball fans will find thousands of sites to encourage their interest. To begin with, try All American Amateur Baseball Association (**www.johnstownpa.com/aaaba**) and United States Amateur Baseball Association (**www.usaba.com**) for results, tournament information, and directions to playing grounds.

TRAVEL

You can use the Internet to plan and book a holiday, read about other people's experiences, or just check that your daily morning train ride to work won't be delayed. The quantity of travel-based sites available worldwide is astounding, and you'll save a fortune on travel guides by trying the web first. Even if you want a paper companion to take with you, there are sites that review them and can recommend an appropriate title. Of course, an online bookshop is usually just one click away. Medical advice and information on safe places to travel is always instantly available.

— Cruises and flights

Airline Network
www.airnet.co.uk
Make sure you don't overspend on your airfares by searching this database of discounts on flights from the UK to international destinations. There are also travel insurance and limited car hire services. The hotel price guide seems wide-reaching, although travellers to more exotic places may have trouble.

British Airways
www.britishairways.com
Find out where and when BA is flying, and tell the site your future plans – it will respond with appropriate special offers when they become available. Occasionally there are auctions for flight seats announced here, too. The mini travel guides are a nice touch, although for the real deal you should try **travel.roughguides.com** and **www.lonelyplanet.com** (see page 300).

Cunard cruises
www.cunardline.com
Not a place to visit for those who are low on funds, the company that owns the QE2 has its own site for the well-at-heeled to find a cruise that suits them. Find

Bob Geldof has created the simple yet useful www.deckchair.com to pick up cheap flights from

out all about the history of their ships and details of the various destinations that those still on the water visit. There is even a section on themed voyages.

Deckchair
www.deckchair.com

This site is mostly famous for its knighted benefactor, Sir Bob Geldof, but it is a deceptively simple search engine for cheap flights. Register your details and then search for the cheapest flight that money can buy.

Expedia Travel
www.expedia.com

This site deals in all aspects of travel – flights, hotels, cars, holidays – just enter the dates that you need in the "Express Search" and the database will do the rest. Its prices are extremely competitive, and there are many other bargains to be had here – check out the best deals at the bottom of the home page. It also includes useful tools such as a currency converter, fare tracker, and an airport guide.

P&O Cruises
www.pocruises.com

Have a look at the ships, itineraries, and what you can expect if you book a cruise with this well known company. You can sort of book online, by sending in a reservation by email, but it's probably wise to request a brochure first (by email too). The online database will let you search for the best option to suit your vacation time.

Thomson Holidays
www.thomson-holidays.com

Find out all about Thomson's holiday cruises and resorts, although to book you'll have to either visit an agent or call Thomson Direct on the old-fashioned telephone. There aren't any online brochures, either, but you can get an idea of the holidays that are available and see which cruises are available for (cheaper) late booking.

Travel Master
www.travelmaster.com

Plan your trip to the second with this set of online tools. You can book flights, car pickups, and hotel reservations in a huge number of countries, with any dangerous options thoughtfully flagged with warning notices. Specify your preferred airline and how you want your ticket options sorted (by price, departure time, or vendor, for example). You can also say when you want to pick up and drop off your car once you have chosen your car rental company. Focused business travellers will probably get the most from this service.

Virgin Atlantic
www.virgin-atlantic.com

Providing more than just trans-Atlantic flights, this airline has a website containing a full route list and map, a searchable schedule timetable, and useful information for passengers – including baggage allowances. Frequent flyers can also read about the perks that they may be able to claim.

— For the adventurous —

Adventure Network
www.adventurenetwork.com

Concentrating on offering the core activities of rock climbing and kayaking, Adventure Network also emphasizes the need to be fit, follow safety procedures, and use appropriate equipment. There are articles on camping, layering your clothing effectively, choosing different technical items such as harnesses, and the best ways to walk yourself fit.

Backpacker Magazine
www.backpacker.com

Pick up essential tips on how to pack and carry a heavy rucksack safely without crippling yourself, choose the best gear for you and the requirements of your trip,

If you fancy Antarctica rather than the Algarve, then we suggest that you visit www.gorp.com

and how to make tasty, easy meals while you are away. A photo gallery is provided to tempt you into leaving the house, and the gear finder takes note of your specific needs and suggests something suitable.

Berghaus
www.berghaus.com

Browse through this specialist clothing and equipment site, complete with price guides. You can also find out what features you should be looking for when shopping, and there are articles on how the gear is tested. The site also explains which skills you might need in the outdoors – some of this information has been written by celebrity explorers Chris Townsend and Clive Garret. For the hardcore, there are endurance and snowsports microsites.

The Great Outdoors
www.gorp.com

This is a big site, providing help and information on just about any outdoor activity you can imagine. As well as helping plan trips and tips on know how, there are debates on toilet habits, dealing with high altitudes, and camping with the family, as well as more mundane subjects like "The scoop on the food fish go for".

Outdoor equipment
www.cotswold-outdoor.co.uk

Buy your mountaineering, cycling, walking, and camping gear from the online shop and order a catalogue if you want to browse in bed. There is a seriously

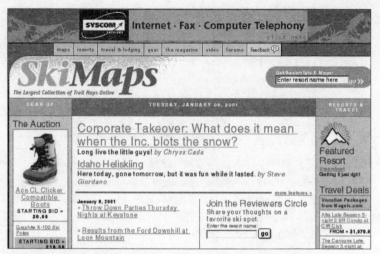

www.skimaps.com has the largest database of ski maps that you will find online

comprehensive set of links for travellers, including in-house technical information on choosing a sleeping bag, as well as contact details and websites of travel companies and map suppliers.

Outdoor gear for women
www.mountainwoman.com

Buying outdoor gear if you're a woman has traditionally been tricky, but things have improved and now there is even a website devoted to supplying ladies with clothes, safety equipment, and packs. There is even a selection of specialized mountaineering underwear. The squeamish might want to avoid the article on al fresco bodily functions…

Ski Resorts
www.skiresorts.com

Find a ski resort to suit your needs (and costs). There are online snow reports for when you're out there (so remember to pack a PC), and a section where you can get a local perspective on what to do and when, which are the best runs, and where the action is. Webcams will reveal the current conditions for you. A calendar will also tell you about the events both on and off the slopes in your chosen resort.

Skiing: piste maps, resort guides, and reviews
www.skimaps.com

Claiming to host the largest online collection of skiing trail maps, SkiMaps provides just that. Well, that, and a resort guide with contact details and reviews from the people who regularly visit. Articles on how to save money when on holiday, and the best way to choose a pair of ski boots, could prove handy, and there are also links to online ski equipment shops and auctions, too.

Space Adventures
www.spaceadventures.com

Book yourself a trip around space mission launch sites, ancient places of astronomy, and high-tech labs. If you feel really adventurous you can pay (lots) to take a zero-gravity flight or even pre-book a proper sub-orbital experience. You can also view the flight suit that you can order – and have personalized – by phone. This is the starting point for the holiday you never dreamed would happen.

Trailfinders
www.trailfinder.com

Priding itself on providing tailor-made holidays, Trailfinders can put together flights, hotel reservations, local tours, and car connections to suit your special needs. You can also sort out travel insurance online, order a brochure, and find your nearest agent here.

— Holiday bargains ————

Bargain flights and holidays
www.onetravel.com

Discover a pile of cheap flights, alternative airports, and other money-saving schemes. Go through the fast fare finder to get the best prices. There is an air travel "survival guide", which publishes various airlines' rules and regulations, as well as a page that will tell you how delayed your flight is.

Bargain holidays
www.bargainholidays.com

Use this site to choose your holiday location according to the style of break you want, whether Ski Bargain or Holiday Sun. You can pick up discounted city breaks, flights, and last-minute deals on package holidays. A live weather link lets you check out the current conditions all over the world.

Budget Travel
www.budgettravel.com

Designed for people who don't want to spend a fortune to travel the world, Budget Travel's avoidance of design frills (or any element of friendly design) will put many people off. But if you are a true bargain hunter, and want advice on how and where to get the best deals, you should put up with it as there is plenty here.

Cheap Flights
www.cheapflights.com

The simple design of this bargain-holiday finding site is quite brilliant. Choose your intended destination and you'll find a list of flights from the UK complete with links to the company offering them, some of which can take your order directly online. Other links will take you to extremely useful currency converters and weather forecasts.

Co-op Travelcare
www.co-op-travelcare.co.uk

You can choose from a selection of special deals from holiday, ferry, and airline companies on this site. You can specify your budget, time of departure, and destination, and you will be provided with loads of options, making choosing a holiday much less painful than running between travel agents in the high street. Go on, try it.

EasyJet
www.easyjet.com

One of the cheapest airlines and a pioneer of online buying – they cut down on costs by cutting out the middle man (ie travel agencies) and running a ticketless, therefore less bureaucratic, business. There are often ridiculous offers (flights from £4) regularly throughout the year, so it is worth subscribing to their newsletters to find out about these bargains first. You get an extra discount for booking your flights online.

Flights, hotels, and holiday offers
www.ebookers.com

Grab discounted flights and other offers and find the appropriate flight, car hire, hotel, and insurance deals easily, using the customizable search engine. You can even tell the site to inform you when a flight to your destination becomes available at a palatable price.

Last minute ideas
www.lastminute.com

Buy airline tickets, reserve hotel rooms, and even buy presents and concert tickets from this online shop with a difference. Each item for sale is only available for a short length of time and the details change frequently. **Lastminute.com** gets special offers directly from the suppliers, claiming that in doing so it can give you

Get everything last minute at www.lastminute.com, but especially flights and weekend breaks

the very lowest prices. And the site does not just sell flights – most things last minute are available here, from presents right through to theatre tickets.

Thomas Cook
www.thomascook.co.uk

Late holiday deals, and the ability to search for your ideal holiday without leafing through thick brochures, make this otherwise sparse site ideal for when you are weighing up the holiday budget. If you want to buy a holiday home, you'll find an introduction to "Thomas Cook's Resort Properties Service", too. There are also a fair number of late deals at extra discount.

Tripquote
www.tripquote.com

This site aims to find you the optimum price for flight tickets for North American travellers. The online shop should still be able to sell you luggage though, wherever you are in the world – what a surprise! There is also a handy "Link Library", connecting you to other travel-related websites for whatever your destination and these are all sorted by category such as cruises, maps, and business travel.

US bargain flights

www.priceline.com

This US company has an innovative system, which lets you name your ideal price for a flight and then offers your deal to the airline companies. If one of the airlines accepts your price, the tickets are yours. They also do the same deals for car rentals and even home finance.

— Holidays in Europe —

British Tourist Authority

www.visitbritain.com

Visit Britain is the official British Tourist Authority's website, and it is available to read in numerous languages with the express purpose of offering plenty of ideas and information for those wishing to spend their holidays in the UK. You can also buy touristy merchandize from the online shop but it does also stock much more useful things too, you'll be relieved to hear, such as maps, road atlases, and pub and restaurant guides.

Canal boat breaks in the UK

www.drifters.co.uk

If you prefer the idea of messing around in boats to hanging around in airports, then suss out what it takes to organize a canal boat holiday with the information on this site. There is a list of UK operators and a map of the country, marking out the different water systems.

Ferry and Channel Crossing Guide

www.a2beurope.com

Search the timetables for UK ferry services, the Eurostar trains, and Le Shuttle. You can also choose breaks in Europe based on price and town, and select the nature of your holiday – with suggestions including luxury, activity, and touring. There is also a guide to shopping in Calais with online calculators for metric/imperial conversions and live weather forecasts to tell you how choppy the water will be.

France

www.tourisme.fr/us

The English may not be that good on this site, but the average Francophile will get a great deal out of this site. There is a search engine that lets you search for the town that you want to visit and it has links into the tourist board for that

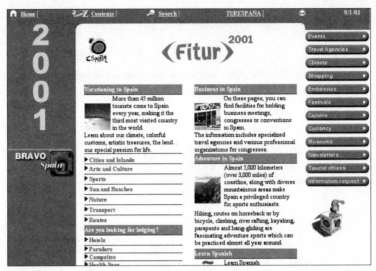

For those who want more than a package deal, visit the Spanish tourist site www.tourspain.es

region for information. You can also search the whole site by activities, type of accommodation, and to find what monuments can be found in the vicinity.

French tourism
www.w3i.com
Focusing mainly on Paris, and more sparingly on the rest of France, this site organizes your travel for holidays or business. Search through over 3000 hotels, find out about the marvellous French wine of the south, and trawl through the usual on museums, shows, and other tourist info.

Spain
www.tourspain.es
Available in English, this is the official guide to the tourist's favourite – Spain. There is general information on vacationing in the country, resources to find hotels, a breakdown on the climate (ie it's very hot), the cuisine, the many festivals, and much more.

Virtual London
www.virtual-london.com
This site aims to hold your hand, virtually of course, from your arrival in London, through each visit to the theatre, the shops, and sights, ending up with handy tips on transport, news stories, and weather reports. There is also a link to London Life (www.londonlife.co.uk), a strange, apparently amateur online magazine.

Travelling to the United States? Then visit www.usatourist.com before embarking on your trip

— Holidays in North America —

American tourism
www.usatourist.com

Ignore the embarrassing name and revel in this site, which is full of great information, as well as having a Hot Tips section with advice on visas, driving, and shopping. It focuses mainly on the major tourist areas and attractions (such as New York, Las Vegas, and the Grand Canyon), with long descriptions of each location accompanied by excellent photographs and handy tips. You need never buy a travel book again if you use this site, though USA Tourist also sells these through its online shop – surprise, surprise…

California
www.gocalif.ca.gov

The Sunshine state, where dreams come true etc. This is the site to come if you want to know about this place of extremes. There is a good search facility for hotels and motels, as well as many useful maps. The site does not strictly just cover California as there is information on Las Vegas (in Nevada), but it is very informative nonetheless.

Interstate travel
www.freetrip.com
Sort out your US or Canada interstate trip, finding the best route and booking accommodation along the way, using this trip planner. You can choose to avoid or favour certain types of road, and specify what kind of places you'd like to stay at and what kind of price you are willing to pay. An excellent resource.

Universal Studios
www.uescape.com
Home of Universal Studios in Florida and various other resorts, this is the place to come when you want details of that "holiday of a lifetime". You can view the offers and special package deals available at various resorts, some of which you can book and pay for online, and generally work the kids up into a frenzy with the photos and descriptions of the attractions.

See also "Disney online" in Entertainment, page 101.

— Information and advice —

The Currency Site
www.oanda.com
Find out what your holiday change is worth, or when the best time to buy your travel currency is. The "Classic" converter has been around for ages, and will show the worth of any amount of any currency in any other currency that you choose. Other features offer multiple conversions, currency trends, and forecasts.

European Routeplanner
www.shell.com/euroshell/routeplanner
Want to know the best route from A to B when travelling through Europe? Then put your start off point and your destination into this site, and it will give you a map of how to get there. (Unfortunately, you also get shown where all the Shell petrol stations are en route.)

For a smooth holiday experience
www.ticked.com
The advice offered by this site aims to help you prevent annoyances from ruining your trip. "Cheap Charlie's" column points you towards the bargains and there are also details on how to save money in other, sometimes possibly unscrupulous, ways. Health and safety concerns are also addressed.

Foreign and Commonwealth Office
www.fco.gov.uk

If you intend to travel anywhere off the beaten track, then check here first to find out the official government line. There are lists of countries that the Trade Advice Unit advises against visiting, as well as ones that should be avoided unless it is absolutely necessary. You can search here for the Office's opinion on more than 150 countries.

Hotel finder service
www.hotelnet.co.uk

Locate hotels all over the world and find directions on how to reach them when you finally arrive in your chosen country. The companies whose hotels appear on the site have little pages showing where their other branches are to be found.

Insights and advice for holiday makers
www.cdc.gov

Going abroad needn't mean you suffer from the inevitable upset stomachs and other nasty, potentially dangerous, diseases. Check with the Centers for Disease and Prevention site to find out what jabs you'll need and where you really should avoid if you are of a sensitive constitution.

International Student Travel Confederation
www.istc.org

Aimed at encouraging students to blow their loans seeing the world, the information here highlights the value of the various student and youth cards available, as well as giving details of which countries and cities support student discounts and benefits. Further information on what to do, see, and where to eat is also provided.

MASTA online
www.masta.org

For those travelling to exotic parts of the world, health advice is an absolute must. And the information you'll get from MASTA (Medical Advisory Services for Travellers Abroad) is the best you'll find online. A range of travel ailments is discussed, including antimalarial drugs, with treatment advice and precautionary measures suggested. If in doubt, though, see a doctor!

Online travel information and booking resource
www.a2btravel.com

Completely organize your holiday using the features on this website, which include mileage counters, accommodation locators, last minute bookings, links to

Visit www.a2btravel.com to organize every aspect of your holiday

specialized holiday sites, and live flight arrival information. There are also links to auction sites, shops that stock travel books, and travel insurance sites.

Passenger Rights
www.passengerrights.com

If you like a moan, you'll love this. It details your rights as a passenger as well as documenting rules and tips on transporting pets and looking after your papers. The site's newsletter claims to offer controversial secrets that will make your travelling less stressful and better value. It costs though...

Take the fuss out of business travel
www.biztraveler.org

Aimed at business travellers, the tips and advice found here should help clarify your rights and ensure that your luggage stays in one piece. There is even a complaints procedure that lets you moan online; the site will forward your grievances to the people who need to hear them.

Tropical Medical Bureau
www.tmb.ie

Before you go anywhere too exotic, visit this top site to find out which jabs you should have, and how far in advance of travelling you need to get them done.

There are some general health tips, too. However, don't bother wasting your time on the "news" and "chat forum" sections as they are more or less dead now.

Virtual Tourist
www.vtourist.com

A place where travellers can exchange information – click on the world map on the home page and create your own travel pages, perhaps even about your own town, and have a look at others and rate them. There are lots of forums where you can find good, personal advice that you will never find in the travel guides.

Worldwide tourist information
www.travel-library.com

Find the tourist boards of other countries, read other travellers' travelogues, locate tour companies. There is a guide to planning your own round-the-world tour, and links to other types of holiday, such as motorcycle vacations and, bizarrely enough, travelling on a containership.

— Transport and maps —

Hertz: car rental
www.hertz.com

If you need to rent a car, Hertz's site will make sure that when you do, it'll be from one of its fleet. You can specify all sorts of requirements and get a price quoted online immediately. Cars are available in just about every country, whether it's safe to visit or not. There is a vehicle guide to help you decide on your car.

Maps and atlases
www.maps.com

View detailed maps, in various formats, and even check out satellite imagery at this commercial site. The hope is that you'll buy the digital images for use in research and other projects. There are also travel guides to buy, an online route planner, and a Top 10 listing of extreme world locations.

Online atlas
www.multimap.com

Explore the world from your armchair with this online atlas. Type in anything from a road name (in the UK) to a country (worldwide) and adjust the scale to produce handy maps. You don't pay anything to use this service, but you're not supposed to copy maps to your own website.

t

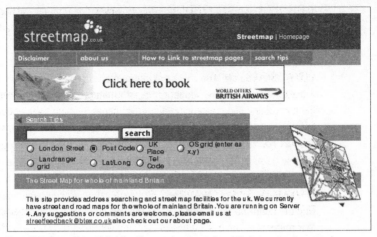

You will never need to ask for directions again once you've visited www.streetmap.co.uk

Street Map
www.streetmap.co.uk

This seemingly simple site will take a postcode or OS map reference and produce a map of the area, which can be enlarged, printed, or panned to find the places you are looking for. London street names are also recognized. The maps are ideal additions to party invitations, when no-one knows where you live. US residents or visitors will find **www.streetmap.com** useful.

UK railway information
www.rail.co.uk

Access Railtrack's train timetables, find out why your transport is late in "real time", and get the contact details of the operating companies so you can complain. Links to other sites include newsletters and software for simulating a train company.

— Travel guides —

Guides to getting away
www.away.com

This site provides information and inspiration for would-be travellers, whether you are on your own or with others. There are articles written by guide book consultants and tips for making the most out of your visit. You can read international travelogues and, if you fancy yourself as a travel journalist, you can even submit your own.

Lonely Planet online
www.lonelyplanet.com

Pick up some essential, general travelling tips as well as the low-down on your destination. If you want a different opinion to that voiced in these great online guides, then you can also check out information supplied directly to the site from other travellers – this will doubtless be of varying quality.

Rough Guides to Travel
travel.roughguides.com

Browse through the spotlighted features, including insights into different cultures and religions, or just find out the history behind some of the world's most popular cities and the world's "cool places". Places to eat at, seek entertainment, and rest are listed and the site claims to carry the complete texts of the paper versions of the guides.

The UK Travel Guide
www.uktravel.com

Do you tip hairdressers, hotel staff, and waiters in the UK? This site offers plenty of advice on where to go and how to get by in London and other places in Britain. Learn about the Royal Family, send a virtual postcard home, or discover the histories of Britain's castles.

US Travel Guides
www.ego.net

Planning a trip to the US may be made easier with the services of this site. It offers travel guides, profiles of "favourite destinations", and a list of contact details for hotels. The map can produce a few national statistics for each state, as well as links to other, more informative, sites.

— see also...

The beauty of the free travel guides you'll find on the Internet is that many have been created from the personal experiences of "real" people. The huge list of guides-based sites includes UK Travel Guide (**www.ukguide.org**), which contains interactive guides to UK cities, with extra information on London, and the World Travel Guide Online (**www.travel-guides.com**), providing a wider range of guides to countries all over the globe. Follow the author of Magical Places (**www.earthwisdom.com**) through her holidays at spiritually charged locations. If you decide you just can't make it out of the house, check out CAM Scape's (**www.onworld.com/CAM**) live, or nearly live, cameras at worldwide locations.

t

It's not hard to find a travel agent online. If you have no luck with the links listed above, try Locate a Travel Agency (**www.locateatravelagency. com**), assuming you're in the US. Uniglobe Travel (**www.uniglobe.com**) will also help. Cape Tours (**www.capetours.co.uk**) can organize you a holiday in South Africa, while Castaways Travel (**travelnude.com**) specializes in naturist holidays (you have to state your age before entering the site)! Try Orient Express (**www.orient-expresstrains.com**) for a sophisticated journey. Great Train Escapes (**www.greattrainescapes.com**) will also do you a deal on a rail-based break, and if you like to shoot animals to relax, try the Hawkeye Sporting Agency (**www.hawkeye-sporting.co.uk**). More "normal" packages may be found at Lunn Poly (**www.lunn-poly.co.uk**) and the coach operator Wallace Arnold Holidays (**www.wallacearnold.com**). Some of the best cruise ship rates can be found at **www.cruise.com**. You can sometimes get flights direct from some of the major airlines such as TWA (**www.twa.com**), KLM (**www.klm.com**), and United Airlines (**www.ual.com**) or more cheap flights at Ryanair (**www.ryanair.com**). Only millionaires need log into **www.learjet.com**.

Travellers on a budget will find advice on Arthur Frommer's Budget Travel Online (**www.frommers.com**), which also provides discussion noticeboards. There are more hints at Backpack Europe on a Budget (**www.backpackeurope.com**) and, for real bargains, try buying a holiday from an online auction house, like Internet Travel Auctions (**www.holidayauctions.net**). Some of the most beautiful scenery in the world can be found down under, so visit the Australia Tourism Net site at **www.atn.com.au** to find out more about accommodation and the tours available. There are more sites for travellers at The Alive! Global Network (**www.alincom.com**), while Holiday Wizard (**www.holidaywizard.co.uk**) will allow you to browse and order brochures online. Air tickets, hotels, and holidays can be bought, booked, and reserved at **www.travelocity.co.uk**.

For those with a special interest in train travel, including commuters who have to use them every day, there is plenty on offer. The Trainline (**www.thetrainline.com**) has timetables and an online service where you can buy and reserve tickets and seats. Enthusiasts will love Rail Serve (**www.railserve.com**), with its directory of all things to do with trains – from models to the real thing. Trains Community (**communities.prodigy.net/trains**) is a truly awesome directory of train links.

You can also find your way around London via the Internet – with Digistreets UK (**www.digistreets.com**), which hosts a photo guide to London neighbourhoods with handy information for home-buyers. Map quest (**www.mapquest.com**) will provide you with map, directions, and local city information for just about anywhere in the world. Try the Ordnance Survey (**www.ordsvy.gov.uk**) for free online maps of the UK.

NETIQUETTE AND SECURITY

The Internet can be a very impersonal place, where people communicate with each other using hastily typed notes. Web chat forums, email mailing lists, and Newsgroups are all places where people can get together and share their ideas and opinions. But in an environment like this, where you can't hear voice tones, see faces, and are often dealing with complete strangers, this collective goodwill can sometimes turn more than a little sour. "So what?" you may ask. Well believe me, the vitriol some people are capable of putting into an email message would ruin anyone's day. However, if you follow a few simple rules then you'll find that most people are very nice. And when a nasty message inevitably pops up, you'll be likely to find support from more reasonable "cyber-citizens". Many of the following suggestions apply when using email with your own friends and family, too.

— Do's and don'ts on the net —

Know your environment

This is crucial. If you want to participate in a particular discussion group then you should spend some time reading other people's messages there first. You will then get a flavour of what is and isn't acceptable. You might even find that the group is not for you. Don't jump straight in and start firing off questions. If you've misjudged what a group is about you may be politely told to ask somewhere else. Unlucky souls will be harshly abused, which is totally unnecessary, but an unfortunate fact of life. The Internet is used by people from all walks of life and, as ever, there are plenty of mean ones around, especially when they can hide behind their PCs.

Avoid humour

This might sound a bit harsh, but unless you are completely convinced that your correspondent will "get you", you run the risk of causing offence. Irony rarely comes across well, which is a shame. Some people try to spell things out by using a device called a smiley. For example, on a rainy day you could type:
What a great day we're having :-)
There are other such devices, which are called emoticons. If you can't "see" any of them, try leaning your head to your left shoulder and look again:

:-(	Sad
;-)	Winking (this is one of the best if you do decide to use humour)
:-p	Cheeky – sticking your tongue out
:-o	Surprised
:*)	Drunk

For a comprehensive list of "amusing" emoticons visit The Unofficial Smiley Dictionary (**www.eff.org/papers/eegtti/eeg_286.html**).

Type with care

Using poor punctuation, spelling, and grammar doesn't help when asking questions. The cardinal sin is to type every word using capital letters. This is hard for some people to read, and in Internet circles is counted as shouting. Silly, but these are the people that you will be relying on for help, so humour them.

Be careful who you reply to

Sometimes you'll receive an email that has been sent to lots of other people too. If you want to reply to the sender, make sure that you do just this and use the standard Reply option. Some email programs have a Reply to All (or similar) feature, which sends your reply to everyone as well as the original sender. Do this and you risk an annoyed email from at least a few of those email addresses. If you do make a mistake, don't compound it by sending apologies to everyone!

Reply quickly

Email is fast to write and faster to send. This means that some people will expect to receive a reply within a day. If someone is offering you help and needs more information, then don't keep them waiting. They're doing you a favour, after all.

Some email programs have a feature that will send automatic replies when you are on holiday. Don't use this if you are a member of a mailing list. Every time someone sends a message to the list, each member (and we could be talking hundreds of people here) receives a copy. So will you. And your email program will reply. Everyone will be informed that you are on vacation right now, and will reply to their message as soon as possible. This will go on until you return or, more likely, until the person in charge of the list removes you from the group.

A few terms and their explanations

A troll is someone who causes mischief by posting a contentious view on a Newsgroup or chat forum, with the express purpose of stirring up a fuss. For example, Christian forums might expect regular contributions from Satanists, while PC-based chat rooms are frequently invited to debate whether a Mac is better than a PC. The troll doesn't really care about God, Satan, or Macintosh computers, so there is no point in responding.

A few members of the group won't be able to resist replying, though, and may post reprimanding messages. If they send angry messages directly to the perpetrator, they are said to be "flaming" them. If you ask inappropriate questions on a chat forum you run the risk of being flamed yourself. Again, the best defence is to ignore it, although you should maybe think about why you've received such a harsh response.

"Spam" is a term used for unsolicited email. If you receive email messages promising quick and easy money, or access to pornography, then you have been "spammed". Spamming also occurs when messages advertising goods or services appear on chat forums or mailing lists. Don't respond, even if the message invites you to unsubscribe from a mailing list you've never joined and you are itching to sort the "mix-up" out. All you'll achieve is to confirm to the advertiser that there is a real person using your email account and then you'll receive even more spam. Sometimes, you may receive emails from companies selling you their wares – most likely you accidentally allowed a site that you have registered to in good faith to pass on your information to other companies. The best advice that can be offered in this situation is to always read the small print before you submit your details to an online company.

—Security on the Internet—

There are three things related to the Internet that are guaranteed to make headlines: viruses, hackers, and child pornography. Movies, books, and news reports would have you believe that not only are we all vulnerable to these threats, but it is almost inevitable that we will be attacked at some point. Let's clear up a few of these myths first.

Computer viruses

You cannot get a computer virus without downloading and running a program. Just using the Internet to access the web will not put you at risk. There are a few ways that bad web authors could, theoretically, attack your computer. However, software updates for all the main web browsers become available whenever a loophole is discovered. These updates can be downloaded from the web or are often found on CDs mounted on the front of computer magazines. A relatively new type of virus has been found circulating via email. It abuses a feature in Microsoft's Outlook Express email program to automatically distribute itself.

There is a straightforward way to avoid such viruses. If you receive an email from someone you don't know, don't open any attached files – whatever they are. Even if a friend sends a program, try to avoid running it unless you are expecting something important. Joke animations, computerized birthday cards, and other "entertainments" are usually very uninspiring at the best of times. Add the fact that they have the potential to carry computer viruses and you can see that they are just not worth the time it takes to download them. It goes without saying that you ought to consider not forwarding these things on to other friends. And always use a virus checker, like Norton Antivirus, to check any attachments that you might receive with your emails.

To keep up-to-date with the latest virus software, get your browser patches from the download areas at Microsoft (**www.microsoft.com/downloads**) and Netscape (**www.netscape.com/computing/download**). You can also find the latest virus announcements at Symantec's AntiVirus Research Center (**www.symantec.com/avcenter**). Is the virus warning you've received through the email system a hoax? Find out at the Computer Incident Advisory Capability website (**www.ciac.org**).

Hackers

The term "hacker" is usually used to refer to a computer literate criminal who has misused a network to commit fraud or damage files. There is a community of computer experts who consider themselves to be hackers, but get upset when tarred with the same brush as vandals and fraudsters. They label the irresponsible people as crackers, among other things. Whatever you call them, the sort of people who infiltrate computer systems to blackmail companies, steal software, or create general havoc are not interested in touching your computer. They may try to steal your credit card number from an online shop's system, but your PC is quite safe! A hacker would need a certain type of software, called server applications, to be running on your computer before he or she could even think about gaining control of your system. Ordinary home PCs do not have any of this server software.

Even if your details are stolen from a third party, like a shop, credit card companies will indemnify you against misuse of your card, with the proviso that you've looked after it properly and taken reasonable steps to secure its use. Most consider Internet shopping to be safe, while VISA even goes as far as to claim that Internet shopping is more secure than giving your number over the phone. Check with your bank, if you're unsure of its Internet policy.

When you buy something from the Internet using a secure server, your details are encoded using quite strong encryption. However, what can you do to protect your email from prying eyes? There are a number of free encryption programs available on the Internet that will do the job nicely, the most famous being Pretty Good Privacy (PGP). Considering the millions of messages that are flying around the Internet at once, you can see that the probability of yours being compromised is low. But although a stereotypical hacker would find it hard to access your email, it's not so hard for the various people who work at your ISP, the ISP of your correspondent, and even co-workers in your office to do so. Email stays on your computer and copies are made on others as the message progresses on its journey. Encryption protects your right to privacy, even if you have nothing to hide. Get PGP from The International PGP Home Page (**www.pgpi.org**).

Filtering out the filth

One criticism of the Internet, which is unfortunately true, is the proliferation of pornography. You can find it purely by accident, although most of the time you'll need a credit card handy before you can even gain any access to the bulk of the material. But often a few introductory pictures of the most explicit nature are flashed up first. There are programs and special web browsers that aim to filter out this kind of content, to avoid the corruption of minors. The latest versions of the main web browsers now feature built-in filters that aim to avoid sexual pictures, as well as articles containing swearing and violence. Many of these programs are quite effective, but nothing will work as well as a parental presence when children are online. More details on NetNanny, a content filtering and blocking program, can be found at **www.netnanny.com**.

Finally, a word about child pornography. It is true that the Internet can and is used to distribute this illegal material. However, it is very rare that someone can gain access to it, accidentally or otherwise. This is because the Internet is not completely open, and there are secret areas that are available only to those in the know. And the paedophiles who use these areas have a vested interest in keeping them secret. They want to avoid you, and the police, so you'd be very unlucky to uncover pornographic images of this nature. That said, some live chat forums have been used by men to contact and mislead children. This is a strong reason to provide parental guidance when using the Internet. You wouldn't let your child talk to strangers or use telephone chat services on their own – the Internet falls into the same category. The Internet is the perfect place for people to hide their identities and/or create new ones, so beware. Having said that, follow the simple advice above and soon you will be having hours of fun browsing with your family!

GLOSSARY

Adobe Acrobat
A file format (PDF) that keeps large documents together in a single file, including pictures. The advantage to this is that the content looks the same on every computer. The disadvantage is that it is usually a very large file to download.

ADSL
Asymetric Digital Subscriber Line. This is a very fast type of Internet connection using ordinary phone lines. Requires special hardware and a costly service subscription.

ASCII
American Standard Code for Information Interchange. The predominant way of encoding characters for computers. It includes upper and lower case letters, but no accented letters or those not used in English, such as the German sharp-S, "ß".

Cable
Very fast Internet access can be offered using cable networks. Often cheaper than ADSL, cable is certainly also more widely available. There are potential speed problems when lots of local people use the service simultaneously, however.

Chat
Live chat lets you "talk" to other people using your web browser in real time. You type your reply and then read the answers as soon as they are written. Chat forums are web-based bulletin boards. You leave questions and answers on a web page, and visit the site later to see the replies.

Cookie
Some retail sites store your personal information on your hard drive to "personalize" the page when you log back in. Don't worry, it is completely safe!

Directory
A massive list of websites, organized into handy categories to aid searching.

Domain
An essential part of a web address, the domain name of a site offers substantial clues about its nature. Yahoo.com and Apple.com are both domain names.

Download
When you open a web page in your computer's web browser program, you are actually downloading information onto your hard disk. This information will be automatically deleted from your computer after a certain period of time. You can also download files from the Internet, such as software drivers for your printer, or shareware programs.

Emoticon
A picture made out of text characters used to denote an emotion. They are handy to use to depict the mood you are trying to express, which can otherwise be difficult in an email (see page 303 for examples).

Encryption
Used to encode information to prevent unauthorized access. All good online shops will use encryption to protect its customers' details from criminals.

Flame
An angry, aggressive email message that is likely to be of a very personal nature.

Flash

Software used by web authors to make their sites look more attractive and interactive. If you don't have a Macromedia Flash plugin installed, you will often be given the chance to download it, and some considerate sites will offer a non-Flash version for older browsers.

Frames

A technique used on websites that creates separate areas on a screen.

FTP

File Transfer Protocol. A way of providing files that can be downloaded using either a web browser or a dedicated FTP program. You would also use FTP to upload your files when creating a website.

Gif

A type of graphics file often used to create small pictures, logos, and buttons.

Hacker

Someone who can access computers using advanced networking techniques. They are far more likely to infiltrate the networks of large companies than your home computer.

HTML

Hypertext Markup Language. This is the computer language that is used to create web pages.

HTTP

Stands for Hypertext Transport Protocol. This is the software that is used to send web page information from the server directly to your browser.

Hyperlink

A selected word or phrase, picture, or button that provides access to another part of the website when clicked with a mouse.

Internet

A global network of computers, providing many services including the world wide web.

Intranet

A network of computers that provides services similar to those found on the Internet. However, this network is located within a company or building and will have been tailored to suit their own specific needs.

ISDN

Integrated Services Digital Network. A reasonably fast, but rather over-priced,

service that brings you quicker Internet access.

ISP

Internet Service Provider. This is the company you use to gain access to the Internet. Home computers use modems to dial into the ISP, which then forwards information from the Internet onto your screen. When you send an email message, it leaves your computer and passes through the ISP onto the Internet, towards its final destination.

Java

A programming language that allows programs to run in your web browser, regardless of the operating system or type of computer you have.

Jpeg

A type of graphic file that uses compression to allow the production of photo-quality pictures that download quickly.

Lurker

Someone who reads messages posted in chat forums and on Newsgroups, without ever contributing. Lurk for a while before joining a discussion group to check whether it is suitable for you but don't spend too long doing it!

Mac

A type of personal computer made by Apple.

Mirror

A copy of a website. Mirrors of very popular websites are made all over the world, so that Internet users can use the closest one and therefore get the fastest possible performance.

Modem

A device used by computers to establish Internet connections over a phone line. Most can also be used to send and receive faxes.

MP3

Mpeg 1 layer 3. This is a type of sound file that offers near-CD quality. MP3 files are around one tenth of the size of a normal sound file, making them ideal for distributing music over the Internet. MP4s also exist, though are not widespread as yet.

Network

A network is formed when at least two computers are wired together and are able to communicate with each other. The Internet is the largest network in the world. You can connect two PCs together, forming the most basic kind of network. This is useful for sharing files and printers, and when playing games.

Newsgroups

An area of the Internet consisting of thousands of very specific bulletin boards within which people can share their ideas and opinions with others.

Offline

It is possible to download pages from the Internet onto your hard disk and then view them after disconnecting. Doing this is called working offline.

Online

When a computer is connected to the Internet, it is online.

Operating system

The software that allows a computer to run programs like word processors, web browsers, and games.

PC

The most popular type of home computer, PCs are made by a large number of different companies.

PGP

Pretty Good Privacy. An encryption program available free via the Internet to help protect your email from prying eyes.

Plugin

A piece of software that increases the abilities of a web browser program.

Search Engine

A website that attempts to index the websites on the Internet, providing visitors with the opportunity to search through its records.

Secure Site

If a site is secure then it is encrypted, meaning that any details that you submit should be safe. The URL often begins with https://

Server

A computer program that provides a service. Websites exist on web servers, email is dealt with by email servers, and files by FTP servers.

Shareware

Software, available on the Internet, for which the author requests payment, usually in the accompanying documentation files or in an announcement made by the software itself.

Shockwave

As with Flash, a website that uses Shockwave requires you to install a plugin to reap the benefit of its features. It is used to improve a website's design.

Site

A collection of web pages held under the same domain name.

Spam

Unsolicited, junk email that usually bears unlikely promises of wealth, health, and sexual fulfilment.

SSL

Secure Socket Layer. This security feature, which is found in all good web browsers, uses encryption to exchange information between computers. It is used by conscientious online shops to protect customers' details from the potential threat of criminals.

TLD

Top Level Domain. The ".com", ".org", and ".co.uk" part of a web address.

Troll

Someone who agitates the inhabitants of Internet chat forums and other "virtual communities". Also a verb,

as in to utter a posting on Usenet designed to attract predictable responses.

URL

Uniform Resource Locator. The technical name for a web address, for example **http://www.apple.com/press.htm**, which is made up of the following components:
http:// – The network software used to distribute web page data.
www. – The first part of the web server's name.
apple – The name of the computer that holds all of the pages.
.com – The top level domain name (TLD).
/press.htm – A web page.

Virus

This is a malignant computer program, more likely to be found hyped up in newspaper reports and Hollywood films than actually on your hard disk. Viruses are usually transferred when programs are downloaded, and are often received as an attachment to an email.

WAP

Wireless Application Protocol. Specially created Internet pages can be accessed through mobile

phones. Originally just text, more development has meant that pictures can now be included in the latest models of phone.

Web browser

A program that displays web pages. There are different types and versions, although they all perform basically the same function. Later versions tend to work better with some websites. Microsoft's Internet Explorer and Netscape's Navigator are among the most popular browsers around.

Webmaster

The person responsible at a site providing world wide web information for maintaining the public pages and keeping the web server running.

www

The world wide web. Arguably the easiest part of the Internet to use, the web contains over a billion pages of information.

Zip

A file format that creates a compressed archive, thus reducing the size of large files, and making them faster to download.

INDEX